喚醒你的英文語感！

Get a Feel for English !

作　者 / 大賀理惠、Bill Benfield
Ann Gleason
總編審 / 王復國

to take care of this crisis caused by the battery recall before we do anything else. In case of emergency, break
and push the red button to stop the train. He had to go to New York on urgent business. The ceremony was
mmemoration of the members of the armed forces who were killed in the war. It was our 20th wedding
ry yesterday, but I completely forgot about it. A huge celebration ceremony took place on the 50th
ry of Cedar City. Computer companies lose a great deal of revenue every year as a result of
iracy. Reports of unusual crimes in the media often give rise to copycat crimes. Mimicry is
ant skill to master if you want to become a good actor. Joe could not understand the
eaning, and expressed his frustration by throwing the book across the room.
n is one of the symptoms of a nervous breakdown. Our house-building
ffered a serious setback when the contractor went bankrupt. The
on Ernest's novels will be the property of his heirs after his death. A
es division is our firm's most valuable asset. In order to save the
we will have to sell our 20 acres of real estate in
ut as soon as possible. According to our fiscal report,
o have managed to come through this period of
with some gain. There has been an
increase in the number of cooking
on television in the last few years.
full-time workers get an annual
in the form of a fixed
According to my rental
have to give the
ny apartment

本書原是日美會話學院專門學校 TOEIC 800 分目標特訓講座的教材，在重新增修後，已成為一本以突破 TOEIC 860 分為目標的自學教材。本套自學教材在 2007 年以《速讀即解！突破 TOEIC TEST 860 分單字書》為名出版，而此次再版，其重點在於跟讀學習法的例句練習，同時針對例句的內容進行了編修。

想在 TOEIC 的考試中拿到 860 分，需具備何種程度的語彙能力？860 分的水準大約位在 TOEIC 分數分布圖的前 8% 左右，是絕對無法一蹴可幾的。若學習者擁有 TOEIC 860 分的程度，即代表其能「即時理解一定長度的英文句子」並能「確實地掌握該例句裡的單字」。而為了幫助學習者達到這樣的英語能力，本書編撰了最適當的例句，同時介紹效果顯著的「跟讀學習法」。

15 年前筆者使用自編的教材創立了 TOEIC 特訓講座，最初僅有一班，但轉眼間，班數即增加至 8 班之多。本人所主持之講座之所以能受到如此多數學生的支持，其原因無二，就是因為上過課的同學，TOEIC 分數確實有了顯著的進步。本講座與一般的英文或英語會話課程不同的是，所有的學習目標都集中於提升 TOEIC 測驗的分數。而其中最具效果的正是本書介紹的語彙學習方法。

參加過本講座的學習者，TOEIC 的分數平均提升了 50-280 分左右。此外，持續參加講座 6 個月～ 1 年的學習者之中，有許多人的 TOEIC 總分也從原本的 200-300 分成長至 750-800 分。筆者相信，本書的使用者只要每天不懈怠地努力，必可達到同樣的效果。請仔細地閱讀「跟讀學習法」章節 (p.10)，並依照指示一步一步地學習。

最後，要感謝在本書改版之際參與修訂的共同作者 Ann Gleason 與 Bill Benfield 先生，以及 ASK 出版社的天谷修平社長和賜予許多寶貴意見的編輯影山洋子小姐。有了他們的鼎力協助，本書才能以今日之風貌呈現給讀者。

作者 大賀理恵

CONTENTS 目錄

Chapter 2 動詞片語

Chapter 3 形容詞・副詞・介系詞片語

Chapter 4 慣用表現

Chapter 5 商務與時事英語

◎ 附錄

TOEIC 測驗與單字能力

■ TOEIC 測驗多以哪些領域為出題的題材？

TOEIC 出題的題材常選自必須使用英文的職場，或是在公共場合中常用的英語會話或書寫用語。換言之，題材涵蓋了下列各個主題。

商業

製造業、工廠經營管理、財務會計、開發企業經營、行銷、採買等。

住宅、不動產

購屋、租賃、契約、訂金等。

金融

存款、支票、房貸、匯款、ATM、銀行窗口業務等。

辦公室

會議、電話用語、傳真、電子郵件、辦公用語等。

人事、人力開發

任用、退休、待遇、福利、人力招募廣告、退休金、獎勵表彰等。

技術

電子業、電腦業、研究機構、研究器材等。

日常話題

旅行、同事聚餐、外食、娛樂、購物、健康、保險、醫療、犯罪等。

交通

飛機、火車、電車、公車、計程車等之相關資訊；路況與事故之相關資訊；運費、交通時刻表等之相關資訊。

氣象狀況

天氣預報、警報、自然災害等之相關資訊。

動植物及環境

動植物檢疫、禁止規定、保護原則與法條、環保等之相關資訊。

公共事務

稅金、社會福利金、官方活動、行政命令、選舉、紀念日、活動通知，以及圖書館、美術館這類公共設施的使用規範。

■ 參加 TOEIC 測驗要具備何種單字能力？

✎ TOEIC 測驗有兩項值得關心的重點：

第一點，同時也是 TOEIC 測驗近來的趨勢，就是考生應具備的單字量大幅增加。例如，Listening Section: Part 3、Part 4 以及 Reading Section: Part 6、Part 7 的考題幾乎就是在測驗考生的單字能力。

第二點則是，絕大部分的考題都與商業與公共事務有關。舉辦 TOEIC 測驗的 ETS (English Testing Service) 也在其官網明白指出：「TOEIC 測驗是職場專用英語能力之測驗」。剛畢業的學生與甫就職的社會新鮮人大多不熟悉商業領域的單字，因此希望讀者透過本書的商業用語詞彙來加強此方面的能力。

學習本書的「Chpater 1 重要單字」時，千萬別以個別背誦的方式來學習，而是要將書中整理在同一頁中的三個相關單字一起研讀，除了能有效地建構記憶網絡之外，也能同時理解這些單字之間語意與用法上之差異。

「Chapter 2 動詞片語」、「Chapter 3 形容詞、副詞、介系詞片語」、「Chapter 4 慣用表現」的內容全都是母語人士常用的話語。為了讓學習者身歷其境地熟悉這類說法，我們還特別編寫了極具故事性的例句。

最後，我們也編入常出現於 TOEIC 考題的商業用語。雖然 TOEIC 的官網指出，TOEIC 的考題不會出現專業用的英文，但是一旦考題裡的情境牽涉到商業場合，就難免出現一些專業用語，例如新型辦公機器的用法、業務話術、企業組織改造等相關詞彙。對於這些用法的理解在要求快速閱讀的考試中，即為取得高分的關鍵。本書中的例句雖然已大量使用商業、生活用語，但是為了幫助讀者掌握重要商業用語，我們將商業詞彙統一整理成 Chpater 5。

■ 本書的語彙是如何選出來的？

✎ 本書主要由以下三處資料來源歸納寫成：

❶ 過去 15 年內，筆者除了曾是 TOEIC 測驗的考生，也曾擔任數十次 TOEIC 測驗的出題考官。憑藉這十幾年參與測驗的經驗，筆者整理了一份 TOEIC 測驗的基本單字集。

❷ 筆者曾為自己的 TOEIC 講座編了模擬測驗集，而本書單字即從模擬測驗集 800-860 分程度的單字中挑選而出。筆者共挑選了約為講

座兩學期分量的內容與問題集。

❸ 由於本書是專為想突破 TOEIC 測驗 860 分的人所寫，所以除了 TOEIC 測驗應試所需的單字之外，我們也挑選了一些英文學習者應知的 ADVANCED LEVEL 單字。若學習者想在 TOEIC 測驗獲得 800-900 分，就必須學習更高階的英文，否則不太容易達成目標。

編寫本書所參考的字典與辭典如下：

- 《朗文當代高級辭典》
  LONGMAN Dictionary of Contemporary English
- 《牛津高階英漢雙解辭典》
  OXFORD ADVANCED LEARNER'S Dictionary（牛津大學出版社）
- 《柯林斯高階美式英語辭典》
  Collins COBUILD ADVANCED DICTIONARY of American English（Heinle Cengage Learning 出版社）
- 《大英百科全書》
  ENCYCLOPAEDIA Britannica（Britannica 出版社）
- 《世界年鑑》
  THE WORLD ALMANAC AND BOOK OF FACTS（World Almanac Education 出版社）
- IMIDAS（集英社）
- 《朝日年鑑》（朝日新聞社）
- 《Genuis 英日辭典》
- 《英辭郎》（ALC）

此外，爲了了解每個單字在網路上的使用頻率，我們還利用 Google 查詢。不過搜尋結果僅供參考，不會成爲挑選單字的標準。挑選單字的標準仍然是以筆者長年參與 TOEIC 測驗的經驗爲主。

效果驚人的跟讀學習法

■ 什麼是「跟讀學習法」？

本書所採取的主要練習方式為「跟讀學習法」。所謂的「跟讀」(Shadowing) 指的是先仔細聆聽語音教材，緊接著把聽到的英語以同樣的發音、語調、腔調確實複誦出來。在經過反覆練習之後，發音與腔調將變得更為自然，也能同時學會句型與單字的用法，效果可謂「一石四鳥」。請讀者跟著下列指示的步驟學習。

在實際開口練習之前，請先聽一遍 MP3 的錄音，並看一遍英文的內容。

■ 運用「跟讀學習法」有效學習本書

STEP 1 一邊閱讀書裡的內容，同時跟著 MP3 一起開口複誦例句。

STEP 2 開始跟讀學習法的練習。一邊跟著 MP3，慢個一拍左右將語句複誦出來。如果跟不上語音播放的速度，每次播放一頁的內容即可；若能輕鬆跟上，建議您每次播放一個單元的內容。絕對不要在速度跟不上時就立刻停止播放 MP3。即便您跟不上語音的速度，也希望您能盡可能將聽到的內容念出聲音來。

STEP 3 請就每個單元的內容，反覆做三遍的跟讀練習。盡可能大聲開口跟讀，並模仿語音教材的發音、語調和腔調。本書特別仿照 TOEIC 聽力測驗，收錄英、美、加、澳四國口音，在學習單字和語句外，可同步強化聽力反應！

STEP 4 當您針對單元內容反覆做了三遍跟讀練習之後，請開始閱讀該單元中的單字、相關用語、TOEIC POINT、Useful POINT 等內容。如果遇到不懂的單字，也可以查字典。

STEP 5 接著請把書本闔上並播放 MP3，再一次重複跟讀整個單元的內容。此時千萬別中途就停止 MP3 的播放。

■ Check Test 測驗以及 Chart 的填寫

STEP 6 如果覺得自己已把大部分的單字記起來，就可以進行 Check Test。

① 將計時器設定為每題 30 秒（10 題就設定為 5 分鐘；15 題就設定為 7 分 30 秒；20 題就設定為 10 分鐘）。不能以散漫的態度接受測驗，也不能在沒有計時的狀態下進行測驗。

② 測驗中不得翻閱字典

③ 作答時間結束時，尚未作答的題目為 0 分。

STEP 7 作答時間結束後立刻停筆。請利用附錄的解答核對答案，並將正確率記錄在 Power Builder Chart (p.434-435) 裡。（沒作答的題目為 0 分）

STEP 8 合格基準為 90%。如果未達此標準，請從 STEP 1 的步驟從頭開始。在每次進行測驗之後，將分數累積在第一次測驗的長條圖長條上。（請參考下方「Power Builder Chart」的填寫方式）

STEP 9 正確率達 90% 之後，請重新從 STEP 1 開始進行下一單元的學習。

【Power Builder Chart 的填寫範例】

100%							
90%	第三回						
80%							
70%							
60%	第二回						
50%							
40%							
30%	第一回						
20%							
10%							
	U01	U02	U03	U04	U05	U06	U07

本書使用說明與符號意義

本書每一頁內容包含「例句與翻譯」、「主題字解說」、「相關用語」、「附加資訊」這四個部分。

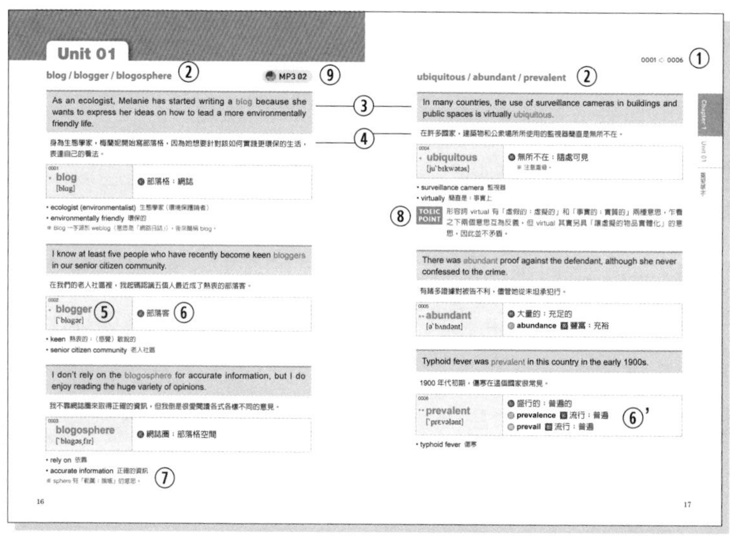

Unit 01

blog / blogger / blogosphere ②　MP3 02 ⑨

As an ecologist, Melanie has started writing a blog because she wants to express her ideas on how to lead a more environmentally friendly life. ③

身為生態學家，梅蘭妮開始寫部落格，因為她想要針對該如何實踐更環保的生活，表達自己的看法。④

0001 * blog [blɑg]　名 部落格；網誌

• ecologist (environmentalist) 生態學家（環境保護論者）
• environmentally friendly 環保的
※ Blog 一字源於 weblog（意思是「網路日誌」），後來簡稱 blog。

I know at least five people who have recently become keen bloggers in our senior citizen community.

在我們的老人社區裡，我起碼認識五個人最近成了熱衷的部落客。

0002 * blogger [ˋblɑgər] ⑤　名 部落客 ⑥

• keen 熱衷的；（感覺）敏銳的
• senior citizen community 老人社區

I don't rely on the blogosphere for accurate information, but I do enjoy reading the huge variety of opinions.

我不靠網誌圈來取得正確的資訊，但我倒是很愛閱讀各式各樣不同的意見。

0003 blogosphere [ˋblɑgəs,fɪr]　名 網誌圈；部落格空間

• rely on 依靠
• accurate information 正確的資訊
※ sphere 有「範圍；領域」的意思。 ⑦

16

0001 ⇨ 0006 ①

ubiquitous / abundant / prevalent ②

In many countries, the use of surveillance cameras in buildings and public spaces is virtually ubiquitous. ③

在許多國家，建築物和公眾場所所使用的監視器簡直是無所不在。④

0004 * ubiquitous [juˋbɪkwətəs]　形 無所不在；隨處可見
※ 注意重音。

• surveillance camera 監視器
• virtually 簡直是；事實上

⑧ TOEIC POINT 形容詞 virtual 有「虛假的；虛擬的」和「事實的；實質的」兩種意思，乍看之下兩個意思互為反義，但 virtual 其實另具「讓虛擬的物品實體化」的意思，因此並不矛盾。

There was abundant proof against the defendant, although she never confessed to the crime.

有諸多證據對被告不利，儘管她從未坦承犯行。

0005 ** abundant [əˋbʌndənt]　形 大量的；充足的
衍 abundance 名 豐富；充裕

Typhoid fever was prevalent in this country in the early 1900s.

1900 年代初期，傷寒在這個國家很常見。

0006 ** prevalent [ˋprɛvələnt]　形 盛行的；普遍的
衍 prevalence 名 流行；普遍 ⑥'
衍 prevail 動 流行；普遍

• typhoid fever 傷寒

17

Chapter 1　Unit 01

❶ 該跨頁中所收錄的單字編號

❷ (Chapter 1) 收錄在該頁的單字群組

(Chapter 2) 收錄在該頁的常用動詞

❸ 例句

❹ 例句的翻譯

❺ 主單字的編號以及主題字出現的頻率

** 表示為最重要的單字，常出現在 TOEIC 測驗裡的基本單字。

* 表示為重要單字，可能出現在 TOEIC 測驗裡的單字。

（沒有 * 號的單字代表在 TOEIC 測驗裡出現頻率較低，但如果想拿高分，不妨將這些單字背起來。）

❻ 主題字的詞性與翻譯

名 名 名詞　　動 動 動詞

形 形 形容詞　　副 副 副詞

❻' 相關用語

衍 衍生字　　類 類義字

反 反義字　　關 關聯字

❼ 例句裡的重要字詞與翻譯，以及其他相關用法補充。

❽ TOEIC POINT：詳細解說 TOEIC 常考的文法重點、陷阱問題以及易混淆的單字。

Useful POINT：不一定可應用於 TOEIC 考試的重點，但對進階的英文學習者而言，如果能知道這些重點，應該可以增加不少學習樂趣。

❾ MP3 02　MP3 曲目（本書仿照 TOEIC 聽力測驗，隨機收錄英、美、加、澳四國口音，請仔細聆聽以熟悉各國口音之差異）。

Chapter 1

Vocabulary Items

0001 ➔ 0433

重要單字

Unit 01

blog / blogger / blogosphere

As an ecologist, Melanie has started writing a blog because she wants to express her ideas on how to lead a more environmentally friendly life.

身為生態學家，梅蘭妮開始寫部落格，因為她想要針對該如何實踐更環保的生活，表達自己的看法。

0001 * **blog** [blɑg]	名 部落格；網誌

- ecologist (environmentalist) 生態學家（環境保護論者）
- environmentally friendly 環保的

※ Blog 一字源於 weblog（意思是「網路日誌」），後來簡稱 blog。

I know at least five people who have recently become keen bloggers in our senior citizen community.

在我們的老人社區裡，我起碼認識五個人最近成了熱衷的部落客。

0002 * **blogger** [ˋblɑgər]	名 部落客

- keen 熱衷的；（感覺）敏銳的
- senior citizen community 老人社區

I don't rely on the blogosphere for accurate information, but I do enjoy reading the huge variety of opinions.

我不靠網誌圈來取得正確的資訊，但我倒是很愛閱讀各式各樣不同的意見。

0003 **blogosphere** [ˋblɑgəsˏfɪr]	名 網誌圈；部落格空間

- rely on 依靠
- accurate information 正確的資訊

※ sphere 有「範圍；領域」的意思。

ubiquitous / abundant / prevalent

In many countries, the use of surveillance cameras in buildings and public spaces is virtually ubiquitous.

在許多國家，建築物和公眾場所所使用的監視器簡直是無所不在。

0004 * **ubiquitous** [ju`bɪkwətəs]	形 無所不在；隨處可見 ※ 注意重音。

- surveillance camera 監視器
- virtually 簡直是；事實上

TOEIC POINT 形容詞 virtual 有「虛假的；虛擬的」和「事實的；實質的」兩種意思，乍看之下兩個意思互為反義，但 virtual 其實另具「讓虛擬的物品實體化」的意思，因此並不矛盾。

There was abundant proof against the defendant, although she never confessed to the crime.

有諸多證據對被告不利，儘管她從未坦承犯行。

0005 ** **abundant** [ə`bʌndənt]	形 大量的；充足的 衍 **abundance** 名 豐富；充裕

Typhoid fever was prevalent in this country in the early 1900s.

1900 年代初期，傷寒在這個國家很常見。

0006 ** **prevalent** [`prɛvələnt]	形 盛行的；普遍的 衍 **prevalence** 名 流行；普遍 關 **prevail** 動 流行；普遍

- typhoid fever 傷寒

spokesperson / publicity / outspoken

The company spokesperson completely denies attempting to bribe the construction minister.

該公司的發言人完全否認企圖對建設部長行賄。

0007 ** **spokesperson** [ˋspoksˌpɝsn̩]	名（組織的）發言人

- deny 否認
- bribe 行賄（take bribery 收賄）
- construction minister 建設部長

To boost his fading popularity, the singer Tony Tyler pulled a publicity stunt causing a scandal with an up-and-coming actress.

為了提振下滑的人氣，歌手湯尼．泰勒祭出了搏版面的噱頭，跟一位剛嶄露頭角的女演員傳出緋聞。

0008 * **publicity** [pʌbˋlɪsətɪ]	名 宣傳；知名度 衍 **publicize** 動 宣傳；公開

- fading popularity 下滑的人氣
- pull a publicity stunt 祭出搏版面的噱頭

Our CEO is popular with journalists for his outspoken views on the economy. They are always quoting him in their articles.

我們執行長很受記者歡迎，因為他都會直言對經濟的看法。他們總會在文章中引述他的話。

0009 **outspoken** [autˋspokən]	形 直言不諱的 類 **forthright** 直率的

- CEO (Chief Executive Officer) 執行長

co-worker / partner / collaborator

I like to leave the office at 5 o'clock sharp, but my co-workers always want me to go out drinking with them.

我喜歡在五點整離開辦公室，但是我的同事老是要我跟他們出去喝一杯。

0010 ** **co-worker** [ˋkoˋwɝkɚ]	名 同事 類 **colleague** 同事、**partner** 伙伴

We did a lot of detailed research before deciding on a partner for the joint venture.

我們做了很多詳盡的研究，才決定合資企業的合夥人。

0011 ** **partner** [ˋpɑrtnɚ]	名 合夥人；（一起行動的）伙伴 關 **partnership** 名 合夥；加盟 類 **associate** 伙伴；合夥人

I would like to thank Professor Julia Turner, my chief collaborator on this project, who gave me many valuable suggestions.

我要謝謝茱莉亞．透納教授，也就是我在這個案子上的主要合作對象，她給了我許多寶貴的建議。

0012 * **collaborator** [kəˋlæbə͵retɚ]	名 合作者；合著者 衍 **collaborate** 動 合作；共同工作

TOEIC POINT 不要將 collaborate 與 corroborate（證實；確證）混淆。

macrobiotic / macroeconomics / microbe

People who follow a macrobiotic diet believe food affects our bodies in very deep ways.

奉行長壽飲食法的人相信食物對我們的身體有非常深遠的影響。

0013 * **macrobiotic** [ˌmækrobaɪˋɑtɪk]	形 長壽的；延年益壽的 衍 **macrobiotics** 名（複數形）延年益壽的飲食方法

※ macro 的意思為 great，biotic(s) 的意思為 life。macrobiotic food 的意思為「健康飲食、延壽飲食（以糙米與蔬菜為主）」。

The study of macroeconomics will give you an overall idea of how the national economy functions.

研究總體經濟會讓你對於國家的經濟運作有全盤的了解。

0014 **macroeconomics** [ˌmækroˌikəˋnɑmɪks]	名 總體經濟學 衍 **macro** 形 總體的；宏觀的 關 **microeconomics** 名 個體經濟學

Regular hand washing is essential for killing microbes that can cause disease.

若要把會使人生病的細菌殺死，一定要勤洗手。

0015 * **microbe** [ˋmaɪkrob]	名 細菌；微生物 類 **germ**「細菌」的一般說法 衍 **micro** 形 極小的；百萬分之一的

※ 其他以 micro- 為開頭的單字，如：microscope 名 顯微鏡；microphone 名 麥克風。

resume / curriculum vitae / biography

When you are applying for a job, it is important that your resume gives a complete record of your education and employment history.

你在應徵工作時，很重要的是，履歷上要完整記錄你的教育和就業歷程。

0016 ** **resume (résumé)** [ˌrɛzjʊˋme]	名 履歷；概略 類 **curriculum vitae** 履歷（表）

※ 這個字源自於法語，因此原本應寫成 résumé，但最近常直接寫成 resume。

Applicants for the post should send a curriculum vitae and a cover letter.

應徵本職位的人應投寄履歷及求職信。

0017 ** **curriculum vitae** [kəˋrɪkjələm ˋvite]	名 履歷表

※ curriculum vitae 常縮寫成 CV。

John had never been interested in visiting India until he read a biography of Mahatma Gandhi.

約翰從來沒有興趣參訪印度，直到看了聖雄甘地的傳記以後。

0018 * **biography** [baɪˋɑgrəfɪ]	名 傳記 衍 **biographical** 形 傳記的；傳記體的

※ autobiography 則指「自傳」。

plump / obese / corpulent

Don't tell me I'm fat. Tell me I'm "pleasantly plump."

不要說我胖。說我「豐腴地恰恰好」。

0019 * **plump** [plʌmp]	形 豐腴的；豐滿的

• pleasantly 令人愉快地

Heart failure is a common disease among obese people.

心臟衰竭是肥胖人士的常見疾病。

0020 * **obese** [o`bis]	形 肥胖的；過胖的 類 **overweight** 體重過重的 衍 **obesity** 名 肥胖

• heart failure 心臟衰竭

In a temple in Nara, he saw a smiling, corpulent Buddha.

在奈良的一間寺廟裡，他看到了一尊微笑的渾圓佛像。

0021 **corpulent** [`kɔrpjələnt]	形 渾圓的；肥胖的 衍 **corpulence** 名 肥胖

※ plump 有「豐滿」的意思，corpulent 則有「肥大」的感覺，obese 則指「過度肥胖」。

crisis / emergency / urgent

We have to take care of this crisis caused by the battery recall before we do anything else.

在採取其他任何行動前，我們必須先把這場因為回收電池而引發的危機給擺平。

0022 ** **crisis** [ˋkraɪsɪs]	名 危機；緊要關頭

※ crisis management 指「危機管理」。

In case of emergency, break the glass and push the red button to stop the train.

萬一發生緊急狀況，把玻璃打破並按下紅色按鈕，以便把列車停下來。

0023 ** **emergency** [ɪˋmɜdʒənsɪ]	名 緊急狀況；突發事件 衍 **emergent** 形 緊急的；意外的 **emerge** 動 浮現；出現

※ 使用 emergency 的字詞有：
emergency exit（緊急出口）、emergency room (ER)（急診室）、emergency rescue squad（災難救援隊）、emergency reserve（緊急準備金）等。

He had to go to New York on urgent business.

為了緊急業務，他必須去紐約一趟。

0024 * **urgent** [ˋɜdʒənt]	形 緊急的；迫切的 衍 **urgency** 名 緊急；急事 **urge** 名 衝動；強烈的慾望 動 催促；力主

※ emergency 比 urgency 更能形容事故現場的緊急性與突發性。

outfit / wardrobe / apparel

When buying clothes for work, I like to choose a matching outfit from top to bottom.

在買上班要穿的衣服時，我喜歡選從上到下搭配的套裝。

0025 * **outfit** [ˋaʊtˏfɪt]	名 套裝；全套裝備 關 **outfitter** 旅行用品店；運動用品店 類 **attire** 衣著；盛裝

※ outfit 指的不是單件的衣物，而是「整體服裝」。讚美對方「您打扮得真漂亮」時，可說 I love your outfit.。

I chose a blue chiffon dress from my limited wardrobe for the dance.

為了去跳舞，我從有限的衣服當中選了一件藍色的雪紡洋裝。

0026 * **wardrobe** [ˋwɔrdˏrob]	名 服裝；衣櫥

※ wardrobe 為單數形單字，意思為某人「所有的衣服；所有的行頭」。
※ dance party（舞會）為中式英文，一般英語人士會用 the dance 或 the ball 來指「舞會」。

It is important for companies in the apparel industry to correctly predict what the fashions will be like for the coming season.

對服裝業界的公司而言，正確預測下一季的流行時尚是很重要的。

0027 ** **apparel** [əˋpærəl]	名 服裝

anniversary / celebration / commemoration

It was our 20th wedding anniversary yesterday, but I completely forgot about it.

昨天是我們結婚 20 週年紀念日，但是我完全把它給忘了。

0028 ** **anniversary** [ˌænəˋvɝsərɪ]	名 週年紀念（日）

※ wedding anniversary 為「結婚週年紀念日」，anniversary of someone's death 則指「某人的忌日」。

A huge celebration ceremony took place on the 50th anniversary of Cedar City.

錫達市的 50 週年紀念日舉辦了盛大的慶祝典禮。

0029 ** **celebration** [ˌsɛləˋbreʃən]	名 慶祝；慶典 衍 **celebrate** 動 慶祝 關 **celebrity** 名 名人

• ceremony 典禮；儀式

The ceremony was held in commemoration of the members of the armed forces who were killed in the war.

舉行這場典禮是為了紀念在戰時陣亡的軍中袍澤。

0030 ** **commemoration** [kəˌmɛməˋreʃən]	名 紀念；慶祝 衍 **commemorate** 動（以祝詞或儀式）紀念 **commemorative** 形 紀念的

• armed forces 軍隊

TOEIC POINT celebration 只在慶祝喜事時使用，而 anniversary、commemoration 則可使用於婚喪喜慶等各種場合。

CHAPTER 1 UNIT 01

CheckTest

0001 ⇨ 0030

請依照文意將適當的單字填入空格中。可參考第 27 頁所提示的單字來作答。(作答時間：5 分鐘)

① I like to leave the office at 5 o'clock sharp, but my ________ always want me to go out drinking with them.

② People who follow a ________ diet believe food affects our bodies in very deep ways.

③ Heart failure is a common disease among ________ people.

④ In many countries, the use of surveillance cameras in buildings and public spaces is virtually ________.

⑤ I don't rely on the ________ for accurate information, but I do enjoy reading the huge variety of opinions.

⑥ When you are applying for a job, it is important that your ________ gives a complete record of your education and employment history.

⑦ When buying clothes for work, I like to choose a matching ________ from top to bottom.

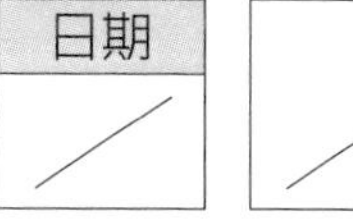

⑧ In case of __________, break the glass and push the red button to stop the train.

⑨ The ceremony was held in __________ of the members of the armed forces who were killed in the war.

⑩ Our CEO is popular with journalists for his __________ views on the economy. They are always quoting him in their articles.

參考用字

resume	co-worker	blogosphere	macrobiotic
outfit	emergency	commemoration	obese
ubiquitous	outspoken		

（解答請參閱第 429 頁）

Unit 02

decade / teens / centenarian

MP3 03

Mr. Howard had been vice-president of the company for almost two decades before he was promoted to president.

豪爾先生在公司當了將近二十年的副總裁才被升為總裁。

0031 ** **decade** [ˋdɛked]	名 十年

※ dec- 是「十」的意思，deci- 則指「十分之一」。

※ decade-long economic boom / slump 即「長達十年的經濟榮景／低迷」。

While still in his teens, Clark Bishop won two tennis championships.

還在十幾歲的時候，克拉克．畢夏普就拿下了兩座網球冠軍。

0032 ** **teens** [tinz]	名 青少年時期（通常指 13 ～ 19 歲） 衍 **teen** 形 青少年的

※ teen workforce（青少年的勞動力）、teen offenders（青少年罪犯）。

My great grandmother enjoyed her longevity and lived to be a centenarian.

我的曾祖母很高壽，活到了一百多歲。

0033 * **centenarian** [ˌsɛntəˋnɛrɪən]	名 百歲人瑞 衍 **centennial** 形 百年的；一世紀的 關 **century** 名 世紀；百年

• longevity 長壽

※septuagenarian 指「70 歲以上的人」，octogenarian 指「80 歲以上的人」，nonagenarian 則指「90 歲以上的人」。

reserve / preserve / conserve

Writers of the book reserve the right to review advertisements when the book is published.

當本書出版時，作者保有審閱廣告的權利。

0034 ** **reserve** [rɪˋzɝv]	動 預約；保有；保留 衍 **reservation** 名 預約；保留；保護區；保留地

TOEIC POINT 商場常用會話：I will go along with your proposal but with reservations.（我有保留地接受您的提案。）另外，without reservations 則是「無條件地、坦誠地」的意思。

It sounds contradictory, but forest trees must be trimmed or cut periodically to preserve nature.

聽起來很矛盾，但是森林裡的樹必須定期修剪或砍伐，才能保護大自然。

0035 ** **preserve** [prɪˋzɝv]	動 保存；維護；保鮮 名 保存食品；保護地 衍 **preservation** 名 保存；防腐；維護

Turning off unnecessary lights in the home and the workplace is an easy and efficient way to conserve energy.

關閉家裡和工作場所中不必要的燈是既簡單又有效率的節約能源方式。

0036 ** **conserve** [kənˋsɝv]	動 保存；保護；節約 衍 **conservation** 名 保全；維持

TOEIC POINT preserve 常用於保存食品時，而 conserve 則常用在「保護天然資源」時。

flyer / draft / manuscript

Bernie got a part-time job handing out flyers for a newly opened restaurant.

柏尼找到了一份兼職工作，替一家新開幕的餐廳發傳單。

0037 * **flyer / flier** [ˋflaɪɚ]	名 傳單

TOEIC POINT part-time job 有別於 1 天 8 小時的 full-time 工作，指的是「在一整天某段短暫時間裡的工作」。另，temporary job 則指「臨時雇用、短期採用」的工作，意思與 part-time job 相近，也常被用來形容打工性質的工作。

I read a draft version of the proposal, and some parts will have to be changed before we submit it to the client.

我看了這個提案的草案，在交給客戶前，有些部分必須修改。

0038 * **draft** [dræft]	名 草稿；草案；選拔（人）；通風；氣流 衍 **drafty** 形 通風良好的

※ I inherited an old drafty house which is over 80 years old from my late grandfather.（我從過世的祖父手上繼承了一間擁有 80 年歷史、通風良好的老房子。）

TOEIC POINT first draft 指「初稿」，final draft 則指「完成稿」。

Publishing companies receive an enormous number of manuscripts from would-be authors every year.

出版公司每年都會收到想當作家的人所寄來的一大堆手稿。

0039 * **manuscript** [ˋmænjə͵skrɪpt]	名 手稿；原稿

TOEIC POINT manu- / mani- 有「手」的意思，如 manual（手冊）、manufacture（製造；加工）、manicure（修指甲）等字皆從此衍生而來。

manual / directions / specification

According to the manual, the satellite dish has to face exactly south by southwest for perfect reception.

根據說明書，小耳朵必須正朝南南西，收訊才會最好。

0040 ** **manual** [ˋmænjuəl]	名 說明書；指南 **instruction manual** 操作指南 形 手工的；手動的 **manual labor** 體力勞動

The directions were so complicated that it took me more than an hour to assemble the bookshelves.

使用說明真複雜，我花了一個多小時才把書架組裝好。

0041 ** **directions** [dəˋrɛkʃənz]	名 使用說明；指示（複數） 衍 **direct** 動 指示；管理 **directional** 形 指示的 **directional signal / indicator**（車子）方向燈

TOEIC POINT 表示「使用說明；指示」這些意思時，通常 directions 這個單字會以複數形出現，若以單數形出現，則是「方向、方位、(僅止一次）的指示」的意思。

We will have to change the specifications of the entire product line if we want it to conform to EU regulations.

假使我們要遵照歐盟的規定，就必須修改整個產品線的規格。

0042 ** **specification** [ˌspɛsəfəˋkeʃən]	名 規格；詳細敘述 衍 **specify** 動 明確說明；指示

• conform (to ...) 遵照
• EU regulations 歐盟的規定

TOEIC POINT 表示「規格」之意時，specifications 多用複數形。

innovative / inventive / groundbreaking

Sally resigned because the company kept rejecting her innovative ideas for new products.

莎莉辭職了，因為公司一直否決她對新產品的創新點子。

0043 ** **innovative** [ˋɪno͵vetɪv]	形 創新的；改革的 衍 **innovate** 動 創新；改革 **innovation** 名 創新；改革

• resign 辭職（注意不要與表「退休」之意的 retire 混淆）

Companies are now looking for people who are capable of coming up with inventive solutions to problems.

各公司現在都在找有能力以具創意之方式來解決問題的人。

0044 ** **inventive** [ɪnˋvɛntɪv]	形 發明的；有創造力的 衍 **invent** 動 發明；創造 **invention** 名 發明（物）

TOEIC POINT innovative 常用來形容獨創的概念、物品或商品；inventive 則用來形容擁有發明才能的人或是其想法。如：innovative product（創新產品）、inventive genius（發明天才）。

Dr. Peters received a major international award for her groundbreaking research on infectious diseases.

彼得斯博士靠著她劃時代的傳染病研究而得到了國際大獎。

0045 **groundbreaking** [ˋgraʊnd͵brekɪŋ]	形 劃時代的；開創性的；（建築工程）破土的 **groundbreaking ceremony** 破土典禮

• infectious 傳染的；傳染性的

resident / occupant / habitat

Residents of the state may send their children to the state university without having to pay tuition fees.

州民可以送子女上州立大學，而不必付學費。

0046 ** **resident** [ˋrɛzədənt]	名 居民；定居者；住院醫師 衍 **residential** 形 居住的；住宅的 關 **residency** 名 居住權；（醫生的）實習期

※ 在此例句中的 resident 代表在該州納稅、可參加選舉同時受法律承認的公民。

Even though I've lived here for more than a year, I've never seen the occupant of the neighboring apartment.

雖然我已經在這裡住了一年多，卻從來沒看過隔壁公寓的住戶。

0047 ** **occupant** [ˋɑkjəpənt]	名 住戶；占有人 關 **occupancy** 名 占有（期）；居住（期） **occupation** 名 工作；職業；占領

One of the most serious threats to the survival of animal species is the disappearance of their habitat.

對於動物物種的存續，棲息地的消失是最嚴重的威脅之一。

0048 * **habitat** [ˋhæbəˌtæt]	名（動物的）棲息地 關 **inhabit** 動 棲息於；居住於 **inhabitant** 名 棲息於某地的動物；居民

piracy / copycat / mimicry

Computer companies lose a great deal of revenue every year as a result of software piracy.

電腦公司每年都會因為軟體盜版而損失慘重。

0049 * **piracy** [ˋpaɪrəsɪ]	名 盜版；侵害著作權 關 **pirate** 名 海盜；盜版商 **pirate DVD** 盜版影音光碟

Reports of unusual crimes in the media often give rise to copycat crimes.

媒體中對於異常犯罪的報導常常引發有樣學樣的犯罪。

0050 * **copycat** [ˋkɑpɪˏkæt]	名（盲目地）模仿他人的人

• copycat crime 模仿犯罪

Mimicry is an important skill to master if you want to become a good actor.

假如你想當個好演員，模仿是需要精通的重要技巧。

0051 **mimicry** [ˋmɪmɪkrɪ]	名 模仿；模擬 關 **mimic** 名 模仿者 動 模仿 形 模仿的

※ mimicry memorization method 模仿記憶法（指老師念完一次，學生再模仿其發音的學習法）。

average / mean / deviation

The per capita income of Connecticut is much higher than the national average.

康乃迪克州的每人平均所得遠高於全國平均值。

0052 ** **average** [ˋævərɪdʒ]	名 平均；平均值 形 一般的；平均的 動 平均起來

• per capita 每人平均的

康乃迪克州為美國東北部的一州，因許多退休之後的有錢人居住而聞名。

The performance of the students at Grover College is significantly above the national mean.

葛羅弗學院的學生成績比全國平均值要高得多。

0053 ** **mean** [min]	名 平均值（mean score 平均分數） 形 平均的；卑賤的；不舒服的；低劣的 動 意謂；意欲

TOEIC POINT 要注意動詞 mean 的過去式、過去分詞為 meant。另外，複數形的 means 為「手段、方法、財力」之意。（參照 0079）

The leaders of the party will expel any members who advocate a deviation from the party's stated aims.

黨的領導人會將任何主張偏離黨的明訂目標之黨員開除。

0054 **deviation** [͵divɪˋeʃən]	名 偏離；偏差；越軌 衍 **deviate** 動 偏離；脫軌

• advocate 提倡；主張

tactic / strategy / approach

Complete honesty is not always the best tactic in negotiations.

在談判時，完全誠實並非永遠是上策。

0055 * **tactic** [`tæktɪk]	名 戰術；策略；手法 衍 **tactical** 形 戰術的；作戰的

TOEIC POINT tactic 為「戰術、策略」之意，通常以複數形出現。另注意，不要把 tactic 的形容詞 tactical 與指「老練、圓融」的 tactful 搞混。

With the proposed changes in the tax law, many companies will have to change their investment strategy.

隨著稅法提出修正，很多公司將必須調整投資策略。

0056 ** **strategy** [`strætədʒɪ]	名 戰略；策略 衍 **strategic** 形 戰略的

The best approach to initiating this joint venture project is to contact Yuan Jones, their company consultant.

推動這件企業合資案的最好辦法，就是跟他們公司的顧問禹安．瓊斯聯繫。

0057 ** **approach** [ə`protʃ]	形（達到某目的的）辦法；路徑 動 接近 衍 **approachable** 形 可接近的；易親近的

※ approach clearance 是指「（飛機的）降落許可」。

infrastructure / subsidiary / affiliate

The financial aid from the World Bank will be used primarily to improve the nation's transportation and telecommunications infrastructure.

世界銀行的金援主要將用來改善該國的交通和電信基礎設施。

0058 * **infrastructure** [`ɪnfrə͵strʌktʃɚ]	名（國家、社會等存續所需要的）基礎建設 衍 **infrastructural** 形 基礎設施的

※ infra- 指「下方」，用到這個字首的字還有 infrared 名 紅外線。

Himero Airlines became a subsidiary of Filipino Air. After that, 50% of the Himero crew was laid off.

希美洛航空變成了菲航的子公司。在那之後，希美洛的員工有一半被資遣。

0059 ** **subsidiary** [səb`sɪdɪ͵ɛrɪ]	名 子公司；附屬物 形 子公司的；附屬的

※ lay off 原指「暫時解雇」，但一般就是「解雇」之意。

This health club is an affiliate of the Metropolitan Health network, and so members are free to use any of its facilities worldwide.

這家健身俱樂部是大都會健身網的分支機構，所以會員可以免費使用它在世界各地的任何設施。

0060 ** **affiliate** [ə`fɪlɪ͵et]	名 分支機構；分會；加入會員 動 聯合；加入 衍 **affiliation** 名 合併；聯繫

• network 網絡

CHAPTER 1 UNIT 02

CheckTest

0031 ⇨ 0060

請依照文意將適當的單字填入空格中。可參考第 39 頁所提示的單字來作答。（作答時間：5 分鐘）

① The per capita income of Connecticut is much higher than the national ________.

② One of the most serious threats to the survival of animal species is the disappearance of their ________.

③ Bernie got a part-time job handing out ________ for a newly opened restaurant.

④ Sally resigned because the company kept rejecting her ________ ideas for new products.

⑤ We will have to change the ________ of the entire product line if we want it to conform to EU regulations.

⑥ Turning off unnecessary lights in the home and the workplace is an easy and efficient way to ________ energy.

⑦ Computer companies lose a great deal of revenue every year as a result of software ________.

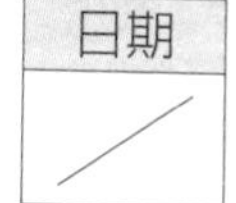

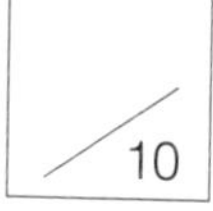

⑧ Mr. Howard had been vice-president of the company for almost two __________ before he was promoted to president.

⑨ With the proposed changes in the tax law, many companies will have to change their investment __________.

⑩ The financial aid from the World Bank will be used primarily to improve the nation's transportation and telecommunications __________.

參考用字

innovative	flyer	conserve	decade
specifications	habitat	piracy	average
strategy	infrastructure		

（解答請參閱第 429 頁）

Unit 03

convention / conference / symposium

MP3 04

In his role as director of an agricultural cooperative, Jerry Condon flies all over the United States to attend farmers' conventions.

身為農業合作社的理事，傑瑞 · 康登要飛到全美各地去參加農民大會。

0061 ** **convention** [kən`vɛnʃən]	名 大會；公約；慣例 衍 **conventional** 形 慣例的；陳腐的

• cooperative 合作社

TOEIC POINT convention 有「同業人員或團隊定期舉辦的集會」的意思，也常用來指「政黨以宣傳或招募基金為目的舉辦的大會」。如：annual convention（年會）、annual convention of the Democratic / Republican Party（民主黨 / 共和黨年會）。

The International Conference of the British Medical Association will take place in Edinburgh this year.

英國醫學協會的國際會議今年將在愛丁堡舉行。

0062 ** **conference** [`kɑnfərəns]	名 會議；會談；協議 衍 **confer** 動 協商；授予

TOEIC POINT conference 指「企業、學校等機構內部召開的會議」。

Professor Alice Wyman read a paper on the novels of Haruki Murakami at a symposium on contemporary Japanese literature.

艾莉絲 · 魏曼教授針對村上春樹的小說，在日本當代文學座談會上發表了一篇論文。

0063 * **symposium** [sɪm`pozɪəm]	名 座談會；討論會

• contemporary 當代的

TOEIC POINT symposium 是指「針對特定主題，專家與學者齊聚一堂參與討論及發表的會議」。

entrepreneur / venture / speculation

It is typical of entrepreneurs to sell off a business once it is successful and move on to a new idea.

一旦成功，創業家一般都會把事業賣掉，並往新的想法邁進。

0064 * **entrepreneur** [ˌɑntrəprəˋnɝ]	㊔ 創業家；企業家

- typical 典型的
- once it is ... 一旦……
- move on 邁進

Our shareholders are worried that the new venture in China may not deliver significant profits for the next five years.

我們的股東擔心在中國的創投事業未來五年或許無法帶來可觀的利潤。

0065 ** **venture** [ˋvɛntʃɝ]	㊔ 投機事業；有風險的事業 ㊯ **venture (into) ...** 冒險去做……

- shareholder 股東
- significant 可觀的；有意義的

Speculation can bring high financial rewards if it's successful, but it can also lead to financial ruin.

假如成功了，投機可以帶來高額的金錢報酬，但是它也可能導致破產。

0066 **speculation** [ˌspɛkjəˋleʃən]	㊔ 投機；推測；臆測 **speculation in futures** 炒作期貨 ㊞ **speculate** 動 投機；推測 **speculative** 形 投機的；推測的 **speculator** 名 投機者

- reward 報酬
- ruin 毀壞；廢墟

Chapter 1
Unit 03 | 重要單字

frustration / breakdown / setback

Joe could not understand the writer's meaning, and expressed his frustration by throwing the book across the room.

喬看不懂作者的意思，於是就把書扔到房間的那頭，以發洩他的挫折感。

0067 ** **frustration** [ˌfrʌsˋtreʃən]	名 挫折（感）；（心理）慾望得不到滿足 衍 **frustrate** 動 使挫折 **be frustrated with ...** 對……感到挫折

Depression is one of the symptoms of a nervous breakdown.

憂鬱是一種神經衰弱的症狀。

0068 ** **breakdown** [ˋbrekˌdaʊn]	名（機械等）故障；（精神、肉體等）衰弱；挫折 衍 **break down** 動 破壞；故障；分解

※ breakdown 另有「明細（表）」之意，例如：As soon as you give us the breakdown, we will discuss it at the board meeting. 你一把明細給我們，我們就會在董事會上討論。

Our house-building project suffered a serious setback when the contractor went bankrupt.

由於包商破產，我們的住宅興建案遭到了嚴重的挫敗。

0069 * **setback** [ˋsɛtˌbæk]	名 妨礙（進步）；挫敗；倒退 衍 **set back** 動 使挫敗

※ setback 可用來指建築法規裡的一項規定。依該項法規規定，建築物在興建時，必須與建築基地的界線保持一定的距離。這項法規的目的在於確保相鄰住戶之間彼此的日照權。

token / hallmark / emblem

As a token of our appreciation, we are very pleased to present this gold watch to Mel for his thirty years of loyal service to our company.

為了表示感謝，我們非常高興把這支金錶送給梅爾，以表彰他為公司忠心服務了三十年。

0070 * **token** [ˋtokən]	名 象徵；表示；（地下鐵、公車等的）代幣；（商品）兌換卷

※ 其他 token 的用法：
by the same token（同樣地）、in token of（表示）、token payment（象徵性償付）。

Senator Agnes Ludlow's hallmark is her integrity, which is rather a rare quality among politicians.

參議員艾格妮絲・拉德洛的註冊商標就是她的誠信，這是政治人物相當難得一見的特質。

0071 * **hallmark** [ˋhɔl͵mɑrk]	名 優良標記；特徵；貴金屬純度的證明印記

• integrity 誠信；正直

The chrysanthemum is an emblem of the Japanese royal family.

菊花是日本皇室的象徵圖案。

0072 **emblem** [ˋɛmbləm]	名 象徵性的花紋（紋章）；標誌；象徵

• chrysanthemum 菊花
• royal family 皇室

property / asset / real estate

The copyright on Ernest's novels will be the property of his heirs after his death.

恩斯特的小說版權在他死後將成為後代子孫的財產。

0073 ** **property** [ˋprɑpətɪ]	名 房地產；財產；所有物

• heir 繼承人

※ intellectuall property rights (IPR)（智慧財產權）、property tax（房地產稅）

A strong sales division is our firm's most valuable asset.

強大的銷售部門是我們公司最珍貴的資產。

0074 ** **asset** [ˋæsɛt]	名（個人或公司團體的）財產；資產

※ 本句中的 asset 指的是 positive feature / strong point（優勢 / 優點）之意。

In order to save the company, we will have to sell our 20 acres of real estate in Connecticut as soon as possible.

為了挽救公司，我們必須盡快把康乃迪克州 20 畝的不動產給脫手。

0075 ** **real estate** [ˋriəl ɪsˋtet]	名 不動產 **real estate agency / agent** 不動產業者 關 **movable / liquid asset** 名 動產

• acre（面積的單位）畝，1 acre ≒ 4,047 平方公尺

saying / proverb / aphorism

There's a saying in our country: "A bright sunset means a good catch the next day."

我國有句俗話說：「夕陽鮮紅代表隔天的漁獲會不錯。」

0076 ** **saying** [ˋseɪŋ]	名 俗話；諺語 類 **cliché** 陳腔濫調

On returning home after many years of working overseas, Ivan really felt the truth of the proverb, "There's no place like home."

在海外工作多年後回家時，伊凡真的覺得這句諺語很對：「金窩銀窩不如自己的狗窩。」

0077 * **proverb** [ˋprɑvɝb]	名 諺語；格言；俗話 衍 **proverbial** 形 諺語的；眾所周知的

Professor Cain used to quote aphorisms of Shakespeare in his lectures.

肯恩教授以前在講課時，常會引述莎士比亞的格言。

0078 **aphorism** [ˋæfəˏrɪzəm]	名 格言

• quote 引述；報價
quote the price 報價

means / measure / ruler

We know the suspect had the means and the opportunity to commit the murder, but he does not appear to have a motive.

我們知道嫌犯有犯下謀殺案的手段和機會，但是他似乎並沒有動機。

0079 ** **means** [minz]	名（複數形）手段；方法；收入 **means of transportation** 交通工具

• appear to ... 似乎

※ 單數形的 mean 指「平均值」。（參照 0053）

Students were impressed by Mr. Wing's inspiring lecture, which clearly showed the measure of his intellect.

學生很欣賞溫先生啓迪人心的演講，他的博學程度也在其中展露無遺。

0080 ** **measure** [\`mɛʒɚ]	名 基準；尺度；度量法；計量單位；手段；措施 動 測量

※「捲尺」叫 tape measure。

When I was in elementary school, the teachers punished us if we did not bring a pencil, a notebook and a ruler to class with us every day.

在我讀小學時，假如我們沒有每天帶鉛筆、筆記本和尺去上課，老師就會處罰我們。

0081 **ruler** [\`rulɚ]	名 尺；統治者

• punish 處罰

※「三角尺」叫 triangle ruler。

fake / shallow / superficial

The criminal used a fake ID to open a bank account and get a driver's licence.

該罪犯利用偽造的身分證去銀行開戶並取得駕照。

0082 * **fake** [fek]	形 偽造的；假的 類 **phony** 假的、**counterfeit** 仿造的

• ID (= identification) 身分證件

John is so shallow. All he ever talks about is sports and video games.

約翰真是膚淺。他開口閉口談的都是運動和電玩。

0083 ** **shallow** [`ʃælo]	形 淺的；膚淺的

Loris talks well, but I feel her knowledge is only superficial. We really need a consultant who is an expert in the field of Asian trade.

蘿莉絲很健談，可是我覺得她的學識只是表面上的。我們真正需要的顧問應該是亞洲貿易方面的專家。

0084 **superficial** [`supɚ`fɪʃəl]	形 浮面的；表面的；膚淺的 衍 **superficially** 副 表面地；淺薄地

gain / increase / increment

According to our fiscal report, we seem to have managed to come through this period of depression with some gain.

根據我們的財務報告，我們似乎勉強度過了這段時期的不景氣，並有一些獲利。

0085 ** **gain** [gen]	名 利益；收穫；獲利 **capital gain** 資本盈利（出售資產或投資所獲得的利潤） 動 獲得；增加

- fiscal report 財務報告
- manage to 勉強

There has been an enormous increase in the number of cooking programs on television in the last few years.

過去幾年來，電視上的料理節目數量大增。

0086 ** **increase** [ˋɪnkris]	名 增加；增長 動 增加；提高（注意發音為 [ɪnˋkris]） 反 **decrease** 名 減少 動 減少

Not all the full-time workers get an annual pay raise in the form of a fixed increment.

並非所有的全職員工都是以固定增量的方式調漲年薪。

0087 **increment** [ˋɪnkrəmənt]	名 增加；增加量；增額 反 **decrement** 減少；減少量

TOEIC POINT increase 一般指「生產力、業績、人數、獲利等的增加」，而 increment 則多指「固定基本金額（存款或基本薪資）因利率而增加的額度」。

compromise / admit / concede

The two governments had no choice but to compromise on certain conditions so that the beef would be promptly imported into the country.

兩國政府別無選擇，只能在某些條件上妥協，使牛肉很快就能進口到國內。

0088 ** **compromise** [ˋkɑmprəˏmaɪz]	動 妥協；和解 名 折衷；妥協 類 **conciliate / arbitrate** 動 和解；調停 **conciliation / arbitration** 名 和解；調停

※ conciliate 是指自發性的和解，而 arbitrate 則是透過法律強制和解。

Frank admitted that the fire at the factory broke out as a result of his negligence.

法蘭克坦承由於他的疏忽，工廠才會失火。

0089 ** **admit** [ədˋmɪt]	動 承認；錄取 衍 **admission** 名 承認；錄取；（入場、入學的）許可 **admittance** 名 入場許可；加入許可

The administration finally conceded its employees' right to take child-care leave.

管理部門總算讓步，承認員工有權請育嬰假。

0090 **concede** [kənˋsid]	動（勉強）承認；讓步 衍 **concession** 名 讓步；特許權

※ concede 與 conceit（自負）發音相近，要小心避免混淆。

CheckTest

0061 ⇨ 0090

請依照文意將適當的單字填入空格中。可參考第 51 頁所提示的單字來作答。(作答時間：5 分鐘)

① As a ________ of our appreciation, we are very pleased to present this gold watch to Mel for his thirty years of loyal service to our company.

② It is typical of ________ to sell off a business once it is successful and move on to a new idea.

③ Depression is one of the symptoms of a nervous ________.

④ In his role as director of an agricultural cooperative, Jerry Condon flies all over the United States to attend farmers' ________.

⑤ A strong sales division is our firm's most valuable ________.

⑥ According to our fiscal report, we seem to have managed to come through this period of depression with some ________.

⑦ Students were impressed by Mr. Wing's inspiring lecture, which clearly showed the ________ of his intellect.

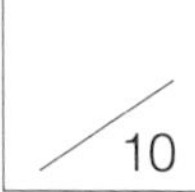

⑧ The criminal used a __________ ID to open a bank account and get a driver's licence.

⑨ Professor Cain used to quote __________ of Shakespeare in his lectures.

⑩ The two governments had no choice but to __________ on certain conditions so that the beef would be promptly imported into the country.

參考用字

breakdown	aphorisms	conventions	entrepreneur
compromise	token	measure	fake
asset	gain		

（解答請參閱第 429 頁）

Unit 04

confiscate / forfeit / waive

Sorry, your pine cone object has to be confiscated. You are not allowed to bring any plants or plant-related products into this country.

抱歉，您的松果物件必須沒收。您不能把任何植物或與植物相關的產品帶進這個國家。

0091 * **confiscate** [ˋkɑnfɪs͵ket]	動 沒收；充公 衍 **confiscation** 名 沒收 類 **seize** 捉住；查封；沒收

• pine cone 松果

Useful POINT 機場因恐怖攻擊頻傳而開始對行李進行嚴密檢查，乘客欲將液體帶入機艙時，必須受新規則管制。

If a full month rent is not paid in 10 days, you will forfeit your right to keep this condominium.

假如月租沒有在 10 天內繳清，你就會喪失保留這間公寓的權利。

0092 ** **forfeit** [ˋfɔr͵fɪt]	動（因犯罪、失職、違約等）喪失權利 名 沒收物；罰金 類 **be deprived of ...** ……遭到剝奪（參照 0556）

• condominium 公寓大樓

You should never waive your right to demand payment for the damage of your car. The accident was entirely his fault.

你絕對不該放棄要求賠償車子損失的權利。車禍完全是他的錯。

0093 * **waive** [wev]	動 放棄（權力）；撤回（要求） 衍 **waiver** 名 棄權聲名（書） 類 **abandon** 拋棄、**give up** 放棄、**not claim** 不主張

• damage 損害；損失

alumni / alma mater / fraternity / sorority

Smith College Alumni Association will hold its annual overnight retreat in Mt. Snow on July 15.

史密斯學院的校友會將於 7 月 15 日在雪山舉行一年一度的隔夜靜修。

0094 ** **alumni** [ə`lʌmnaɪ]	名 校友；畢業生 **alumni association** 校友會

※ alumnus 為單數，但通常多使用複數形的 alumni。

※ overnight 指「二天一夜」。另，retreat 原指「退隱處、靜居處」。

If your daughter is interested in applying to Pheaton College, my alma mater, I shall be happy to introduce her to the dean.

假如你女兒有意申請我的母校費頓學院，我很樂意向院長引薦她。

0095 ** **alma mater** [`ælmə`metɚ]	名 母校

• dean（大學的）院長；學務長；教務長

※ 大學的校長為 president【美】或 principle【英】。

Many of my fellow fraternity / sorority members have become my lifelong friends, while others have given me invaluable career advice.

我在兄弟會 / 姊妹會的會員有很多都成了我一輩子的朋友，有的還給過我無價的生涯建言。

0096 **fraternity** [frə`tɝnətɪ]	名 兄弟會
0097 **sorority** [sə`rɔrətɪ]	名 姊妹會

※ fraternity / sorority 指的是學校男 / 女聯誼會的成員，彼此因同住一個屋簷而有著深厚的感情。

Chapter 1 Unit 04 重要單字

status / standing / reputation

Teachers have high social status, but earn relatively low salaries.

老師擁有崇高的社會地位，但是所賺取的薪資相對偏低。

0098 ** **status** [ˋstetəs]	名 地位；身分；立場

- relatively 比較的；相對的

George's standing in his local community fell drastically after he was convicted of drunk driving.

在因酒駕而被判有罪後，喬治在當地社區的聲望便一落千丈。

0099 ** **standing** [ˋstændɪŋ]	名 聲望；立場；地位 類 **position** 地位

- drastically 大幅地
- be convicted of 被判有罪
- drunk driving 酒駕

Useful POINT 在美國 DUI (=driving under the influence) 指「受酒精與藥劑影響之下的駕駛行為」。

The reputation of the workforce in the city had a big impact on our decision to relocate our factory there.

該市的勞動力之風評，對於我們將工廠遷移的決定有很大的影響。

0100 ** **reputation** [ˌrɛpjəˋteʃən]	名 名聲；風評 衍 **reputable** 形 有聲望的；風評不錯的

- workforce 勞動力
- impact 影響；衝擊
- relocate 重新安置；遷移

notice / alert / warning

According to my rental contract, I have to give the owner of my apartment two months' notice if I want to move out.

根據我的租約，假如我要搬離，我必須在兩個月前通知房東。

0101 ** **notice** [ˋnotɪs]	名 通知；公告 動 注意 衍 **notify** 動 通知；通告 **notification** 名 通知；通告

• rental contract 租約

The weather bureau's tornado alert was issued too late for the residents to evacuate safely.

氣象局太晚發布龍捲風警報，居民來不及安全撤離。

0102 ** **alert** [əˋlɜt]	名 警報；警戒 **on the alert** 保持警戒 動 示警；使警覺 形 警覺的；機伶的

• evacuate 撤離

All the flights have been canceled due to the hurricane warning in Florida.

所有的航班都因為佛羅里達的颶風警報而取消了。

0103 ** **warning** [ˋwɔrnɪŋ]	名 警告；警報 衍 **warn** 動 警告；提醒 類 **caution** 名 小心；謹慎 動 提醒；告誡

TOEIC POINT alert 比 warning 更能形容事情的急迫性，快速反應與處置為重要關鍵。

policy / premium / surcharge

This insurance policy guarantees the payment of $500,000 in case of your death.

萬一你身故了，這份保單保證償付 50 萬美元。

0104 ** **policy** [ˋpɑləsɪ]	名 政策；方針；保單 **health insurance policy** 健康保險保單 類 **guidelines** 準則；守則

※ policy 常指「政策、方針」，例如：Our father's policy was to be always honest with his children.（我爸爸的方針是，永遠要對子女誠實。）

The premium for health insurance policies gets more expensive as people get older.

人的年紀愈大，健康保險的保費就愈貴。

0105 ** **premium** [ˋprimɪəm]	名 保費；獎金；附加費 形 高品質的 **premium gasoline** 高級汽油

There will be no surcharge for transferring all your calls and messages to your cell phone.

把所有的來電和訊息轉到您的行動電話上不用額外收費。

0106 ** **surcharge** [ˋsɝˌtʃɑrdʒ]	名 額外收費；附加費 **surcharge on imports** 進口附加費

due / overdue / expiration

Right now, I'm in my 20th week. And our baby is due early July.

目前我是第 20 週。我們的寶寶預計在 7 月初誕生。

0107 ** **due** [dju]	形（支票等）應給付的；到期的；預計的 名 應付款

※ due date 截止日期 (=deadline)；到期日；預產日

His flight is overdue; it should have arrived half an hour ago.

他的班機延誤了；它半小時前就該到了。

0108 ** **overdue** [ˋovɚˋdju]	形 過期的；遲到的 類 **delayed** 延誤的

I'm afraid you can't use this credit card; the expiration date was last month.

你這張信用卡恐怕不能用了；到期日是上個月。

0109 ** **expiration** [ˏɛkspəˋreʃən]	名 到期；期滿 衍 **expire** 動 到期

※「有效日期至……」說成 valid until ...。

identify / classify / categorize

Bar codes are used to identify not only merchandise but also individual insects such as bees and beetles.

條碼不僅被用來識別商品，還用來識別個別的昆蟲，比如蜜蜂和甲蟲。

0110 ** **identify** [aɪˋdɛntəˏfaɪ]	動 識別；確認 衍 **identification** 名 身分證明；識別；認同 **identical** 形 相同的；一模一樣的

※ 在台灣所使用的「身分證」稱為 ID (identification card)。

The books in the library are classified according to subject matter and author.

圖書館的書是依照主題和作者來分類。

0111 * **classify** [ˋklæsəˏfaɪ]	動 分類；分級；列為機密 衍 **classified** 形 列為機密的 **classification** 名 分類；分級

※ the classifieds 指「(報紙的) 分類廣告，相當於 classified ads」。另，求職、求才、徵租、讓售等之「徵求廣告」稱為 want ad。

I would categorize Henry as a habitual liar; he never tells the truth.

我會把亨利歸類為撒謊的慣犯；他從來不說實話。

0112 * **categorize** [ˋkætəgəraɪz]	動 歸類 衍 **category** 名 類別；類目

TOEIC POINT categorize 與 classify 的意思相近，但 categorize 就如本例，可用於個性、性格這類的分類，而 classify 則不用來形容個性。

drive / impose / compel

China's demand for raw materials is driving the economic expansion of resource-rich countries such as Australia and Canada.

中國對原物料的需求帶動了資源豐富國家的經濟擴展，像是澳洲和加拿大。

0113 ** **drive** [draɪv]	動 帶動 名 動力

- raw material 原物料
- economic expansion 經濟擴展
- resource-rich country 資源豐富的國家

The new tax law will impose a great burden on people in the middle-income bracket.

新的稅法將對中等收入階層的民眾造成重擔。

0114 * **impose** [ɪm`poz]	動 強加；實施 **impose on / upon ...** 強加於…… 衍 **imposition** 名 強加；課徵

- burden 負擔
- middle-income 中等收入的
- bracket 括弧【】的一邊；等級

You cannot compel the audience to applaud. Applause has to come spontaneously.

你不能強迫觀眾鼓掌。鼓掌必須出於自願。

0115 * **compel** [kəm`pɛl]	動 強迫；強求 衍 **compelling** 形 強制的；令人注目的；有說服力的

- applaud 鼓掌喝采；稱讚（名詞為 applause）
- spontaneously 自發地；自然自發地

generous / lenient / indulgent

You shouldn't give **generous** gifts just to look good in the eyes of others.

你不該只為了讓別人看了有面子而大方送禮。

0116 ** **generous** [ˋdʒɛnərəs]	形 大方的；寬大的；豐盛的 衍 **generosity** 名 寬宏大量；大方

• in the eyes of others 在他人眼裡

A teacher's **lenient** attitude may be considered his or her weak point.

一個老師的態度溫和可能會被視為是他 / 她的缺點。

0117 * **lenient** [ˋlinjənt]	形 溫和的；寬大的；仁慈的 衍 **leniency** 名 寬大；仁慈 類 **easygoing** 隨和的

• weak point 弱點（反義字為 strong point 優點）

His parents were very **indulgent** toward him; they let him do whatever he wanted.

他爸媽對他非常放縱；他們讓他為所欲為。

0118 * **indulgent** [ɪnˋdʌldʒənt]	形 縱容的；放任的 衍 **indulge** 動 縱容；沉迷 **indulge oneself in ...** 沉浸在…… **indulgence** 名 沉溺 類 **tolerant** 容忍的

TOEIC POINT indulge 常用於否定的意思。例如：If parents indulge their children's every desire, they risk spoiling them.（如果父母隨意滿足孩子們的每一個慾望，有可能會寵壞他們。）

profitable / beneficial / lucrative

The general view is that most new businesses do not become profitable for at least three years.

一般認為，大部分的新企業至少要經過三年才會獲利。

0119 ** **profitable** [ˋprɑfɪtəbl̩]	形 賺錢的；獲利的 衍 **profit** 動 獲利；受益 名 利益；利潤

• general view 一般的看法

We would very much like to be given the opportunity to discuss how our technology could be beneficial to your industry.

我們非常希望能有個機會，討論我們的技術如何能對你們的產業有所助益。

0120 ** **beneficial** [ˏbɛnəˋfɪʃəl]	形 有益的；有利的 衍 **benefit** 動 利益；好處；救濟金；福利 **pension benefit** 退休給付

• technology 技術；科技

※ benefit concert / performance 指「慈善音樂會／表演」。

It is unrealistic to expect to get a lucrative job immediately after you graduate from university.

期望大學畢業後就立刻找到賺錢的工作是不切實際的。

0121 * **lucrative** [ˋlukrətɪv]	形 賺錢的；有利可圖的

TOEIC POINT profitable 用於「從事業而獲得利潤」的情況，lucrative 則有「輕易地一獲千金」之意。

CHAPTER 1 UNIT 04

CheckTest

0091 ⇨ 0121

請依照文意將適當的單字填入空格中。可參考第 63 頁所提示的單字來作答。(作答時間：5 分鐘)

① According to my rental contract, I have to give the owner of my apartment two months' __________ if I want to move out.

② His parents were very __________ toward him; they let him do whatever he wanted.

③ The __________ of the workforce in the city had a big impact on our decision to relocate our factory there.

④ Sorry, your pine cone object has to be __________. You are not allowed to bring any plants or plant-related products into this country.

⑤ The __________ for health insurance policies gets more expensive as people get older.

⑥ I'm afraid you can't use this credit card; the __________ date was last month.

⑦ Bar codes are used to __________ not only merchandise but also individual insects such as bees and beetles.

日期 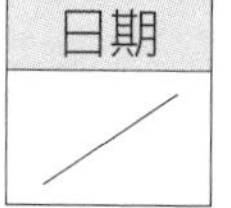 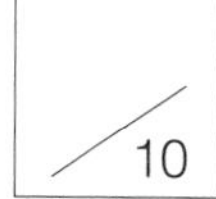

⑧ The new tax law will ________ a great burden on people in the middle-income bracket.

⑨ Smith College ________ Association will hold its annual overnight retreat in Mt. Snow on July 15.

⑩ We would very much like to be given the opportunity to discuss how our technology could be ________ to your industry.

參考用字

reputation	premium	confiscate	alumni
expiration	notice	impose	identify
indulgent	beneficial		

（解答請參閱第 429 頁）

Unit 05

potential / probability / prospect

MP3 06

Trudy has the potential to become the most successful sales executive in the history of the company.

楚迪有潛力成為公司歷來最成功的業務主管。

0122 ** **potential** [pə`tɛnʃəl]	名 可能性；潛力 **has the potential to ...** 有潛力…… 形 可能的；潛在的 衍 **potentiality** 名 潛能；潛在性

• sales executive 業務主管

You have a higher probability of dying in an air crash than of winning first prize in the lottery.

死於空難比贏得樂透頭獎的機率要高。

0123 ** **probability** [ˌprɑbə`bɪlətɪ]	名 機率；或然率 衍 **probable** 形 大概的；可能發生的

※ 與 possible 相較，probable 指「發生的機率較高的可能」。

After a successful round of talks between the leaders of the two countries, prospects for peace in the region seem brighter.

在兩國領袖經過一輪成功的會談後，該地區的和平前景似乎較為光明。

0124 ** **prospect** [`prɑspɛkt]	名 前景；預期 衍 **prospective** 形 預期的；盼望中的；未來的 類 **expectation** 預期；期待、**outlook** 展望；視野

• a round 一輪

versatile / adaptable / diverse

Will is not a great musician but he is very versatile; he plays piano, guitar, trumpet and violin.

威爾並不是了不起的音樂家，但是他非常多才多藝；他會演奏鋼琴、吉他、喇叭和小提琴。

0125 ** **versatile** [ˋvɜsətaɪl]	形 多才多藝的；多功能的 衍 **versatility** 名 多才多藝；多功能 類 **multi-talented** 多才多藝的

Being adaptable and also trilingual, Cathy was immediately chosen to work in the UN Office in Geneva.

適應力強又精通三種語言，凱西立刻就被選派去日內瓦的聯合國總部服務。

0126 ** **adaptable** [əˋdæptəbḷ]	形 適應力強的；適合的 衍 **adapt** 動 使適應；改編 **adaptation** 名 適應；改編 類 **flexible** 有彈性的、**adjustable** 可調整的

Because of his diverse experience, David Goodwin developed strong skills as a business consultant.

由於有多樣化的歷練，大衛 · 古德溫培養出擔任企業顧問的高超本領。

0127 **diverse** [daɪˋvɜs]	形 不同的；多樣的 衍 **diversity** 名 差異；不同點 **diversify** 動 多樣化；多角化 類 **various** 各式各樣的、**miscellaneous** 五花八門的

significant / considerable / noteworthy

The City just landed one of the most significant investments in years: a factory to manufacture two million printers annually.

該市剛獲得多年來其中一筆最重大的投資：一座每年可製造 200 萬台印刷機的工廠。

0128 ** **significant** [sɪg`nɪfəkənt]	形 重大的；有意義的 衍 **signify** 動 表示；象徵；有重要性 **significance** 名 重要性；意義

• land 獲得；著陸
• investment 投資
• annually 每年的

Keen's considerable experience in the field of robotics will make him a great asset to our organization.

基恩在機器人學方面的可觀經驗將使他成為我們組織的一大資產。

0129 ** **considerable** [kən`sɪdərəbḷ]	形 重要的；可觀的；相當多的 衍 **considerably** 副 相當地

• robotics 機器人學
• asset 資產

請小心不要將 considerable 與 considerate（體貼的）混淆。

Professor Gregory has written more than 50 academic papers, but unfortunately only two or three are noteworthy.

桂格利教授寫過 50 多篇學術論文，但可惜的是，只有兩、三篇值得留意。

0130 * **noteworthy** [`notˌwɝðɪ]	形 值得留意的；顯著的 類 **remarkable** 出色的；了不起的 **notable** 著名的；顯著的

• academic papers 學術論文

valid / applicable / legitimate

Everyone who uses a company vehicle must have a valid motor pool checkout card.

每個使用公司座車的人都必須持有車輛調度處的有效通行卡。

0131 ** **valid** [ˋvælɪd]	形 正確的；有效的 衍 **validity** 名 效力；正確性 類 **official** 官方的；正式的 反 **invalid** 無效的

• vehicle 車輛 • motor pool 車輛調度處

※ invalid 也可指「久病的；傷殘的」或「病弱者；傷殘者」，但發音為 [ˋɪnvəlɪd]。

We regret to inform you that we cannot offer you the post because your experience, though very impressive, is not entirely applicable to this type of work.

我們很遺憾地通知您，我們無法請您來任職，因為您的資歷雖然非常亮眼，但是並不完全適合這類型的工作。

0132 * **applicable** [ˋæplɪkəbl̩]	形 適任的；合用的 衍 **apply** 動 應用；申請；塗抹 **application** 名 申請；應用；塗抹

• impressive 令人印象深刻的 • not entirely ... 不完全……

TOEIC POINT 「到一家公司應徵」說成 apply to a company，而「應徵某個職位或是申請獎學金」則說成 apply for a position / apply for a scholarship。

The lawyers decided that my claim to my late uncle's estate was a legitimate one.

律師們斷定，我要求繼承已故伯父的遺產是合法的。

0133 **legitimate** [lɪˋdʒɪtəmɪt]	形 合法的；正當的 類 **lawful** 法律上正當的、**legal** 合法的 反 **illegitimate** 非法的

• claim 名 主張；要求

current / contemporary / topical

Our current CEO has succeeded in rescuing the company from possible bankruptcy and putting it back in the black.

我們目前的執行長成功挽救了可能破產的公司，並使它回復到有盈餘。

0134 ** **current** [ˋkɝənt]	形 目前的；現行的 名 流動；潮流；趨勢 衍 **currently** 副 目前 類 **present** 現在的

My professor believes that we must read literary classics before we can appreciate contemporary novels.

我的教授認為，我們必須先讀文學經典，才懂得欣賞當代小說。

0135 ** **contemporary** [kənˋtɛmpəˏrɛrɪ]	形 當代的 名 同時代的人；同時期的東西

TOEIC POINT modern 與 contemporary 在文學或美術作品的領域裡分指「現代」與「當代」。

We always try to pick up the most topical subjects for our morning news show, "Good Morning USA."

我們總是盡量替我們的晨間新聞節目「早安美國」挑選最有話題性的題材。

0136 * **topical** [ˋtɑpɪkl̩]	形 時下關注的；時興話題的 類 **up-to-date** 最新的；新潮的

※ topical 另有「局部的」之意，例如 a topical ointment「局部用藥膏」。

award / grant / runner-up

Gareth Foster won the award for the most promising young novelist. The prize was a Rolex wrist watch.

葛瑞 · 佛斯特贏得了最有希望的年輕小說家獎項。獎品是一支勞力士手錶。

0137 ** **award** [ə`wɔrd]	名 獎項；獎賞 動 獎賞；授予 **award a prize** 頒獎

• promising 有希望的；有前途的

The government is thinking of cutting its grants to museums and encouraging them to raise funds from private sources.

政府在考慮要削減對博物館的補助，並鼓勵它們向民間募款。

0138 ** **grant** [grænt]	名 撥款；補助金 動 授予；准許

• encourage 鼓勵
• raise funds 募款
• private sources 民間來源

The winner of the race was disqualified for using illegal drugs, and so the gold medal went to the runner-up.

比賽的優勝者因為使用禁藥而被取消資格，所以金牌頒給了亞軍。

0139 * **runner-up** [`rʌnə`rʌp]	名 亞軍

• be disqualified 被取消資格

TOEIC POINT 「亞軍」的精確說法為 first runner-up，「季軍」則稱為 second runner-up。

land / obtain / acquire

After a lot of behind-the-scenes effort, our office finally landed the project.

經過幕後的諸多努力，我們的辦事處終於拿下了這個案子。

0140 ** **land** [lænd]	動 得到；獲得

• behind-the-scenes effort 幕後的努力

※ land 也有「著陸、登陸、著地」的意思（參見 0128）。例如：The plane landed safely in the storm.（飛機在暴風雨中安全降落。）

If you are sick for more than two days, you must obtain a doctor's letter.

假如你生病超過兩天，就必須取得醫生的診斷證明。

0141 ** **obtain** [əb`ten]	動 取得；獲得 衍 **obtainable** 形 可獲得的

• doctor's letter 醫生診斷證明

※「診斷書」可說成 doctor's diagnosis。

Some people believe it is more important to acquire wisdom than to acquire wealth.

有些人認為，獲取智慧比獲取財富重要。

0142 * **acquire** [ə`kwaɪr]	動 取得；獲取；習得 衍 **acquisition** 名 取得；購得 **Mergers and Acquisitions**（M & A）企業併購 類 **gain** 獲得（參見 0085）

odd / peculiar / bizarre

I think Frank might be under too much pressure at work; his behavior has been rather odd recently.

我想法蘭克可能在工作上承擔了太多的壓力；最近他的行為相當怪異。

0143 * **odd** [ɑd]	形 怪異的；奇數的 **odd number** 奇數（偶數為 even number） 類 **strange** 奇怪的、**eccentric** 古怪的

• pressure 壓力
• behavior 行為；舉止

There were some peculiar characteristics about the case that eventually led to the identification of the criminal.

這個案件有一些怪異的特徵，最後終於使罪犯現了形。

0144 ** **peculiar** [pɪˋkjuljə]	形 獨特的；怪異的 衍 **peculiarity** 名 獨特；怪異 類 **strange** 奇怪的、**abnormal** 異常的

• lead to 導致

I think body-piercing is bizarre, but some people consider it perfectly normal.

我覺得人體穿環很怪異，但是有些人認為那十分正常。

0145 **bizarre** [bɪˋzɑr]	形 奇異的；古怪的 類 **weird** 怪誕的

• body-piercing 人體穿環

tactful / discreet / prudent

Try to be very tactful when you approach a would-be client for the first time.

第一次接觸潛在客戶時，要盡量地圓融。

0146 ** **tactful** [ˋtæktfəl]	形 老練的；圓融的 衍 **tactfully** 副 機伶地；圓滑地

The chairperson of the board asked the executive members to be discreet in passing their judgment.

董事長要求執行董事們在下判語時須謹慎。

0147 * **discreet** [dɪˋskrit]	形 謹慎的；慎重考慮的 衍 **discretion** 名 判斷力；謹慎 反 **indiscreet** 不謹慎的；欠考慮的

• executive 執行的；行政的

TOEIC POINT chairperson of the board 指「董事長」，而這裡的 board 指的就是 board of directors（董事會）。

It was not prudent of you to invest all your money in the stock market.

你真是不明智，把所有的錢都砸進股市裡。

0148 * **prudent** [ˋprudn̩t]	形 審慎的；明智的 衍 **prudence** 名 審慎；精明

• stock market 股市

swell / inflate / expand

We could see the swelling river from the helicopter.

我們從直升機上可以看到高漲的河水。

0149 ** swell [swɛl]	動 高漲；膨脹；增加 （過去式、過去分詞為 swelled、swollen） 名 上漲；膨脹

TOEIC POINT 「腫起來」也可用 swell 來表示，例如：My foot swelled up like a melon.（我的腳腫得跟哈密瓜一樣大。）除此之外，swell 還有形容詞的用法，指「很棒；極好」之意，例如：Hello, Jim. You're looking swell ！（哈囉 Jim ！你看起來氣色真好。）

It took 20 minutes to inflate the enormous balloon.

那顆巨大的氣球花了 20 分鐘才膨脹起來。

0150 ** inflate [ɪn`flet]	動 使膨脹；膨脹；充氣 衍 **inflatable** 形 可充氣的 **inflatable boat** 充氣船 **inflation** 名 膨脹；通貨膨脹

※「通貨緊縮」叫 deflation。

Ralph decided to expand his publishing business.

拉夫決定擴大他的出版事業。

0151 ** expand [ɪk`spænd]	動 擴大；擴充 衍 **expansion** 名 擴大；擴充 類 **stretch** 延伸；伸展

CHAPTER 1 UNIT 05

CheckTest

0122 ⇨ 0151

請依照文意將適當的單字填入空格中。可參考第 75 頁所提示的單字來作答。（作答時間：5 分鐘）

① The City just landed one of the most ________ investments in years: a factory to manufacture two million printers annually.

② Will is not a great musician but he is very ________; he plays piano, guitar, trumpet and violin.

③ Trudy has the ________ to become the most successful sales executive in the history of the company.

④ Everyone who uses a company vehicle must have a ________ motor pool checkout card.

⑤ My professor believes that we must read literary classics before we can appreciate ________ novels.

⑥ Try to be very ________ when you approach a would-be client for the first time.

⑦ Some people believe it is more important to ________ wisdom than wealth.

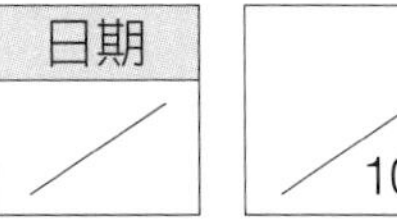

⑧ There were some ________ characteristics about the case that eventually led to the identification of the criminal.

⑨ The winner of the race was disqualified for using illegal drugs, and so the gold medal went to the ________.

⑩ Ralph decided to ________ his publishing business.

參考用字

significant	peculiar	potential	versatile
contemporary	runner-up	valid	tactful
expand	acquire		

（解答請參閱第 429 頁）

Unit 06

income / remuneration / proceeds

While credit cards are very useful, there is a danger that they can lead us to spend more than our income.

信用卡雖然非常有用，但有個危險：它會導致我們花費超過我們收入的錢。

0152 ** **income** [ˋɪn͵kʌm]	動 所得；收入 **income disparity** 所得差距 類 **earnings** 盈餘、**revenue** 歲入；營收 **internal revenue**（美國）國稅局

The law firm offers a high remuneration, but works you like a slave.

該律師事務所給的薪酬很高，但是會把你操得跟奴隸一樣。

0153 ** **remuneration** [rɪ͵mjunəˋreʃən]	名 薪酬；酬勞 衍 **remunerate** 動 酬謝；給酬勞 **remunerate sb. for his trouble** 酬謝某人的辛勞 類 **wage** 工資、**salary** 薪水

※ 本句中的 work 為及物動詞，意思是「使（人）工作」。

The proceeds from the sale of the building paid off the debt.

出售大樓的收益把債還清了。

0154 ** **proceeds** [prəˋsidz]	名 所得；收益 衍 **proceed** 動 行進；出發 **proceedings** 名（複數形）議事錄；訴訟

※ 注意，proceeds 為複數形。類似的用法還包括 earnings（收入）、savings（存款）、finances（財務狀況）等。

support / endorse / ratify

After his parents died in an accident, Seiji had to support himself by taking whatever jobs came his way.

在父母意外喪生後，誠二必須有什麼工作就做什麼工作，以養活自己。

0155	
** **support** [sə`port]	動 支持；養活 **support oneself** 養活自己；自立 名 支持；扶養 **child support** 子女扶養費 衍 **supportive** 形 支持的；贊助的

• come sb.'s way 被某人碰到

If you would like to cash this check, you will have to endorse it.

假如你想兌現這張支票，就必須在上面背書。

0156	
* **endorse** [ɪn`dɔrs]	動 在（發票、票據等）背面簽名；背書；簽署 衍 **endorsement** 名 背書；簽署

• cash a check 兌現支票

Useful POINT endorsement（背書）的意思是為了讓支票等同現金使用，領受人必須在支票背面簽名的行為。

The treaty will not come into force until every signatory nation ratifies it.

要等每個簽約國都認可，條約才會生效。

0157	
* **ratify** [`rætə͵faɪ]	動 批准；認可 衍 **ratification** 名 批准；認可 類 **enact** 制定（法律）

• signatory 簽署者；締約國（從 sign 衍生而來）

TOEIC POINT signature 以及 autograph 的用法容易混淆。「請（在文件上）簽名」可說成 Sign your name, please，但如果要請「某位名人簽名」則要說 May I have your autograph?

refuge / deport / exile

After the volcano erupted, residents of the island were forced to take refuge.

火山爆發後，島上的居民不得不去避難。

0158 ** **refuge** [`rɛfjudʒ]	名 庇護所；避難處 **take refuge** 避難 衍 **refugee** 名 難民

• volcano 火山
• erupt 爆發（名詞為 eruption）

Immigration Services have deported 520 people who illegally entered the country this year.

移民署今年遣返了 520 個非法入境的人。

0159 ** **deport** [dɪ`port]	動 遣返；驅逐 衍 **deportation** 名 遣返；驅逐

• Immigration Services 移民署
• illegally 非法地

The new people's government decided to exile their country's former king.

新的人民政府決定流放該國的前任國王。

0160 * **exile** [`ɛksaɪl]	動 放逐；使流亡 名 放逐；流放

TOEIC POINT exile 有「將國民流放至國外」的意思，而 deport 則是「以違法留滯的理由，強制遣返外國人士」的意思。

faint / collapse / incapacitate

The rush-hour train was so hot and crowded that an elderly woman fainted.

尖峰時間的那班列車十分悶熱擁擠，使得一位老婦人暈倒。

0161 ** **faint** [fent]	動 暈倒；昏厥 名 昏厥 形 快要暈倒的；微弱的 類 **pass out** 昏倒

TOEIC POINT pass out 當不及物動詞使用時，指「昏倒」；作為及物動詞使用時，則有「分發」的意思，如：pass out the test papers（發考卷）。

Betty collapsed into bed after an exhausting day.

累了一天後，貝蒂癱倒在床上。

0162 ** **collapse** [kə`læps]	動 癱倒；崩塌 名 倒塌；崩潰 衍 **collapsible** 形 可摺疊的 **collapsible umbrella** 折疊傘

During the Big Blackout in New York, the train system was completely incapacitated, and many people were forced to walk home.

在紐約大停電期間，火車系統完全停擺，有很多人被迫走路回家。

0163 * **incapacitate** [ˌɪnkə`pæsətet]	動 使喪失功能；使癱瘓 衍 **incapacitated** 形 喪失正常功能的

Useful POINT Big Blackout 指的是 1977 年與 2003 年 8 月紐約市發生的全市大停電。當時造成交通混亂，大部分的人都沿著電車線走路回家，或是步行登上幾十層的高樓。由於沒有交通訊號，居民都自行擔任交通指揮的工作。

※ 一般的「停電」可說成 power outage。

circumstance / circumference / circumvent

To understand why a child is failing in school, it is important to find out about his or her domestic circumstances.

如果要了解孩子在學校為什麼達不到標準，弄清楚他 / 她的家庭狀況就很重要。

0164 ** circumstance [ˋsɝkəm͵stæns]	名 狀況；環境 衍 **circumstantial** 形 狀況的；偶然的；間接的 **circumstantial evidence** 旁證；間接證據

The circumference of this island is only three kilometers. We can easily paddle around it in a canoe.

這座島的周長只有三公里。我們可以輕鬆地划著獨木舟繞行。

0165 * circumference [sɚˋkʌmfərəns]	名 周長；圓周 衍 **circumferential** 形 周長的；圓周的 關 **diameter** 名 直徑、**radius** 名 半徑

• paddle 划行

If you know someone in the city office, you might be able to circumvent the red tape.

假如你在市府裡有認識的人，或許就能避開繁文縟節。

0166 circumvent [͵sɝkəmˋvɛnt]	動 繞行；設法規避 類 **get around** 逃避、**avoid** 避免

• red tape 繁文縟節；官樣文章；費時的繁瑣手續

commitment / devotion / dedication

Helen could not take the job in New York because she had such strong family commitments in Los Angeles.

海倫沒辦法去紐約任職，因為她在洛杉磯家庭責任很重。

0167 ** **commitment** [kə`mɪtənt]	名 責任；承諾；獻身；支持 衍 **commit** 動 託付；承諾；投入；犯（罪） **commit oneself to ...** 承諾、致力於……

Devotion to one company for the whole of one's working life now seems an old-fashioned idea.

把自己的整個工作生涯奉獻給一家公司現在似乎是個過時的觀念。

0168 ** **devotion** [dɪ`voʃən]	名 奉獻；熱愛；虔誠 衍 **devote** 動 奉獻；投身 **devote oneself to ...** 獻身於……

• old-fashioned 老式的；過時的

I really admire Mary's dedication to helping people less fortunate than herself.

我相當欽佩瑪莉致力於幫助比自己不幸的人。

0169 * **dedication** [ˌdɛdə`keʃən]	名 致力；投身；奉獻 衍 **dedicate** 動 致力；投身；奉獻

• less fortunate 比較不幸運

※「弱勢族群」可說成 underprivileged groups。

refund / reimbursement / compensation

I took back the sweater to the store for a refund because it didn't fit.

我把毛衣拿回店裡退錢，因為不合身。

0170 ** **refund** [`rifʌnd]	名 退款；退錢 動 退還錢款（發音為 [rɪ`fʌnd]） 衍 **refundable** 形 可退款的

※「更換的商品」用 replacement 表示。

The accounting department deals with reimbursement of travel expenses at the end of each month.

會計部在每個月的月底都會處理差旅費的退款。

0171 ** **reimbursement** [ˌriɪm`bɝsmənt]	名 核銷；償付 衍 **reimburse** 動 核銷；償付

If the company does not pay Jerry sufficient compensation for his injury, he is threatening to take legal action.

假如公司不付給傑瑞足額的傷害賠償，他就威脅要採取法律行動。

0172 ** **compensation** [ˌkɑmpən`seʃən]	名 補償（金）；賠償（金）；酬勞 衍 **compensate** 動 補償；賠償；彌補

• take legal action 採取法律行動

TOEIC POINT reimbursement 是指「償付代墊的金額」，compensation 則指「蒙受損失時所得的賠償」。

privilege / immunity / exemption

It was a great privilege for me to do research under the supervision of such an eminent scholar as Professor Lucas.

在像盧卡斯教授這麼傑出的學者指導下做研究，是我的莫大榮幸。

0173 ** **privilege** [ˋprɪvl̩ɪdʒ]	名 特權；榮幸

- supervision 監督；指揮；指導
- eminent 著名的；傑出的

The criminal was promised immunity from prosecution if he gave testimony against his associates.

犯人得到保證，只要他供出不利於同夥的證詞，就能免於遭到起訴。

0174 ** **immunity** [ɪˋmjunətɪ]	名 免除；免疫力 **diplomatic immunity** 外交豁免權 衍 **immune** 形 免除的；免疫的 **immune system** 免疫系統

- testimony 證詞
- associate 夥伴；同事

Military service is compulsory, but members of religious organizations can be granted exemptions.

服兵役是義務，但是宗教組織的成員可以獲准免除。

0175 * **exemption** [ɪgˋzɛmpʃən]	名（義務等）免除；減免 **tax exemption** 免稅（額） 衍 **exempt** 動 免除 形 被免除的

fatal / lethal / toxic

Cancer is no longer a fatal disease if it is treated at an early stage.

假如早期治療，癌症就不再是致命的疾病。

0176 ** **fatal** [ˋfetl̩]	形 致命的；毀滅性的 **fatal mistake** 致命的錯誤 衍 **fatality** 名 死亡人數（可數）；致命性

The victim was murdered by a lethal dose of poison.

被害者是被一劑致命的毒藥所殺害。

0177 * **lethal** [ˋliθəl]	形 致命的；致死的 類 **deadly** 致命的；勢不兩立的

An overdose of this pain reliever is toxic, and may harm your health.

這種止痛藥使用過量會中毒，並且可能有害健康。

0178 ** **toxic** [ˋtɑksɪk]	形 有毒的；有害的 衍 **toxin** 名 毒素 關 **detox** 動（使）戒毒；（使）戒酒 **poisonous** 形 有毒的；有壞影響的

- overdose 攝取過量
- pain reliever 止痛藥

※ detox 為 detoxify 之簡略。另，「止痛藥」通俗的說法是 pain killer。

permit / consent / sanction

After passing the written test, you will be given a learner's permit, which allows you to practice on the road.

通過筆試後，你會拿到學習駕照，這樣你就可以上路練習了。

0179 ** **permit** [`pɜmɪt]	名 許可證；執照 動 許可；允許（發音為 [pɚ`mɪt]） 反 **prohibit** 動 禁止；阻止

TOEIC POINT learner's permit 是「學習者駕照」，筆試之後可領取此證。只要教練或擁有駕照的人在副駕駛座同乘，就能在馬路上練習駕駛。

I'm afraid you can't use this parking space without written consent from the building management.

沒有大樓管委會的同意，恐怕你不能使用這個停車位。

0180 * **consent** [kən`sɛnt]	名 答應；同意 動 答應；同意 **My parents finally consented to our marriage.** （我爸媽總算同意我們結婚了。）

• parking space 停車位

The economic sanctions against the country are making it harder for the people to obtain daily necessities such as food and fuel.

對該國的經濟制裁，使得民眾較難取得食物與燃料之類的日常必需品。

0181 **sanction** [`sæŋkʃən]	名 批准；認可；制裁；懲罰

• daily necessities 日常必需品

sanction 這個字具有「許可」和「制裁」兩種彼此對立的意思，所以必須從句子來判讀其意。例如，sanction mark 指「許可章」，而 sanctions against the terrorist country 則是指「對恐怖主義國家所進行的制裁」。

CheckTest

0152 ⇨ 0181

請依照文意將適當的單字填入空格中。可參考第 87 頁所提示的單字來作答。(作答時間：5 分鐘)

① The law firm offers a high ________, but works you like a slave.

② Cancer is no longer a ________ disease if it is treated at an early stage.

③ After the volcano erupted, residents of the island were forced to take ________.

④ The accounting department deals with ________ of travel expenses at the end of each month.

⑤ To understand why a child is failing in school, it is important to find out about his or her domestic ________.

⑥ Helen could not take the job in New York because she had such strong family ________ in Los Angeles.

⑦ During the Big Blackout in New York, the train system was completely ________, and many people were forced to walk home.

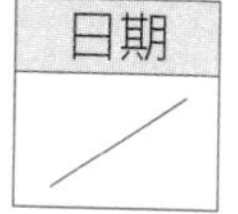

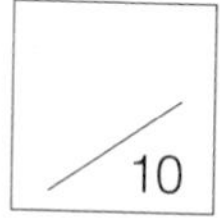

⑧ It was a great ________ for me to do research under the supervision of such an eminent scholar as Professor Lucas.

⑨ If you would like to cash this check, you will have to ________ it.

⑩ I'm afraid you can't use this parking space without written ________ from the building management.

參考用字

commitment	remuneration	circumstance	endorse
incapacitate	privilege	reimbursement	fatal
refuge	consent		

（解答請參閱第 429 頁）

Unit 07

finalize / terminate / cease

MP3 08

We are now finalizing the details of our round-the-world trip with our travel agent.

我們現在正在跟旅行社敲定環球之旅的細節。

0182 ** **finalize** [ˋfaɪnḷˌaɪz]	動 敲定；完成；結束 衍 **finality** 名 定局；完成；終結

• travel agent 旅遊代辦業者

I regret having to terminate your employment due to the financial difficulties our company is currently going through.

我很遺憾必須解雇你，因為公司目前遇到了財務困難。

0183 * **terminate** [ˋtɝməˌnet]	動 終止；使終結 衍 **termination** 名 終止；結束

TOEIC POINT regret having to 是 regret + have to 的動名詞形，有「因不得不做某件事，而感到遺憾」的意思。

Fighting between the two countries officially ceased as soon as the peace treaty was signed.

和平協定一經簽署，兩國便正式停止交戰。

0184 * **cease** [sis]	動 中斷；中止；停止 **cease fire** 停火

• peace treaty 和平協定

antique / replica / hand-me-down

My wife wants to replace all our antique furniture to give our house a more contemporary look.

我太太把我們的骨董家具全換掉，好讓我們家比較有現代感。

0185 ** **antique** [æn`tik]	形 古風的；骨董的 名 骨董；古物

• contemporary look 現代感

This bracelet is an exact replica of one that was worn by Princess Diana.

這副手鐲完全是複製戴安娜王妃所戴的那副。

0186 ** **replica** [`rɛplɪkə]	名 複寫；複製（品） 類 **reproduction** 複製品

Helen comes from a big family, and spent her childhood wearing hand-me-down clothes.

海倫出身自大家庭，小時候都是穿別人穿過的舊衣服。

0187 * **hand-me-down** [`hændmɪˌdaʊn]	形 他人（兄姊）穿過的 名 他人（兄姊）穿過的舊衣 類 **second-hand** 二手的

TOEIC POINT 名詞 hand-me-down 的複數形為 hand-me-downs。

gourmet / gourmand / connoisseur

You should ask Pat about the recipe. He is a real gourmet, especially where French cuisine is concerned.

你應該向派特問一下做法。他是個道地的美食家，尤其是在法國料理方面。

0188 ** **gourmet** [ˋgʊrme]	名 美食家 類 **gastronome** 美食家

• recipe 烹飪法；食譜

Dave's doctor told him to eat less, but he is such a gourmand that he's finding it very difficult to do.

戴夫的醫生要他少吃點，可是他是標準的老饕，所以他覺得很難做到。

0189 **gourmand** [ˋgʊrmənd]	名 老饕；美食家

※ gourmand 也可做「美食家」解，但較常用來指「老饕」。

My mother is quite a connoisseur of Louis XV furniture. She can go on talking about it for hours.

我媽可說是路易十五時代家具的行家。她可以連講上好幾個小時。

0190 * **connoisseur** [ˌkɑnəˋsɝ]	名 行家；鑑賞家

• Louis XV furniture 路易十五時代的家具

Useful POINT 歐洲的國王們（尤其是法國或英國）一旦繼承王位後，就開始為自己創造專屬的建築風格、室內設計或是家具。雖然 TOEIC 不會把這些設計風格當成考題，但 *NEWSWEEK* 或是 *TIME* 這類的英語雜誌卻常出現與這些時代背景或設計風格有關的內容，建議英文學習者最好能擁有這類的基礎知識。

humane / sympathetic / compassionate

Kendall Inc. seems to attract many job applicants due to their humane management policies.

拜人性化管理方針之賜，肯德爾公司似乎吸引了不少求職者。

0191 ** **humane** [hju`men]	形 人道的；人性化的；仁慈的 **humane management policies** 人性化的管理方針 衍 **human** 名 人類 形 人的；人類的 **humanism** 名 人道主義；人本主義

TOEIC POINT humane 與 human 拼字相近，要小心不要混淆。

As human resources manager, you should try to be sympathetic to all employees if they come to you with a complaint.

身為人事經理，對於所有來找你抱怨的員工，你都應該盡量發揮同理心。

0192 ** **sympathetic** [ˌsɪmpə`θɛtɪk]	形 同情的；贊同的；有同理心的 衍 **sympathy** 名 同情；共鳴；贊同

TOEIC POINT 人事部也可稱為 personnel department，但最近比較常使用 human resources department（人力資源部門）來指人事部。另外，human resources development department 則指「人力資源開發部門」。

Living near the dog pound taught Laura to be compassionate toward abandoned animals.

住在流浪狗收容所附近讓蘿拉學習到要同情棄養動物。

0193 **compassionate** [kəm`pæʃənɪt]	形 憐憫的；有同情心的 衍 **compassion** 名 同情；憐憫

• dog pound 流浪狗收容所
• abandoned animals 被棄養的動物

argue / persuade / induce

If you are not prepared to argue with people, you will never get what you want in life.

假如你沒準備好跟別人爭論，你永遠爭取不到人生中所要的東西。

0194 ** **argue** [`ɑrgjʊ]	動 爭論；辯論；爭吵 **The counsel argued the case.** （律師辯論該案件。） 衍 **argument** 名 爭論；辯論；爭吵 **argumentative** 形 爭論的；辯論的 類 **quarrel** 不和；爭吵

• be prepared to 準備好做……

An extensive report on the disastrous earthquake persuaded many people to volunteer to help the victims.

對於慘烈地震的廣泛報導打動了許多人自願去協助災民。

0195 ** **persuade** [pɚ`swed]	動 說服；使信服 衍 **persuasion** 名 說服；說服力 **persuasive** 形 說服的；有說服力的 類 **convince** 使相信；說服

• extensive report 廣泛報導
• disastrous 慘烈的；災害的
• volunteer to 自願做……

It is rather difficult to induce those reckless teenagers to obey the traffic laws.

要促使這些無法無天的青少年遵守交通規則相當困難。

0196 **induce** [ɪn`djus]	動 促使；引起 衍 **induction** 名 誘導；引起；歸納法

※ induction 可指邏輯學的「歸納法」，而與其相對的「演繹法」則稱為 deduction。

naive / candid / ingenuous

Wendy thinks all Japanese people still wear kimonos in Japan. She is so naive.

溫蒂以為在日本所有的日本人還是穿和服。她真是天真。

0197	
** **naive** [nɑ`iv]	形 天真的；質樸；輕信他人的 衍 **naivety** 名 天真；單純 類 **inexperienced** 缺乏經驗的

TOEIC POINT naive 雖然有「純真」的意思，但在英文中，通常用於形容「無知」，具有負面的意思。

If you want to sell your products, you must be prepared to listen to our customers' candid opinions.

假如你想要把產品賣出去，就必須作好準備去聽取顧客直言不諱的意見。

0198	
** **candid** [`kændɪd]	形 直言不諱的；坦率的 類 **frank** 坦白的、**truthful** 誠實的

Kyle gave ingenuous answers to all of his students' questions about sex.

對於學生問到性方面的一切問題，凱爾都回答得很坦白。

0199	
ingenuous [ɪn`dʒɛnjuəs]	形 坦白的；天真無邪的 類 **honest** 誠實的、**guileless** 不狡詐的

TOEIC POINT ingenuous 這個字的拼法與 ingenious（富有創意的）相近，請小心不要混淆。

immense / enormous / hefty

There is an immense amount of work to do before we can even begin to build a new model spaceship.

在我們真正能開始建造新型的太空船之前，還有無數的工作要做。

0200 ** **immense** [ɪ`mɛns]	形 巨大的；無窮的；無邊無際的 衍 **immensity** 名 巨大；廣大 類 **colossal** 龐大的

※ 本句中 even begin to build 的 even 是強調用語。

This enormous fall in company profits must be dealt with as soon as possible.

這次公司獲利的重挫必須盡快處理。

0201 ** **enormous** [ɪ`nɔrməs]	形 極大的；極惡的 衍 **enormity** 名 龐大；極惡

- company profits 公司獲利
- deal with 處理（deal 的過去式與過去分詞為 dealt）

The hefty policeman was able to lift the fallen rock off the road very easily.

這位壯碩的員警輕而易舉地就把落石搬離路面。

0202 * **hefty** [`hɛftɪ]	形 壯碩的；魁梧的 衍 **heftiness** 名 壯碩；魁梧 類 **burly** 大塊頭的、**stout** 粗壯的

icebreaker / defrost / thaw

Bernice's icebreaker speech helped all the new trainees feel less nervous.

柏妮絲的破冰演說有助於所有的新學員感覺比較不緊張。

0203 ** **icebreaker** [ˋaɪsˌbrekɚ]	名 破冰船；活絡氣氛的事物

• trainee 受訓者；實習生
• nervous 緊張的

※ icebreaker 由動詞片語 break the ice（破冰；打破僵局）而來。

This refrigerator is a 50-year-old antique; it is still in good working condition, but has to be defrosted every two weeks or so.

這台冰箱是 50 年的骨董；它的運轉情況還是很好，但是每兩週左右就必須除霜一次。

0204 ** **defrost** [diˋfrɔst]	動 除霜；解凍 反 **frost** 結霜

※ de- 這個字首為「除去」之意。常用到 de- 的字還有 defog（除霧）、dehydrate（脫水）、depose（免職）、derail（使出軌）等。

Every year, mountain climbers die in the Alps due to avalanches during the spring thaw.

每年都有登山客在春天融雪時，因為山崩而葬身在阿爾卑斯山。

0205 ** **thaw** [θɔ]	名 融雪；解凍 動 融雪；解凍 **thaw frozen meat** 將冷凍肉品解凍

advantage / merit / virtue

I still have one advantage over you: my expertise in the car industry.

我還有一個強過你的優勢：我有汽車產業方面的專門技術。

0206 ** **advantage** [əd`væntɪdʒ]	名 優點；優勢 衍 **advantageous** 形 有利的 反 **disadvantage** 不利；缺點

• expertise 專門技術

The new spaceship is not perfect; nevertheless, it has merit.

新的太空船並非十全十美，但是還是有它的優點。

0207 ** **merit** [`mɛrɪt]	名 優點；價值 反 **demerit** 缺點；過失

• nevertheless 儘管如此；然而

Alison's only virtue is that she is an expert in developing design software, and so she is indispensable to our company.

愛莉森唯一的長處是，她是開發設計軟體的專家，所以我們公司少不了她。

0208 * **virtue** [`vɜtʃu]	名 長處；美德 衍 **virtuous** 形 有品德的；貞潔的

• design software 設計軟體

• indispensable 不可或缺的；必需的

Useful POINT 商場上常有人說 Nobody is indispensable（沒有一個人是不可或缺的）。職場中競爭之激烈可見一斑。

immigrate / emigrate / migrate

Europeans who immigrated to America in the early 1900's first landed on Ellis Island in New York.

1900 年代初移居美國的歐洲人，最早是在紐約的艾利斯島登陸。

0209 ** **immigrate** [ˋɪmə͵gret]	動 移居入境 衍 **immigration** 名 移居；移民局 **immigrant** 名 移民

The first group of Japanese people to emigrate to Seattle arrived in the early Meiji Period.

第一批移居西雅圖的日本人在明治初期抵達。

0210 ** **emigrate** [ˋɛmə͵gret]	動 移居外國 衍 **emigration** 名 移居 **emigrant** 名 移民

TOEIC POINT immigrate 是指「移民至某個國家」（im- 是 in 之意），emigrate 則是指「自某個國家移出」（e- 是 out 之意）。

Canada geese migrate south in the fall and spend the winter in Florida.

加拿大雁在秋天時會南遷，並在佛羅里達過冬。

0211 ** **migrate** [ˋmaɪ͵gret]	動 遷徙 衍 **migration** 名（候鳥等的）遷徙 **migratory** 形 遷徙的 **migratory birds** 候鳥

CheckTest

0182 ⇨ 0211

請依照文意將適當的單字填入空格中。可參考第 99 頁所提示的單字來作答。（作答時間：5 分鐘）

① I regret having to __________ your employment due to the financial difficulties our company is currently going through.

② An extensive report on the disastrous earthquake __________ many people to volunteer to help the victims.

③ You should ask Pat about the recipe. He is a real __________, especially where French cuisine is concerned.

④ Kendall Inc. seems to attract many job applicants due to their __________ management policies.

⑤ Helen comes from a big family, and spent her childhood wearing __________ clothes.

⑥ If you want to sell your products, you must be prepared to listen to our customers' __________ opinions.

⑦ The __________ policeman was able to lift the fallen rock off the road very easily.

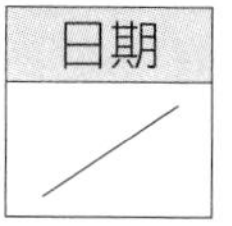
日期

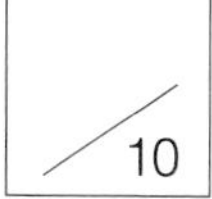
10

⑧ Canada geese __________ south in the fall and spend the winter in Florida.

⑨ I still have one __________ over you: my expertise in the car industry.

⑩ Every year, mountain climbers die in the Alps due to avalanches during the spring __________.

參考用字

advantage	terminate	hand-me-down	humane
gourmet	migrate	persuade	candid
thaw	hefty		

（解答請參閱第 429 頁）

Unit 08

administration / execution / minister

My boss is very dynamic and creative, but his weak point is administration of the business.

我老闆非常有幹勁和創意，但是經營事業是他的弱點。

0212 ** **administration** [əd͵mɪnə`streʃən]	名 經營；管理 衍 **administer** 動 經營；管理 **administrator** 名 管理人；行政官員

• dynamic 有活力的

These orders are vital for national security; there must be absolutely no delay in their execution.

這些命令對國家安全至關重要，在執行時絕對不可延誤。

0213 ** **execution** [ɛksɪ`kjuʃən]	名 執行；處決 衍 **execute** 動 執行；處決 **executive** 名 主管；執行者 **executioner** 名 死刑執行人

• vital 極其重要的
• absolutely 絕對地

The minister declared the couple husband and wife, and the newly married couple kissed each other.

在牧師宣布兩人成為夫妻後，這對新人便互吻。

0214 ** **minister** [`mɪnɪstɚ]	名 牧師；部長 衍 **ministry** 名（政府的）部會

TOEIC POINT 在美國政府機關的層級中，「部」級單位為 Department、「局」級單位則為 bureau。如：Department of State（DOS）為「美國國務院」、Federal Bureau of Investigation（FBI）為「聯邦調查局」。

issue / agenda / minutes

Dealing with global warming is perhaps the most important issue currently facing the human race.

因應全球暖化或許是人類當前所面臨最重要的課題。

0215 ** issue [ˋɪʃjʊ]	名 議題；課題；（雜誌的）刊號 動 發佈；發行

• global warming 全球暖化

With permission of the Chair, I would like to begin with the first item on today's agenda, "How to deal with the new mega-shopping complex project."

要是主席允許的話，我想從今天議程的第一項議題談起：「大型購物商場的新案子要如何處理」。

0216 ** agenda [əˋdʒɛndə]	名 議程；待議事項

TOEIC POINT 本句中的 the Chair 指「會議主持人」，為 chairperson 之略。

If no one volunteers to take the minutes for today's meeting, we will have to take turns and start from the top of the alphabet.

假如沒有人自願在今天開會時做會議記錄，我們就只好輪流，從最前面的字母輪起。

0217 * minutes [ˋmɪnɪts]	名 會議記錄（複數形） **take minutes** 做會議記錄

※ 作「分鐘」解時，minute 為普通名詞，可為單數或複數。另，注意同樣拼法的 minute 亦可作為形容詞，意思是「微小的；極小的」，但念成 [maɪˋnjut]。

process / procedure / protocol

For non-EU citizens, obtaining a work visa in an EU country is a long and difficult process.

對非歐盟區的民衆來說，取得歐盟國家的工作簽證是個漫長而辛苦的過程。

0218 ** **process** [ˋprasɛs]	名 過程；流程；訴訟程序 動 處理；加工

- EU (=European Union) 歐盟
- visa 簽證

When shutting down the computer system, it is important to follow the correct procedure.

在關閉電腦系統時，遵照正確的程序很重要。

0219 ** **procedure** [prəˋsidʒɚ]	名 程序；手續

- shut down 關閉

TOEIC POINT procedure 指「處理事務的順序」，而 process 則指「處理事物的過程」。

When you're allocating seats for the banquet, please study the seating protocol carefully so that none of the guests is offended.

在分配筵席的座位時，請仔細研究排位禮節，以免得罪任何客人。

0220 * **protocol** [ˋprotəˌkal]	名 禮節；協定

- allocate 分配
- banquet 筵席；宴會
- offend 使不快；犯法

TOEIC POINT banquet 指「宴會」，通常為正式邀宴，buffet 則指「自助餐」，一般非正式之餐會常採這個方式。

delinquent / mischievous / disobedience

In regard to your delinquent account, we will be forced to discontinue your telephone service as of this coming Friday, May 13th.

由於您拖欠款項，我們不得不自這星期五，5 月 13 日，起將您斷話。

0221 ** **delinquent** [dɪˋlɪŋkwənt]	形 拖欠的；怠忽職守的 名 違法者；犯過者 **juvenile delinquent** 不良少年 衍 **delinquency** 名 違法；怠忽職守

- in regard to 關於
- discontinue 中斷
- as of ... 自……起

Lily was suspended from school for three days for her mischievous behavior. She was found writing graffiti on the bathroom wall.

莉莉因為行為不檢而被停學三天。她被人發現在廁所的牆上塗鴉。

0222 ** **mischievous** [ˋmɪstʃɪvəs]	形 淘氣的；調皮的 衍 **mischief** 名 調皮；惡作劇

- be suspended from 遭到停止
- graffiti 塗鴉

At our factory we have to deal with several explosive chemicals. Disobedience of work rules may cost you your life as well as your job.

我們在工廠裡必須處理好幾種具爆炸性的化學物品。不遵照工作守則可能會使你丟掉性命和飯碗。

0223 **disobedience** [ˏdɪsəˋbidɪəns]	名 不服從；違命 衍 **disobedient** 形 不服從的；違抗的 反 **obedience** 服從；順從

- explosive chemical 具爆炸性的化學物品
- as well as 和；及

modest / unassuming / inconspicuous

Don't be so modest! We all know that you have made extraordinary achievements in the field of genetics.

別這麼謙虛了！大家都知道，你在遺傳學的領域中成就非凡。

0224 ** **modest** [ˋmɑdɪst]	形 謙虛的；適度的 衍 **modesty** 名 端莊；謙虛；節制 類 **humble** 謙遜的；卑下的

Meg Leeds's acceptance speech was unassuming, and she gave most of the credit for her success to her colleagues.

梅格．李茲接受提名的演說並不張揚，她把自己的成功大部分都歸功於同事。

0225 * **unassuming** [͵ʌnəˋsjumɪŋ]	形 不傲慢的；不出風頭的

- acceptance speech 接受提名之演說
- give the credit to ... 歸功於……

Gareth is so shy about speaking French that he always does his best to remain inconspicuous in language classes.

葛瑞對於說法語十分膽怯，所以他在上語言課時總是想盡辦法保持低調。

0226 **inconspicuous** [͵ɪnkənˋspɪkjʊəs]	形 低調的；不顯眼的 反 **conspicuous** 顯眼的；引人注目的

- shy 膽怯的；羞怯的
- remain inconspicuous 保持低調

legend / myth / superstition

According to a legend among Native Americans in Alaska, it was a raven that gave life to everything that exists in this world.

根據阿拉斯加美洲原住民的傳說，這個世界上所存在的一切都是由渡鴉賦予生命的。

0227 ** **legend** [ˋlɛdʒənd]	名 傳說；傳奇故事 衍 **legendary** 形 傳說的

• raven 渡鴉

※ It be ~ that ... 為強調用句型，被強調的部分置於 ~ 處。

Many people still believe in the myth of men being the stronger gender.

有很多人還是相信男性比女性強的這個迷思。

0228 ** **myth** [mɪθ]	名 神話；迷思

• gender 性別

※「神話集」為 mythology，如 Greek mythology（希臘神話）。

It used to be a common superstition among sailors that beginning a voyage on a Friday would bring bad luck.

以往有個常見的迷信是，船員在星期五啓航會帶來噩運。

0229 * **superstition** [ˌsupəˋstɪʃən]	名 迷信 衍 **superstitious** 形 迷信的

TOEIC POINT legend 一般夾雜了一些事實在其中，但 myth / superstition 則通常指非事實、無科學根據之事物。

desert / neglect / abandon

Marla is seeking a divorce because her husband deserted her and their three children.

瑪拉試圖要離婚，因為她先生遺棄了她和三個小孩。

0230 ** **desert** [dɪˋzɜt]	動 遺棄；逃亡 衍 **desertion** 名 遺棄；逃亡 **desertor** 名 逃兵

※ desert 當「沙漠」之意時，念成 [ˋdɛzət]，要多加注意。

Neglecting children and leaving them unattended is one of the major problems in raising children.

對小孩疏忽並棄之不顧是養育小孩時的一大問題。

0231 ** **neglect** [nɪgˋlɛkt]	動 疏忽；忽視 衍 **negligence** 名 疏忽；粗心大意 **negligent** 形 疏忽的；粗心的 類 **ignore** 忽略；不顧

• unattended 沒人照顧的；沒人陪伴的

Somebody has abandoned an old car right outside my front door!

有人就在我的大門外面棄置了一輛舊車！

0232 ** **abandon** [əˋbændən]	動 棄置；遺棄；捨棄；放棄 類 **leave** 拋下、**give up** 放棄

uproar / hubbub / racket

There was an uproar in Parliament yesterday when the governing party tried to force a vote on its controversial new national security measures.

昨天國會一片騷動，因為執政黨試圖強行表決引發爭議的新國安措施。

0233 * **uproar** [ˋʌp͵ror]	名 喧囂；騷亂；騷動 衍 **uproarious** 形 騷亂的；喧囂的

- force a vote 強行表決
- controversial 引發爭議的
- national security 國家安全
- measures 措施（複數形）

Ken raised his voice so that he could be heard above the hubbub of the noisy party.

肯恩把音量提高，好讓別人能在嘈雜宴會的吵鬧聲中聽到他的聲音。

0234 * **hubbub** [ˋhʌbʌb]	名 吵鬧聲；嘈雜聲 **the hubbub of the city streets** 都市街道的嘈雜聲

Students were punished for raising a racket last night in their dorm.

學生因為昨天晚上在宿舍大聲喧嘩而遭到處罰。

0235 **racket** [ˋrækɪt]	名 喧嘩；擾攘

- raise a racket 大聲喧嘩
- dorm 宿舍（為 dormitory 之略）

※ 注意，同樣拼法的 racket 還可以指「（網球等的）拍子」。

sensitive / observant / perceptive

Cats and dogs as animal companions are said to be sensitive to their owners' moods.

像貓狗這些動物夥伴，據說對主人的情緒很敏感。

0236 ** **sensitive** [ˋsɛnsətɪv]	形 敏感的；過敏的 衍 **sense** 名 感覺；合理性 動 感覺到；意識到 **sensitivity** 名 感受性；敏感；過敏 **sensible** 形 明智的；合理性的

TOEIC POINT sensitive 包含「容易受傷；易怒；神經質的」這類較負面的意義。要注意別與具正面意義的 sensible 混淆。

You are employed as a trainee at this store. So during the on-the-job training period, we ask you to be observant and try to learn the trade.

你是被雇用為這家店的見習生。所以在職訓期間，我們要你好好觀察，並試著去了解這個行業。

0237 ** **observant** [əbˋzɜvənt]	形 善於觀察的；留意的 衍 **observe** 動 觀察；注意 **observation** 名 觀察；留意

- on-the-job (OJT) training 在職訓練
- trade 行業

If I had been more perceptive, I would not have missed the chance to buy a house before real estate prices soared.

假如我當時敏銳一點，就不會在不動產價格大漲前錯失買房子的機會了。

0238 * **perceptive** [pɚˋsɛptɪv]	形 敏銳的；感知的 衍 **perceive** 動 感知；察覺 **perception** 名 感知；察覺；洞察力

- soar 大漲

※ 本句屬「與過去事實相反」的假設語氣句型：在 if 子句中用「過去完成式」，在主要句子中用 would / could / might / should 加現在完成式動詞。

obstruct / hinder / impede

Our house is always dark because the big oak in the front yard obstructs the sun.

我們的房子老是暗暗的，因為前院的大橡樹會擋住陽光。

0239 ** **obstruct** [əb`strʌkt]	動 阻礙；妨礙；遮住；擋住 衍 **obstruction** 名 妨礙；阻塞 **obstructive** 形 蓄意阻撓的

A lack of funds has continually hindered George's ambition to be a successful inventor.

喬治有志當個成功的發明家，卻始終受到缺乏資金所阻撓。

0240 * **hinder** [`hɪndɚ]	動 阻礙；阻止 衍 **hindrance** 名 阻礙；障礙物

- inventor 發明家

If those curious onlookers had not impeded the fire engine, the fire would have been put out much sooner.

假如那些好奇的旁觀者沒有擋到消防車，火災會撲滅得更快。

0241 **impede** [ɪm`pid]	動 阻礙；妨礙 衍 **impediment** 名 擋到；妨礙；口吃

- fire engine 消防車
- put out 撲滅

CheckTest

0212 ⇨ 0241

請依照文意將適當的單字填入空格中。可參考第 111 頁所提示的單字來作答。（作答時間：5 分鐘）

① Meg Leeds's acceptance speech was __________, and she gave most of the credit for her success to her colleagues.

② You are employed as a trainee at this store. So during the on-the-job training period, we ask you to be __________ and try to learn the trade.

③ My boss is very dynamic and creative, but his weak point is __________ of the business.

④ In regard to your __________ account, we will be forced to discontinue your telephone service as of this coming Friday, May 13th.

⑤ Many people still believe in the __________ of men being the stronger gender.

⑥ Dealing with global warming is perhaps the most important __________ currently facing the human race.

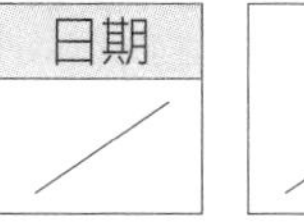

⑦ __________ children and leaving them unattended is one of the major problems in raising children.

⑧ Our house is always dark because the big oak in the front yard __________ the sun.

⑨ When shutting down the computer system, it is important to follow the correct __________.

⑩ Students were punished for raising a __________ last night in their dorm.

参考用字

administration	procedure	observant	delinquent
neglect	unassuming	myth	racket
issue	obstruct		

（解答請參閱第 430 頁）

Unit 09

alternate / substitute / surrogate

We should choose an alternate day for the meeting in case some of the participants can't make it on July 17th.

我們應該替會議挑個預備日，以防有些與會者在 7 月 17 日來不了。

0242 ** **alternate** [ˋɔltənɪt]	形 預備的；交替的；間隔的 名 替補者；替代者 動 使交替；使輪流 衍 **alternative** 名 選擇餘地；替代品 形 可選擇的；替代的

- in case 免得；以防
- make it 到場；成功

This recipe requires sour cream, but if you don't like the flavor, yogurt can be used as a substitute.

這道食譜需要酸奶油，不過如果你不喜歡這個味道，可以用優格來代替。

0243 * **substitute** [ˋsʌbstəˏtjut]	名 代替人；代用品 動 代替；代班 衍 **substitution** 代替；代用；替換

Joan's parents died when she was just a child, but her uncle Albert was so kind to her that she regarded him as a surrogate father.

瓊的父母在她還小的時候就過世了，但是她的叔叔亞伯特對她非常好，所以她也把他視為代理父親。

0244 * **surrogate** [ˋsɜəgɪt]	形 代理的 名 代理人；代用品

- surrogate father 代理父親（cf. surrogate mother 代理孕母）
- regard someone as ... 把某人視為……

※「養父」為 foster father，「養母」為 foster mother；「繼父」為 step father ，「繼母」為 step mother。

distinguish / discriminate / discern

Carrie is so ignorant about plants that she cannot distinguish tulips from pansies.

凱莉對植物一無所知，連鬱金香和三色堇都分不出來。

0245 ** **distinguish** [dɪˋstɪŋgwɪʃ]	動 分辨；區別 衍 **distinguishable** 形 可分辨的；可區別的

• tulip 鬱金香
• pansy 三色堇

The new Civil Rights Act makes it illegal to discriminate against anyone on the basis of age, gender, ethnicity, physical ability or religion.

新的民權法案明訂，基於年齡、性別、種族、體能或宗教信仰而歧視任何人皆屬違法。

0246 ** **discriminate** [dɪˋskrɪməˏnet]	動 歧視；辨別 衍 **discrimination** 名 歧視；辨別 **discriminatory** 形 歧視的；辨別的 類 **differentiate** 區別

• ethnicity 種族特性

※ 相關用法請參照 0316 segregate。

Discerning the faint trail of footprints led to establishing the identity of the murderer.

鑑識模糊的腳印足跡使得以確立凶手的身分。

0247 **discern** [dɪˋsɜn]	動 鑑識；識別 衍 **discernible** 形 可識別的

• trail 足跡；痕跡；鄉間小徑
• establish identity 確立身分

aggressive / hostile / taciturn

I don't care to shop at Foster's; the sales staff are too aggressive.

我不喜歡去佛斯特買東西；那裡的店員太積極了。

0248 ** aggressive [ə`grɛsɪv]	形 侵略的；好鬥的；積極的；進取的 衍 **aggressiveness** 名 侵犯；積極；衝動 **aggression** 名 侵犯；侵略

TOEIC POINT 請注意，aggressive 這個字有正面（積極、進取），也有負面（侵略、好鬥）的意思。

One example of a hostile environment may be an area that has a high dioxin count. It may be hazardous to your health and that of your offspring.

一個地區的戴奧辛含量偏高可能是有害環境的一例。它可能會對你以及後代的健康造成危險。

0249 ** hostile [`hɑstḷ]	形 惡劣的；懷敵意的；敵對的 衍 **hostility** 名 敵意；敵對

- dioxin count 戴奧辛的含量
- hazardous 危險的
- offspring 子孫；後代

I am sorry to say Megan's morose and taciturn attitude is alienating many of her classmates.

我要很遺憾地說，梅根陰鬱、寡言的態度讓很多同學敬而遠之。

0250 taciturn [`tæsə,tɜn]	形 寡言的；無言的 類 **reticent** 緘默的

- morose 陰鬱的
- alienate 疏遠

drench / saturate / immerse

Kim's car stalled in the middle of nowhere, and so she had to walk home and got drenched in the shower.

金的車在荒郊野外拋錨，所以她只好走路回家，並被陣雨淋得全身溼透。

0251 ** drench [drɛntʃ]	動 使溼透；浸透 類 **soak**（使）溼透；浸泡

- stall 熄火；拋錨
- in the middle of nowhere 在荒郊野外

The company had to expand their sales market into remote areas since their product had already saturated the market in the city.

該公司必須把銷售市場拓展到偏遠地區，因為他們的產品在都會區的市場上已經飽和。

0252 * saturate [`sætʃə͵ret]	動 使飽和；使溼透 衍 **saturation** 名 飽和；浸透

- remote area 偏遠地區

※ saturated fat 指「飽和脂肪」，unsaturated fat 則為「不飽和脂肪」。

I was so immersed in my work that I lost track of time and missed an important appointment.

我十分專注於工作，以致於沒注意到時間，錯過了一場重要的約會。

0253 * immerse [ɪ`mɝs]	動 使浸入；沉浸於 **be immersed in sth.** 沉浸、專注於某事 衍 **immersion** 名 沉浸；專注

- lose track of time 沒注意到時間

estimate / evaluate / appraise

The construction costs are likely to rise far above the original estimate as a result of delays caused by bad weather.

由於天候不佳造成延誤，建築成本很可能會漲到遠超出原本的估算。

0254 ** **estimate** [ˋɛstə͵met]	名 估價；估算 動 估計；估算 衍 **estimation** 名 評價；判斷

- far above 遠超出

The committee was unable to evaluate the proposal because it lacked sufficient information on the financing of the project.

委員會無法評估提案，因為它缺乏足夠的專案融資資料。

0255 * **evaluate** [ɪˋvælju͵et]	動 評估；估價 衍 **evaluation** 名 評估；評鑑

- lack 缺乏
- financing 融資

Before we can insure this jewelry, you must have it appraised by an expert to determine its value.

你必須先請專家鑑定並確定它的價值，我們才能替這件首飾投保。

0256 * **appraise** [əˋprez]	動 鑑定；鑑價；評估價 衍 **appraisal** 名 鑑定；評價 **appraiser** 名 鑑定人；鑑價官

- determine 決斷；確定；下決心；作決定

convincing / credible / plausible

Betty's argument was convincing enough for her co-workers to vote for a strike.

貝蒂的論點相當有說服力，使她的同事對罷工投下了贊成票。

0257 ** **convincing** [kən`vɪnsɪŋ]	形 有說服力的 衍 **convince** 動 說服

• vote for ... 對……投下贊成票

The witness's testimony didn't sound credible and failed to convince the jury.

證人的證詞聽起來並不可信，無法說服陪審團。

0258 ** **credible** [`krɛdəbḷ]	形 可信的；可靠的 衍 **credit** 名 信用；功勞；學分 **credit card** 信用卡 **credibility** 名 可信度 反 **incredible** 不可信的；難以置信的；了不起的

• witness 目擊者；證人
• testimony 證詞

Alex's explanation for the staff reshuffle was plausible but not convincing.

愛力克斯對於人員改組的說明看似有理，但是卻難以服人。

0259 * **plausible** [`plɔzəbḷ]	形 似有理的；可能正確的 衍 **plausibility** 名 似有理；似正確 類 **reasonable** 合理的

• reshuffle 改組；重洗（紙牌）

※ plausible 指「似乎正確、合理的」，但實際上並不一定如此，不過此字並無故意欺瞞之意，例如 a plausible argument（似乎有理的論證）。

campaign / ballot / electorate

The senatorial campaign got started today with a debate among the six candidates.

參議員的競選活動今天以六位候選人的相互辯論展開序幕。

0260 ** **campaign** [kæm`pen]	名 競選活動；（社會、政治的）運動；戰役

• senatorial 參議員（senator）的（眾議員為 representative）
• candidate 候選人

It was pointed out that in the last presidential election the ballot card in the state was not clearly formatted and confused many voters.

有人指出，在上次的總統選舉中，該州的投票卡格式不清，使很多選民都弄不清楚。

0261 * **ballot** [`bælət]	名 選票；投票

• point out 指出
• presidential election 總統選舉
• format 格式化
• ballot card 投票卡

If he had visited his electorate more often, Mr. Reynolds would have won.

要是能更常造訪他的選區，雷諾斯先生就會當選了。

0262 **electorate** [ɪ`lɛktərɪt]	名 選區；選民 衍 **electoral** 形 選舉的；選民的

※ 注意，本例句為「與過去事實相反」的假設句。

maintain / retain / uphold

We use a service company to maintain equipment such as elevators and escalators in the facility.

我們找檢修公司維護諸如廠內升降梯和手扶梯之類的設備。

0263 ** **maintain** [men`ten]	動 維護；維持；扶養 衍 **maintenance** 名 維護；維持（發音為[`metənəns]）

• service company 檢修公司

Be sure to retain the bottom half of the ticket in order to claim your luggage.

一定要把票根保留下來，以便領取行李。

0264 * **retain** [rɪ`ten]	動 保留；記住 衍 **retention** 名 保留；存放；記憶力

• claim one's luggage 領取行李

※ 注意，luggage〔英〕與 baggage〔美〕皆指「行李」，並皆為不可數名詞。

It is especially serious when politicians break the law, because it is their duty to uphold it.

政治人物違法尤其嚴重，因為守法是他們的天職。

0265 * **uphold** [ʌp`hold]	動 舉起；支持；擁護

TOEIC POINT 動詞片語 hold up 也有「舉起」之意，但是 hold up 還可作「耽擱」、「使停滯」、「搶劫」等意解。

retrieve / salvage / reclaim

I had to go to the lost and found office to retrieve my briefcase that I had left on a bus.

我必須去失物招領處領回我在公車上所掉的公事包。

0266 ** **retrieve** [rɪ`triv]	動 領回；取回；挽救 關 **retriever** 名（尋回被射中獵物的）獵犬

The survivors of the earthquake are now busy trying to salvage personal possessions from the ruins of their homes.

地震的倖存者現在正忙著從住家的斷垣殘壁中，設法搶救私人財物。

0267 ** **salvage** [`sælvɪdʒ]	動（火災、水災等災難的）搶救；打撈（沉船） 類 **save** 救助；拯救

- survivor 倖存者
- possessions 所有物；財產（常用複數）
- ruins 斷垣殘壁；廢墟（常用複數）

A new war broke out because the nation wanted to reclaim territory it had lost in the previous war.

新的戰爭爆發了，因為該國想奪回在前一次戰爭中所失去的領土。

0268 * **reclaim** [rɪ`klem]	動 重新贏回；回收；開墾 名 矯正；改過 類 **regain** 重新獲得

- territory 領土；版圖
- previous 先前的；在前的

appropriately / consequently / aptly

We are expected to dress appropriately for the reception: a long dress or a tux.

我們參加接待會時衣著必須得體：長禮服或晚禮服。

0269 ** **appropriately** [ə`proprɪˌetlɪ]	副 得體地；適合地 衍 **appropriate** 形 得體的；適合的

• tux（男士）晚禮服（tuxedo 之略）

※ be expected to 的意思是「被期待要⋯⋯」，也就是「必須」、「應該」之意。

Henry has already bounced two checks this month. Consequently, his bank has charged him a $24 fee per check for insufficient funds.

亨利這個月已經跳票了兩次。因此，對於餘額不足的支票，每一張銀行都向他收取 24 美元的費用。

0270 ** **consequently** [`kɑnsəˌkwɛntlɪ]	副 因此；所以 衍 **consequence** 名 結果；後果；重大

• bounce a check 跳票

• insufficient funds 金額不足

Veronica's report aptly described the crises our company currently faces.

維若妮卡的報告，適切地說明了我們公司目前所面臨的危機。

0271 * **aptly** [`æptlɪ]	副 適切地；合宜地 衍 **apt** 形 適切的；合宜的；傾向於

※ 注意，本例句中的 crises [`kraɪsiz]（危機）為不規則複數名詞，其單數形為 crisis [`kraɪsis]。

CheckTest

0242 ⇨ 0271

請依照文意將適當的單字填入空格中。可參考第 123 頁所提示的單字來作答。(作答時間：5 分鐘)

① It was pointed out that in the last presidential election the __________ card in the state was not clearly formatted and confused many voters.

② One example of a __________ environment may be an area that has a high dioxin count. It may be hazardous to your health and that of your offspring.

③ Carrie is so ignorant about plants that she cannot __________ tulips from pansies.

④ Be sure to __________ the bottom half of the ticket in order to claim your luggage.

⑤ We should choose an __________ day for the meeting in case some of the participants can't make it on July 17th.

⑥ The company had to expand their sales market into remote areas since their product had already __________ the market in the city.

⑦ Henry has already bounced two checks this month. __________, his bank has charged him a $24 fee per check for insufficient funds.

⑧ The committee was unable to __________ the proposal because it lacked sufficient information on the financing of the project.

⑨ I had to go to the lost and found office to __________ my briefcase that I had left on a bus.

⑩ The witness's testimony didn't sound __________ and failed to convince the jury.

參考用字

alternate	distinguish	hostile	ballot
retain	saturate	evaluate	credible
retrieve	consequently		

（解答請參閱第 430 頁）

Unit 10

bilateral / mutual / reciprocal

MP3 11

Japan and the US have a bilateral agreement about accepting short-stay travelers without visas.

日本和美國達成了雙邊協議，同意短期停留的旅客不必簽證。

0272 ** **bilateral** [baɪˋlætərəl]	形 雙邊的 反 **unilateral** 單邊的；單方面的

Meg and Ted found out that they had some mutual hobbies that drew them together.

梅格和泰德發現，他們有一些互相吸引的共同嗜好。

0273 * **mutual** [ˋmjutʃʊəl]	形 共同的；互相的 衍 **mutuality** 名 相互關係；相互依存

Shortly after Japan's prime minister visited China, the Chinese premier made a reciprocal visit to Japan.

日本首相一訪問過中國，中國總理就到日本展開互惠參訪。

0274 **reciprocal** [rɪˋsɪprəkḷ]	形 互惠的；回報的 衍 **reciprocate** 動 互惠；交換；回報 **reciprocation** 名 互惠；交換；交互作用

※ reciprocation 的口語表現為 give-and-take。另外，You scratch my back and I'll scratch yours. 這句俗語的意思為「互相抓背後的癢」，指的是政治人物等互相交換利益。

budget / revenue / financial statement

The budget forecast for the next fiscal year is going to be discussed at the next board meeting.

下一次董事會將討論下一個會計年度的預算預測。

0275 ** **budget** [ˋbʌdʒɪt]	名 預算（額）；經費 **fiscal budget** 財政預算 動 編列預算；預定 衍 **budgetary** 形 預算的 **budgetary surplus** 預算盈餘

• board meeting 董事會

One of the responsibilities of the regional manager is to monitor revenues and expenses.

區域經理的職責之一是要控管營收與開銷。

0276 ** **revenue** [ˋrɛvə͵nju]	名（企業的）營收；（國家的）歲入；財源 **Internal Revenue Service (IRS)** 美國國稅局

• regional manager 區經理
• monitor 監視；控管

The company's financial statement confirms my suspicion that it is in danger of bankruptcy.

公司的財務報表證實了我的懷疑，公司有破產的危險。

0277 ** **financial statement** [faɪˋnænʃəl ˋstetmənt]	財務報表 類 **the books** 帳簿

• suspicion 懷疑
• bankruptcy 破產；倒閉

※「記帳」說成 keep / do the books。另，bookeeping 指「簿記」。

commence / implement / instigate

The new school year will commence earlier than usual this year on September 6th.

今年的新學年將從 9 月 6 日展開，比以往要早。

0278 ** **commence** [kə`mɛns]	動（事業、計畫等）開始；展開 衍 **commencement** 名 開始；畢業典禮 類 **begin** 開始、**start** 開始

※「畢業典禮」也可說成 graduation ceremony。

The situation hasn't improved drastically even though the Equal Employment Opportunity Law was implemented a long time ago.

即使就業機會平等法在很久以前就實施了，但是情況並沒有大幅改善。

0279 * **implement** [`ɪmpləmənt]	動（法律等的）實施；實行 衍 **implementation** 名 實施；實行 類 **put into practice** 落實、**become effective** 生效

- drastically 劇烈地；大幅地
- Equal Employment Opportunity Law 就業機會平等法

The demonstration was peaceful until a few radical demonstrators instigated violence against the police.

示威一直很平和，直到少數激進的示威分子對警方施暴。

0280 **instigate** [`ɪnstə,get]	動 施展；唆使；煽動 衍 **instigation** 名 煽動；教唆

- demonstration 示威
- radical 激進的
- demonstrator 示威人士

vow / pledge / oath

Nowadays, couples are increasingly writing their own wedding vows rather than sticking to the traditional ones.

現今的夫妻愈來愈多人自己寫結婚誓詞，而不拘泥於傳統誓詞。

0281 ** **vow** [vaʊ]	名 誓詞；誓約；誓言 動 發誓；許願 類 **swear** 發誓；宣誓

- stick to ... 堅守……；遵守……
- wedding vow 結婚誓詞

※「誓言要……」可說成 vow to。例如：The prime minister vowed to pull the country's economy out of its long slump.（總理向國民宣誓，要讓國家擺脫長期以來的經濟不振。）

At the initiation ceremony, Wei pledged to obey all the rules faithfully. After that he became a full-pledged member of the Boy Scouts.

在入會儀式上，魏發誓會謹守所有的規定。接著他就成了童子軍的正式成員。

0282 * **pledge** [plɛdʒ]	動 發誓；許諾；以……為抵押 名 誓言；諾言；抵押品

- initiation ceremony 入會儀式
- a full-pledged member 正式成員

In law courts, it is customary for witnesses to swear an oath to tell the truth before giving testimony.

在法庭上，證人照例要先宣誓會據實以告才能作證。

0283 **oath** [oθ]	名 誓約；宣誓

- customary 照例的；習慣上的
- swear an oath 宣誓
- give testimony 作證；提供證詞

※ 本例句中的 swear an oath 也可說成 take an oath。

progressive / conservative / conformist

I usually like progressive artists, but Hirst's work is too experimental for my taste.

我通常喜歡前衛的藝術家，但是就我的品味而言，赫斯特的作品太具實驗性。

0284 ** **progressive** [prə`grɛsɪv]	形 前衛的；進步的；前進的 名 革新派；進步分子 衍 **progress** 名 進步；進展 動 前進；發展

• experimental 實驗（性）的

My father's views on marriage were very conservative. He believed the husband should go out to work, and the wife should stay at home.

我爸對婚姻的看法非常保守。他深信丈夫應該外出工作，妻子則應該待在家裡。

0285 ** **conservative** [kən`sɜvətɪv]	形 保守的；守舊的 名 保守派；保守的人 衍 **conservation** 名 保護；保存；節約 類 **conventional** 守舊的、**old-fashioned** 過時的

Bob is such a conformist. He hates to stand out from the crowd.

包伯是個標準的順民。他討厭與眾不同。

0286 **conformist** [kən`fɔrmɪst]	名（法律、慣例、常規等的）遵循者；墨守成規的人 衍 **conform** 動 遵照；遵守

• stand out 引人注目；突出

mortgage / collateral / deposit

Since interest rates went up, I've had trouble keeping up with my mortgage payments.

由於利率走高，我都快繳不出房貸了。

0287 ** mortgage [`mɔrgɪdʒ]	名 房貸；抵押貸款 **take out a mortgage** 申辦房貸

- have trouble Ving 做……有困難
- keeping up with ... 趕上……

※ mortgage broker「房貸掮客」指的是替人進行房貸申請、擔保設定手續的代理人。

The bank agreed to let Mark have a business loan on condition that he put up his house as collateral.

銀行同意讓馬克取得商業貸款，條件是他要拿房子來抵押。

0288 ** collateral [kə`lætərəl]	名 抵押品；擔保品 形 附帶的；並行的

※ collateral damage 是指伴隨著戰爭而來的損害，有「池魚之殃」的意思。

Nancy was lucky to find an apartment in the center of town that did not require a security deposit.

南西很幸運在鎮中心找到了一間不需要押金的公寓。

0289 ** deposit [dɪ`pazɪt]	名 定金；押金；保證金 動 存付；寄存

Useful POINT 一般在美國租房時，必須繳交一個月的保證金。

petition / appeal / sue

A group of citizens who care for wild animals filed a petition to abolish the city zoo.

有一群關切野生動物的市民遞交了一份請願書，要求關閉市立動物園。

0290 ** **petition** [pə`tɪʃən]	名 請願；請願書 **file a petition** 遞交請願書 動 向……請願

• abolish 廢除；取消

After losing his case at the district court, the defendant decided to appeal to the higher court.

在地方法院輸掉官司後，被告決定上訴到高等法院。

0291 ** **appeal** [ə`pil]	動 呼籲；懇求；上訴 名 呼籲；懇求；上訴

• lose a case 敗訴；輸掉官司

※ 如本例所示，appeal 為不及物動詞，在其後須接介系詞，再接名詞。另，appeal to 亦可作「吸引」解。

The company sued us for not having the merchandise delivered in time for their annual sale, thus causing them a lot of financial damage.

該公司告我們送貨沒有及時趕上他們的年度銷售，因而造成了他們重大的財務損失。

0292 **sue** [su]	動 控告；提起訴訟

• merchandise 商品

• financial damage 財務損失

※ 本例中的 have (having) ... delivered 為「使役動詞＋受詞＋過去分詞」的結構。注意，此處用過去分詞表「被動」。

qualification / eligibility / criteria

The school needs to find someone who has the qualifications to teach English-to-Chinese translation.

學校要找個有資格可以教英翻中的人。

0293 ** **qualification** [ˌkwɑləfə`keʃən]	名 資格；能力；證明 衍 **qualified** 形 合格的；勝任的 **qualify** 動 使合格；取得資格 **be qualified to** 有資格做…… 類 **certificate** 證書、**diploma** 文憑

Duncan's application for a scholarship was turned down because he did not fully meet the criteria for eligibility.

鄧肯申請獎學金被打了回票，因為他沒有完全達到合格的標準。

0294 * **eligibility** [ˌɛlɪdʒə`bɪlətɪ]	名 合格性；適任 衍 **eligible** 形 有資格的；適合的

※ 注意，本句中的 meet 為「符合；達到；滿足」之意。

What criteria do you have for selecting candidates?

你們選擇候選人的標準是什麼？

0295 * **criteria** [kraɪ`tɪrɪə]	名 標準；指標

※ criteria 為複數形，其單數形為 criterion，但複數較常使用。

dismiss / adjourn / liberate

Anyone divulging confidential information about the company to outsiders will be dismissed immediately.

任何對外人洩露公司機密資料的人會立刻遭到開除。

0296 ** **dismiss** [dɪsˋmɪs]	動 開除；解散；排除 衍 **dismissal** 名 開除；解散

- divulge 洩露
- confidential information 機密資料（參照 0431）

The board meeting was adjourned as soon as the directors voted on the last agenda item.

董事們一表決完最後一項議程，董事會即告散會。

0297 * **adjourn** [əˋdʒɜn]	動 散會；休會；（使）暫停 衍 **adjournment** 名 休會；散會；暫停

- director (of the board) 董事；理事

The uprising in November liberated the country from foreign occupation.

11 月的起義把國家從外國的占領中解放了出來。

0298 * **liberate** [ˋlɪbəˏret]	動 解放；使自由 衍 **liberation** 名 解放；釋放 **Women's Liberation Movement** 婦女解放運動 **liberal** 形 自由的；開明的 **liberty** 名 自由 關 **release** 動 釋放、**free** 動 使自由

- uprising 起義；造反
- foreign occupation 外國的占領

TOEIC POINT liberty 為「因勝利而獲得的自由」；freedom 則是「原本擁有或是被賦予的自由」。

parliament / judiciary / legislature

Parliament will reconvene on September 1st after the members have returned from the summer recess.

等議員從夏季的休會中回來後，國會就要在 9 月 1 日重新開議。

0299 ** **parliament** [ˋpɑrləmənt]	名 國會；議院 類 **congress** 國會；（政黨的）大會

- reconvene 重新開議
- summer recess 夏天的休會

※ 指英國國會時 parliament 的 p 要大寫。同樣地，指美國國會時 congress 的 c 要大寫。

Last year the government attempted to introduce reforms to the nation's judiciary, but a group of powerful judges and lawyers blocked them.

去年政府企圖對國內的司法實行改革，但是遭到了一群勢力龐大的法官和律師所阻撓。

0300 * **judiciary** [dʒuˋdɪʃɪˏɛrɪ]	名 司法部；司法制度 形 司法的；法官的 衍 **judicial** 形 司法的；法官的；公正的 **judicious** 形 明智的；深思熟慮的

- attempt 企圖 • reform 改革 • block 阻撓

The legislature is now debating a proposed law to completely ban smoking in public places.

立法機關現在正在辯論公共場所全面禁菸的法律提案。

0301 * **legislature** [ˋlɛdʒɪsˏletʃɚ]	名 立法機關 衍 **legislate** 動 立法；制定 **legislative** 形 立法的

- debate 辯論
- ban 禁止

Useful POINT 所謂「三權分立」separation of the three powers 指 executive（行政）、legislative（立法）、judiciary（司法）等三權的獨立運作。

Chapter 1 Unit 10

CheckTest

0272 ⇨ 0301

請依照文意將適當的單字填入空格中。可參考第 135 頁所提示的單字來作答。(作答時間：5 分鐘)

① In law courts, it is customary for witnesses to swear an ________ to tell the truth before giving testimony.

② Japan and the US have a ________ agreement about accepting short-stay travelers without visas.

③ Bob is such a ________. He hates to stand out from the crowd.

④ One of the responsibilities of the regional manager is to monitor ________ and expenses.

⑤ The situation hasn't improved drastically even though the Equal Employment Opportunity Law was ________ a long time ago.

⑥ The company ________ us for not having the merchandise delivered in time for their annual sale, thus causing them a lot of financial damage.

⑦ Nancy was lucky to find an apartment in the center of town that did not require a security ________.

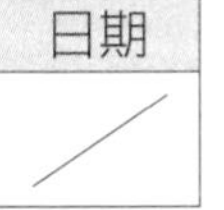

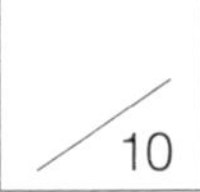

⑧ The board meeting was __________ as soon as the directors voted on the last agenda item.

⑨ Duncan's application for a scholarship was turned down because he did not fully meet the criteria for __________.

⑩ The __________ is now debating a proposed law to completely ban smoking in public places.

参考用字

revenue	oath	bilateral	legislature
conformist	sue	eligibility	implement
adjourn	deposit		

（解答請參閱第 430 頁）

Unit 11

subsidize / sustain / resuscitate

MP3 12

This tourism promotion film was subsidized by the US State Department.

這段觀光宣傳影片是由美國國務院所資助的。

0302 * **subsidize** [ˋsʌbsə͵daɪz]	動 資助；補助 衍 **subsidy** 名 津貼；補貼；補助金

- promotion film 宣傳影片
- US State Department 美國國務院

After sustained losses in the market, the price of steel finally began to pick up as a result of the war that broke out in the Middle East.

在市場上持續虧損後，鋼價終於因為中東爆發戰事而開始走高。

0303 ** **sustain** [səˋsten]	動 持續；持久；維持 衍 **sustainable** 形 可維持的；永續的 **sustenance** 名 食物；生計

- pick up 走高；上揚
- break out 爆發

※ pick up 還有「拿起」、「(用車) 接人」、「收拾」、「學會」、「染病」、「購買」、「接收（電子訊號）」、「注意到」、「勾搭」等意。

The paramedics arrived quickly at the scene of the accident, and were able to resuscitate the driver, who had stopped breathing.

醫務人員迅速抵達了事故現場，因而得以救活已停止呼吸的駕駛。

0304 **resuscitate** [rɪˋsʌsə͵tet]	動 使復活；使復甦 衍 **resuscitation** 名 復活；復甦 **mouth-to-mouth resuscitation** 口對口人工呼吸 **cardiopulmonary resuscitation** 心肺復甦術

- paramedics 醫務人員

riot / vandalism / demolition

The acquittal of the police officer who allegedly killed an unarmed suspect led to a riot outside the courthouse.

涉嫌把手無寸鐵的嫌犯殺死的警官獲判無罪，使得法庭外掀起了暴動。

0305 ** **riot** [ˋraɪət]	名 暴動；騷亂 **riot police** 鎮暴警察

- allegedly 據稱地
- unarmed suspect 手無寸鐵的嫌犯

Over the past few years, there has been an increase in vandalism of art exhibits by visitors to the museum.

過去幾年來，破壞藝術展覽的博物館遊客與日俱增。

0306 * **vandalism** [ˋvændḷˏɪzəm]	名 破壞公物（行為） 衍 **vandalize** 動 任意破壞 類 **destruction** 破壞；毀滅

The old City Hall is scheduled for demolition this summer to make way for a new building on the site.

舊市府預定在今年夏天拆除，以在原址興建新大樓。

0307 * **demolition** [ˏdɛməˋlɪʃən]	名 破壞；拆除 衍 **demolish** 動 摧毀；拆除

- make way 讓位；讓路
- site 地點；工地

degrade / deteriorate / degenerate

Vegetable, meat, wood, and paper products degrade biologically, but plastic, nylon and vinyl products do not.

蔬菜、肉類、木材和紙類等產品會被生物分解，但是塑膠、尼龍和乙烯基等產品則不會。

0308 * **degrade** [dɪ`gred]	動 分解；降級 衍 **degradable** 形 可分解的 類 **decompose** 動 分解；腐爛

※ biodegradable 指「生物可分解的」。

The 600 year-old castle had deteriorated so badly that the city government finally decided to appropriate a budget to restore it.

這座有 600 年歷史的城堡腐朽得很厲害，所以市政府最後決定提撥預算來修復。

0309 * **deteriorate** [dɪ`tɪrɪə͵ret]	動 惡化；變壞 衍 **deterioration** 名 惡化；衰敗 反 **ameliorate** 改善；變好

- appropriate 提撥；挪用
- restore 修復；復原

Throughout history, older people have invariably felt that the moral sense of the younger generation has degenerated.

縱觀歷史，年紀大的人總覺得年輕一輩的人道德感墮落。

0310 **degenerate** [dɪ`dʒɛnə͵ret]	動 退化；墮落 形 墮落的；退化的 名 墮落者 衍 **degeneration** 名 退化；墮落

- invariably 不變地；始終如一地
- younger generation 年輕一輩

expertise / ingenuity / dexterity

Ms. Gonzalez's management expertise was what saved the company from disaster during the depression.

岡薩雷茲女士的管理專長使得公司在不景氣期間得以免於災難。

0311 ** **expertise** [͵ɛkspɚˋtiz]	名 專長；專門技術 關 **expert** 名 專家

• disaster 災害；災難
• depression 不景氣

Frances shows great ingenuity in solving problems, but tends to be a bit lazy if she does not have a challenging task to do.

法蘭西絲很有解決問題的巧思，但是如果沒有具挑戰性的事可做，她往往就會有點懶。

0312 * **ingenuity** [͵ɪndʒəˋnuətɪ]	名 巧思；創造力 衍 **ingenious** 形 有獨創性的；別出心裁的

• tend to 傾向於

Playing any kind of musical instrument requires a high level of physical dexterity.

演奏任何一種樂器都需要很高的肢體敏捷度。

0313 * **dexterity** [dɛksˋtɛrətɪ]	名 敏捷；靈巧；靈活 衍 **dexterous** 形 敏捷的；靈巧的；靈活的 類 **skillfulness** 熟練；技巧高超

• musical instrument 樂器
• physical dexterity 肢體敏捷

isolated / quarantine / segregate

We are worried about our grandfather living in such an isolated area all by himself, but he refuses to move in with us.

我們很擔心爺爺自己一個人住在那麼偏僻的地方，但是他拒絕搬來跟我們住。

0314 ** **isolated** [ˋaɪsḷˏetɪd]	形 隔絕的；偏僻的 衍 **isolate** 動 隔絕；孤立 **isolation** 名 孤立；隔絕

The law requires that any canine entering the country without a vaccination certificate be quarantined for a period of 14 days.

法律規定，任何沒有接種證明的入境犬隻都必須隔離 14 天。

0315 * **quarantine** [ˋkwɔrənˏtin]	動 隔離；檢疫 名 檢疫所；隔離期

- canine 犬科動物
- vaccination 預防接種

Although people are no longer segregated in the country, there still remain the problems of prejudice and discrimination.

雖然該國不再把人種族隔離，但是偏見和歧視的問題依然存在。

0316 * **segregate** [ˋsɛgrɪˏget]	動 實行種族隔離；分離 衍 **segregation** 名 種族隔離；分離 關 **apartheid** 名 南非的種族隔離政策

※ 與歧視相關的名詞有 prejudice（偏見）、discrimination（差別待遇）、segregation（種族隔離）。（參閱 0246 dicriminate）

outstanding / extraordinary / remarkable

Pedro's outstanding achievements in basketball won him a scholarship to the college.

佩卓在籃球方面的傑出成就使他拿到了大學的獎學金。

0317 ** **outstanding** [ˋaʊtˋstændɪŋ]	形 突出的；傑出的 衍 **outstand** 動 突出

※ 在商業上 outstanding 可用來指「未付的」，如 outstanding debts（未清償的債務）。

Peter's extraordinary story about canoeing down the Yukon River made me decide to go there.

彼得在育空河泛舟的不凡故事，使我決定到那裡走一趟。

0318 ** **extraordinary** [ɪkˋstrɔrdn̩͵ɛrɪ]	形 不凡的；令人驚奇的 類 **amazing** 驚人的、**unusual** 不尋常的、**incredible** 令人難以置信的 反 **ordinary** 一般的、**common** 普通的

Considering the fact that Billy is only 10 years old, he gave a remarkable performance on the piano.

如果考慮比利才 10 歲，他的鋼琴演奏算是相當了不起的。

0319 ** **remarkable** [rɪˋmɑrkəbl̩]	形 值得注意的；卓越的；了不起的 衍 **remark** 動 評論；談論

- considering the fact that ... 如果考慮……
- performance 表演；性能；成績

conditional / provisional / contingent

The conditional agreement states that our country will supply rice provided that they do not conduct experiments to test strategic arms.

有條件協議上明訂，假如他們不做實驗來測試戰略武器，我國就會供應稻米。

0320 ** **conditional** [kən`dɪʃənl̩]	形 有條件的 衍 **condition** 名 條件；狀況 **on the condition that** 在……的條件下

- supply 提供；供應
- provided that 假如
- conduct experiments 做實驗
- strategic arms 戰略武器

After the coup d'état, a provisional government was set up, and they began to prepare for the country's first general election.

政變過後，臨時政府成立，並開始準備該國的首次大選。

0321 * **provisional** [prə`vɪʒənl̩]	形 臨時的；暫定的 衍 **provision** 名 供應；條款；預備；（複數形）食材

- coup d'état 政變（法文）
- provisional government 臨時政府

The success of the treatment is contingent upon the doctor's skill and the patient's overall condition.

治療成功與否，要視醫生的技術和病患的整體狀況而定。

0322 **contingent** [kən`tɪndʒənt]	形 附帶的；偶發的；視狀況而定的 衍 **contingency** 名 不測；偶發事件；偶然性

- treatment 治療
- contingent upon 視……而定
- overall condition 整體狀況

prototype / archetype / matrix

Charles Darwin, the author of *The Origin of Species*, is considered to be the prototype of the modern biologist.

《物種的起源》之作者查爾斯．達爾文被認為是現代生物學家的典範。

0323 * **prototype** [ˋprotə͵taɪp]	名 典範；原型

• species 物種；品種（單、複數同形）

Useful POINT 字首 proto- 是「最初的；原始的」的意思，如 protohistory 為「原史學」、protohuman 為「原生人類」、protoplasm 則為「原生質」。

A psychoanalyst said archetypes of guilt, death, redemption and rebirth exist in the myths of many countries.

有位精神分析學家說，罪惡、死亡、贖罪與重生的原型存在於許多國家的神話中。

0324 * **archetype** [ˋɑrkɪ͵taɪp]	名 原型

※ prototype 指的是具體的原型，而 archetype 則是指較抽象的、哲學的概念原型。

Useful POINT 字首 arch- 是「第一；主要」之意，如 archbishop 為「大主教」、archduke 為「大公」、archenemy 為「首敵」。

The city states that developed in the Middle East around 3,000 BC are commonly considered to be the matrix of human civilization.

西元前 3,000 年左右在中東所發展出來的城邦，普遍被視為人類文明的發源地。

0325 **matrix** [ˋmetrɪks]	名 母體；發源地；矩陣

• B.C (before Christ) 西元前
• city state 城邦
• human civilization 人類文明

※「西元後」為 AD（Anno Domini〔拉丁文，即英文 in the year of the Lord 之意〕）。

quotation / excerpt / summary

Kindly fax us a price quotation for 100 of your latest model RH-511 cellular phones.

煩請將你們最新款 RH-511 行動電話 100 支的報價傳真給我們。

0326 * **quotation** [kwo`teʃən]	名 引用；報價 衍 **quote** 動 引用；報價

※ 如今 cellular phone 多略為 cellphone。

To make the screening process more efficient, we would appreciate it if you could attach a three-page excerpt from your treatise.

為了使選拔過程更有效率，假如您能附上三頁的論文摘要，我們會很感激。

0327 * **excerpt** [`ɛksɝpt]	名 節錄；摘要 動 摘錄 類 **abstract** 摘要

- screening process 選拔過程
- treatise 論文

※ abstract 作形容詞用時指「抽象的」。

Professor Brown asked us to write a summary of Jane Austen's novel *Pride and Prejudice*.

布朗教授要我們寫一篇珍．奧斯汀的小說《傲慢與偏見》的摘要。

0328 **summary** [`sʌmərɪ]	名 概述；摘要；總結 衍 **summarize** 動 概述；總結

dehydrate / arid / sterile

Drink lots of water, even in winter, so you won't get dehydrated.

要多喝水，尤其是在冬天，這樣你才不會脫水。

0329 * **dehydrate** [di`haɪ,dret]	動 脫水；使乾燥 衍 **dehydration** 名 脫水 關 **parched** 動 使乾透；使乾渴

※「除溼」為 dehumidify，而「除溼機」即為 dehumidifier。

Native Americans were driven out of their fertile homeland and into vast sterile pieces of land with rocks and pebbles.

美洲原住民被趕出肥沃富饒的家園而來到了幅員遼闊、遍布岩石和卵石的不毛之地。

0330 * **sterile** [`stɛrəl]	形 不毛的；貧瘠的 類 **barren** 貧瘠的；荒蕪的 反 **fertile** 富饒的；肥沃的

※ sterile 也有「無菌的」、「不孕的」之意，sterilize 則指「消毒」或「結紮」。

The farmers despairingly stared at miles and miles of arid soil after the longest drought they had ever experienced.

在經歷所遇到過最久的旱災之後，農民們絕望地凝視著延綿不知多少哩乾旱的土地。

0331 * **arid** [`ærɪd]	形 乾旱的；乾燥的 類 **dry** 乾的；乾燥的

- despairingly 絕望地
- drought 旱災

CHAPTER 1 UNIT 11

CheckTest

0302 ⇨ 0331

請依照文意將適當的單字填入空格中。可參考第 147 頁所提示的單字來作答。(作答時間:5 分鐘)

① Over the past few years, there has been an increase in __________ of art exhibits by visitors to the museum.

② This tourism promotion film was __________ by the US State Department.

③ Ms. Gonzalez's management __________ was what saved the company from disaster during the depression.

④ Charles Darwin, the author of *The Origin of Species*, is considered to be the __________ of the modern biologist.

⑤ The law requires that any canine entering the country without a vaccination certificate be __________ for a period of 14 days.

⑥ Vegetable, meat, wood, and paper products __________ biologically, but plastic, nylon and vinyl products do not.

⑦ Drink lots of water, even in winter, so you won't get __________.

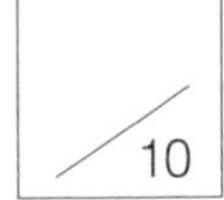

⑧ Kindly fax us a price __________ for 100 of your latest model RH-511 cellular phones.

⑨ Peter's __________ story about canoeing down the Yukon River made me decide to go there.

⑩ After the coup d'état, a __________ government was set up, and they began to prepare for the country's first general election.

參考用字

subsidize	degrade	expertise	quarantine
extraordinary	provisional	vandalism	prototype
quotation	dehydrate		

（解答請參閱第 430 頁）

Unit 12

spontaneously / impulsively / outrageously

MP3 13

After the formal concert, some of the musicians spontaneously began to play some wild jazz.

在正式的音樂會後，有些音樂家自行開始演奏一些狂野的爵士樂。

0332 ** spontaneously [spɔn`teniəsli]	副 自發地；自然地 衍 **spontaneous** 形 自然發生的；自發的 **spontaneity** 名 自發性

Tony tends to buy things impulsively. He has an expensive camera and a state-of-the-art computer, as well as paragliding equipment he never uses.

湯尼買東西常很衝動。他有一台很貴的相機和一部最先進的電腦，還有一套他從來都沒用過的飛行傘裝備。

0333 ** impulsively [ɪm`pʌlsɪvlɪ]	副 衝動地；莽撞地 衍 **impulsive** 形 衝動的；莽撞的 **impulse** 名 衝動；一時的念頭

- state-of-the-art 最先進的；尖端的

※ buy something on an impulse 是指「衝動下買東西」。

Don't shop at the new boutique on Park Avenue; the prices are outrageously high.

不要去公園大道上的那家新精品店買東西；價錢高得離譜。

0334 ** outrageously [aʊt`redʒəslɪ]	副 離譜地；太過分地 衍 **outrageous** 形 離譜的；太過分的 **outrage** 名 惡行；義憤

- boutique 精品店

stimulate / provoke / aggravate

Winning the high jump in the competition stimulated Gen to make further efforts.

在跳高比賽中獲勝激勵了甘恩更加努力。

0335 ** **stimulate** [ˋstɪmjəˏlet]	動 刺激；激勵 衍 **stimulation** 名 刺激；激勵 **stimulant** 名 刺激物；興奮劑 關 **stimulus** 名 刺激（物）；促進因素

• high jump 跳高
※「跳遠」叫 long jump。

The boss's abusive attitude provoked his workers to rebel against him. They made a list of complaints about him and sent it to the president.

該上司惡言相向的態度激起了員工群起反抗。他們把怨言羅列出來，送交總裁。

0336 * **provoke** [prəˋvok]	動 激怒；挑釁 衍 **provocative** 形 激怒的；挑釁的 **provocation** 名 激怒；挑釁

• abusive 辱罵的；施虐的
• rebel against 反抗
※ stimulate 指正面的刺激（激勵），而 provoke 則指負面的刺激（激怒）。

The hot, humid weather aggravated the baby's heat rash.

炎熱潮溼的天氣使寶寶的痱子惡化了。

0337 * **aggravate** [ˋægrəˏvet]	動 使惡化；加重 衍 **aggravation** 名 惡化；加重

• heat rash 痱子
※「痱子」也叫 prickly heat。

desperate / frantic / chaotic

That company must be pretty desperate to borrow money using non-bank loans.

那家公司一定是狗急跳牆了，才會向地下錢莊借錢。

0338 ** **desperate** [ˋdɛspərɪt]	形 絕望的；急切的；情急拚命的 衍 **desperately** 副 絕望地；拚命地 **desperation** 名 絕望；拚命

• non-bank loans 非銀行的借貸（指向地下錢莊借貸）

Useful POINT 「放高利貸者」叫 loan shark。

Danny made a frantic dash for the departing train, and barely made it onto the last car.

丹尼朝著駛離的列車狂奔，驚險地登上了最後一節車廂。

0339 * **frantic** [ˋfræntɪk]	形（因喜悅、憤怒等）發狂似的；狂亂的 衍 **frantically** 副 發狂似地；狂亂地

TOEIC POINT car 指列車的一節車廂。

The cancellation of all morning flights due to a bomb threat led to a chaotic scene at the airport.

早上的所有班機都因為炸彈威脅而取消，導致機場一片混亂。

0340 ** **chaotic** [keˋɑtɪk]	形 混亂的；混沌的 衍 **chaos** 名 混亂；混沌（發音為 [ˋkeɑs]）

centralization / rationalization / privatization

Centralization of all the company's functions will not necessarily lead to greater efficiency.

把公司所有的職責集中起來不必然能提高效率。

0341 * **centralization** [ˌsɛntrəlɪˋzeʃən]	名 集權；集中化 衍 **centralize** 動 集中；集權 反 **decentralization** 分權；權力下放

※ 本例中的 function 指「職務；職責」。

The labor union is fighting the firm's rationalization plans because they are likely to result in the closure of some local plants.

工會正在對抗公司的合理化計畫，因為它很可能會導致某些地方廠的關廠。

0342 * **rationalization** [ˌræʃənləˋzeʃən]	名 合理化（過程） 衍 **rationalize** 動 合理化 **rational** 形 理性的；合理的 **rationale** 名 基本理念

Privatization will lead to more competition in the market, and prices will fall as a result.

民營化將使市場更加競爭，價格也會因此下滑。

0343 **privatization** [ˌpraɪvətaɪˋzeʃən]	名（國營企業的）民營化；私有化 衍 **privatize** 動 民營化；私有化 **privatize postal services** 把郵政事業民營化

• as a result (of ...) 由於（……）

comprehensive / overall / inclusive

We can't deal with this problem one piece at a time; we must try to find a comprehensive solution.

我們對這個問題不能一次處理一點，我們必須設法找出全面性的解決方案。

0344 ** **comprehensive** [ˌkɑmprɪˋhɛnsɪv]	形 全面性的；綜合的；包羅萬象的 衍 **comprehend** 動 理解；領會 **comprehension** 名 理解；理解力 **listening / reading comprehension** 聽力／閱讀測驗

Although a few of the paintings are excellent, my overall impression of Jake Donaldson's new exhibit is that he has run out of new ideas.

雖然有少數的畫很棒，但是我對傑克 · 唐納森新畫展的整體印象是，他已無新意。

0345 ** **overall** [ˋovɚˌɔl]	形 整體的；全面的

- exhibit 展覽（品）；陳列（物）
- run out 耗盡

※「展覽會」用 exhibition 表示。

The university I attended used to be very elitist, but now it is trying to be as inclusive as possible in its admissions policy.

我所上的大學以往非常菁英取向，但是現在它試圖在招生政策上盡可能做到兼容並蓄。

0346 * **inclusive** [ɪnˋklusɪv]	形 兼容並蓄的；包含的 衍 **include** 動 包括；包含 **inclusion** 名 包括；包含（物） **including** 介 包含；包括 反 **exclusive** 排除的；獨有的

- elitist 菁英取向的

※「獨家新聞」英文說成 exclusive。

affable / gregarious / extrovert

Whenever I need company, I call up Donny; he is such an affable person that I can always talk to him.

每當我需要人陪時，我就會打電話給唐尼；他是個相當和藹可親的人，跟他說話很輕鬆。

0347 ** **affable** [ˋæfəbl̩]	形 和藹可親的；平易近人的 類 **amiable** 和藹可親的、**friendly** 友善的

• company 同伴

Both humans and monkeys are gregarious, and have difficulty living alone for long periods of time.

人和猴子都是群居動物，很難長時間獨自生活。

0348 * **gregarious** [grɪˋgɛrɪəs]	形 群居的；合群的 類 **social** 社會的；群居的

• have difficulty Ving 做……有困難

Good salespeople are usually extroverts by nature.

好的銷售人員通常都是天生就外向。

0349 **extrovert** [ˋɛkstrovɜt]	名 外向的人 形 個性外向的 反 **introvert** 內向的人

heterogeneous / miscellaneous / motley

Tokyo has become quite a heterogeneous city. For example, one out of ten residents in Minato-ku is a foreign national.

東京已成為相當異質化的城市。例如，港區就有十分之一的居民是外籍人士。

0350 * **heterogeneous** [ˌhɛtərəˋdʒinɪəs]	形 異質化的；異種的 反 **homogeneous** 同質化的；同種的

• one out of ten 十個中就有一個（十分之一）

After our aunt passed away, we found out that she had left a collection of miscellaneous miniature objects.

姑姑過世後，我們發現她留下了一堆各式各樣的袖珍物品。

0351 * **miscellaneous** [ˌmɪsl̩ˋenɪəs]	形 各式各樣的；五花八門的

• pass away 過世
• miniature 袖珍的；小型的

After the car accident, we noticed we were surrounded by a motley crowd of onlookers.

車禍發生後，我們發現周遭出現了一群混雜的圍觀者。

0352 **motley** [ˋmatlɪ]	形 雜色的；混雜的

• surround 包圍
• onlooker 圍觀者

carnivore / herbivore / omnivore

You can never make a cat eat vegetables; cats are carnivores.

你絕對沒辦法要貓吃蔬菜；貓是肉食動物。

0353 * **carnivore** [ˋkarnə͵vɔr]	名 肉食動物；食蟲植物 衍 **carnivorous** 形 肉食的

Bears are basically herbivores, but they sometimes eat fish or meat.

熊基本上是草食動物，但是有時候牠們也會吃魚或肉。

0354 * **herbivore** [ˋhɜbə͵vɔr]	名 草食動物 衍 **herb** 名 草藥 **herbaceous** 形 草本的 **herbivorous** 形 草食的

Human beings are omnivores, but can live quite healthily as vegetarians.

人類是雜食動物，但是吃素也能活得相當健康。

0355 * **omnivore** [ˋamnə͵vɔr]	名 雜食動物 衍 **omnivorous** 形 雜食的

• vegetarian 素食者

distract / sidetrack / divert

I have to work in complete silence; music or any kind of noise distracts me.

我必須完全安靜才能工作，音樂或任何一種噪音都會使我分心。

0356 ** **distract** [dɪˋstrækt]	動 使分心 衍 **distraction** 名 分心；注意力分散 **distracting** 形 使人分心的 **distracted** 形 注意力不集中的

If you want to succeed, focus firmly on your goal and don't let yourself be sidetracked.

假如你想成功，那就要堅定地鎖定目標，而不要讓自己偏離正軌。

0357 * **sidetrack** [ˋsaɪdˏtræk]	動 使轉移目標；（火車）駛入側線 名（鐵路）側線；旁軌

• focus on 鎖定
• firmly 堅定地

Mike was so absorbed in the TV game that it was impossible to divert his attention.

麥克十分投入電玩遊戲，要轉移他的注意力是不可能的事。

0358 * **divert** [daɪˋvɜt]	動 轉移；轉向；使分心 衍 **diversion** 名 轉移；轉向；分散注意力

• be absorbed in ... 專注於……
• divert one's attention from ... 把某人的注意力從……轉移
※ diversion 可指「消遣」、「娛樂活動」。

elaborate / ornate / sumptuous

Mr. Parker spared no expense on the elaborate dinner for Dye Corporation executives, our best clients for the past 10 years.

派克先生不惜花費請我們過去 10 年來最好的客戶——戴伊公司的主管吃精緻大餐。

0359 ** **elaborate** [ɪˋlæbərɪt]	形 費心的；精巧的；詳盡的 動 詳細說明；精心製作

• spare no expense 不惜花費

TOEIC POINT elaborate 常作動詞用，意思為「詳述（論點等）」，例如：Your explanation is too simple. Please elaborate.（你的說明過於簡單。請進一步詳述。）

At the Academy Awards Presentation, the actress Emily Fisher wore an ornate piece of jewelry studded with large rubies.

在奧斯卡頒獎典禮上，演員艾蜜莉．費雪戴了一副以大顆紅寶石來點綴的華麗首飾。

0360 * **ornate** [ɔrˋnet]	形 裝飾華麗的；過分修飾的 衍 **ornament** 名 裝飾；裝飾品

• studded with 散布於；點綴

※ 注意，jewelry 為珠寶、首飾之總稱，屬不可數名詞；一件一件的珠寶、首飾應用可數的 jewel 表示。

The sumptuous new opera house proved to be an acoustic disaster.

這座豪華的歌劇院被證明在音響的部分是個大失敗。

0361 **sumptuous** [ˋsʌmptʃuəs]	形 豪華的；昂貴的 類 **extravagant** 奢侈的、**luxurious** 奢華的

• acoustic 音響的；聽覺上的

• disaster 災難；大失敗

CHAPTER 1 UNIT 12

CheckTest

0332 ➪ 0361

請依照文意將適當的單字填入空格中。可參考第 159 頁所提示的單字來作答。(作答時間:5 分鐘)

① The labor union is fighting the firm's __________ plans because they are likely to result in the closure of some local plants.

② The hot, humid weather __________ the baby's heat rash.

③ Whenever I need company, I call up Danny; he is such an __________ person that I can always talk to him.

④ Tony tends to buy things __________. He has an expensive camera and a state-of-the-art computer, as well as paragliding equipment he never uses.

⑤ Danny made a __________ dash for the departing train, and barely made it onto the last car.

⑥ We can't deal with this problem one piece at a time; we must try to find a __________ solution.

⑦ I have to work in complete silence; music or any kind of noise __________ me.

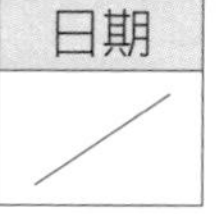

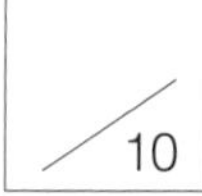

⑧ After our aunt passed away, we found out that she had left a collection of __________ miniature objects.

⑨ Mr. Wong spared no expense on the __________ dinner for Dye Corporation executives, our best clients for the past 10 years.

⑩ Human beings are __________, but can live quite healthily as vegetarians.

參考用字

impulsively	frantic	rationalization	comprehensive
omnivore	affable	aggravate	distract
miscellaneous	elaborate		

（解答請參閱第 430 頁）

Unit 13

improper / inadequate / indecent

MP3 14

It is considered improper for the groom to visit his bride on their wedding day.

新郎在婚禮當天去探訪新娘被認為是不得體的。

0362 ** **improper** [ɪm`prɑpɚ]	形 不得體的；不適當的 類 **inappropriate** 不恰當的 反 **proper** 恰當的；正確的

- groom 新郎（為 bridegroom 之略）
- bride 新娘

Ms. Hart, we are sorry to tell you that your sales figures during the past three months are quite inadequate, and we will have to let you go.

哈特小姐，我們要很遺憾地告訴妳，妳過去三個月的銷售數字相當差，我們必須請妳走路。

0363 ** **inadequate** [ɪn`ædəkwɪt]	形 不夠格的；不足的；不適切的 衍 **inadequacy** 名 不適切；不足 反 **adequate** 足夠的；適切的

- sales figures 銷售數字

When Matt spoke, people began to move away one by one; they were shocked by his use of indecent language.

在麥特發言時，大家開始一個接一個離場；他們被他所說的粗話嚇到了。

0364 **indecent** [ɪn`disn̩t]	形 粗鄙的；下流的；不當的 衍 **indecency** 名 粗鄙；下流 類 **obscene** 猥褻的；淫穢的 反 **decent** 正派的；體面的

※「說髒話」用 swear（原意為「發誓」）表達，例如：Don't swear so much.（不要那麼愛說髒話。）

mannerism / fixation / inhibition

Adam often scratches his neck while talking to someone; it is a nervous mannerism he picked up from his father.

亞當在跟別人說話時，常常會抓脖子；這是被他爸爸傳染到的緊張習性。

0365 ** **mannerism** [ˋmænərɪzəm]	名 獨特之格調；習性；怪癖

• scratch 抓；搔
• nervous 緊張的

Meg's fixation about marrying Tom is beginning to affect her relationship with him.

梅格執意要嫁湯姆，使彼此間的關係開始受到影響。

0366 * **fixation** [fɪkˋseʃən]	名 專注；執著 衍 **fix** 動 使固定；專心於；修理

• affect 影響；佯裝

It is wonderful to listen to what children say because they are so free of inhibitions.

聽小孩子說話很妙，因為他們百無禁忌。

0367 **inhibition** [ˏɪnhɪˋbɪʃən]	名 顧忌；抑制；禁止 衍 **inhibit** 動 禁止；抑制 **uninhibited** 形 不受約束的

※ 注意，不要將 inhibit 與 inhabit「居住」混淆。

diploma / credentials / archive

I'm sending you a copy of my high school diploma and school transcripts with this application letter.

我會把我高中畢業證書的副本和成績單連同這封求職信寄給您。

0368 ** **diploma** [dɪ`plomə]	名 畢業證書；文憑 類 **certificate** 執照；憑證

• transcripts 成績單

When applying for the teaching position, you are required to submit your curriculum vitae accompanied by validated credentials.

在應徵教職時，你必須繳交履歷，並附上有效的證書。

0369 ** **credentials** [krɪ`dɛnʃəlz]	名 證明書；證件（複數形） 衍 **credence** 名 信任；信賴 **add credence to sth.** 提高某事的可信度

The Ministry of Internal Affairs is responsible for keeping all the archives in order.

內政部要負責把所有的檔案保存妥當。

0370 * **archive** [`ɑrkaɪv]	名 檔案；文書 動 存檔；歸檔

• the Ministry of Internal Affairs 內政部
• in order 妥當地；按順序地
※「外交部」為 the Ministry of Foreign Affairs。

zealous / fervent / fanatical

Lithuania's zealous efforts for liberty were finally rewarded. The country won independence from Russia.

立陶宛熱切盼望自由的努力終獲回報。該國從俄羅斯取得了獨立。

0371 ** **zealous** [`zɛləs]	形 熱望的；熱心的 衍 **zeal** 名 熱忱；熱心（發音為 [zil]） **zealot** 名 狂熱者（發音為 [`zɛlət]） 類 **enthusiastic** 熱切的、**eager** 急切的

• win independence 取得獨立

Peter's fervent love for Penny finally persuaded her parents to consent to their marriage.

彼得對潘妮濃烈的感情終於說服她的雙親同意他們的婚事。

0372 * **fervent** [`fɝvənt]	形 熱衷的；熱烈的 衍 **fervor** 名 熱情；熱誠 類 **passionate** 熱情的

• persuade 說服
• consent to 同意

Many young men are almost fanatical in their support of their favorite soccer team.

很多年輕人對於自己最喜愛的足球隊是幾近狂熱地支持。

0373 * **fanatical** [fə`nætɪkḷ]	形 狂熱的；入迷的 衍 **fanatic** 名 狂熱分子；入迷者 **fanaticism** 名 狂熱；入迷

TOEIC POINT 與 zealous、fervent 不同，fanatical 具強烈的否定意涵。

neutralize / annul / invalidate

The new tax law was neutralized by the opposition party, and all its potential benefits were lost.

新的稅法遭到反對黨掣肘，所有可能的福利都化為烏有。

0374 * **neutralize** [ˋnjutrəlˏaɪz]	動 中和；抵銷；使無效；中立化 衍 **neutral** 形 中性的；中立的 **neutralization** 名 中和；中立化

- opposition party 反對黨
- benefit(s) 福利；利益

※ fringe benefits 指「附加福利」。

The water bill was annulled as a result of petitions filed by groups of citizens opposing the rate increase.

在公民團體提出請願反對費率調漲下，水費法案遭到了廢止。

0375 **annul** [əˋnʌl]	動 取消；廢止；使無效 衍 **annulment** 名 廢止；取消

- water bill 水費法案
- file the petition 提出請願

※ 除了指「法案」外，本例中的 bill 常用來指「帳單」，如 telephone bill（電話費單）、water bill（水費單）、electricity bill（電費單）等。

If one party fails to present accurately audited accounts by March 31st, this agreement will be invalidated.

假如有一方無法在 3 月 31 日前提出精確的審計帳目，本協議即告失效。

0376 **invalidate** [ɪnˋvæləˏdet]	動 失效；使無效 衍 **invalid** 名 重病者；傷殘者（念法為 [ˋɪnvəlɪt]） 形 無效的；體弱多病的（念法為 [ɪnˋvælɪt]）

- audited accounts 經審計之帳目

mandatory / compulsory / imperative

Due to the trade imbalance, our country will have to accept mandatory import quotas.

由於貿易失衡，因此我國必須接受強制進口配額。

0377 ** **mandatory** [ˋmændəˏtorɪ]	形 強制的；命令的；義務的

※ mandatory retirement 指「強制退休」。

Attending elementary school and junior high school is compulsory for everyone.

每一個人都強制必須上小學和國中。

0378 * **compulsory** [kəmˋpʌlsərɪ]	形 強迫的；義務的 類 **obligatory** 義務的；強制的

※ compulsory military service 指「義務兵役」。

We are running low on fuel. It is imperative that we land our plane within 10 minutes.

我們的燃料快用完了。我們必須在 10 分鐘內把飛機降落。

0379 * **imperative** [ɪmˋpɛrətɪv]	形 必須的；緊急的；命令式的 名 要務；命令

TOEIC POINT 車子的燃料用 gas（gasoline），飛機的燃料則用 fuel。

corresponding / proportionate / commensurate

You have to understand the rights you insist on always come with corresponding responsibilities.

你必須了解你所堅稱的權利永遠伴隨著相應的責任。

0380 ** corresponding [ˌkɔrɪˋspɑndɪŋ]	形 相應的；符合的；相當的 衍 **correspond** 動 符合；一致；通信 **correspond to / with ...** 與……相符 **correspondent** 名 特派員；通信員

• insist on 堅稱

The tiny windows looked a little odd because their size was not proportionate to the height of the room.

那些小窗子看起來有點怪，因為大小跟房間的高度不成比例。

0381 ** proportionate [prəˋporʃənɪt]	形 成比例的；相稱的 衍 **proportion** 名 比率；比例 **in proportion to / with ...** 與……成比例

• odd 怪的（參照 0143）

Aircraft engineers urgently wanted. Salary commensurate with experience.

急徵飛機工程師。依資歷敘薪。

0382 ** commensurate [kəˋmɛnʃərɪt]	形 相當的；相稱的

• (be) commensurate with 與……相稱

TOEIC POINT 本例為廣告詞。第一句為 Aircraft engineers are ungently wanted. 之省略式；第二句則為 Salary will be commensurate with experience. 之省略式。

enhancement / reinforcement / corroborate

This beautifully designed media center was subsidized by the State Department's Local Identity Enhancement Project and was constructed by our company.

這棟設計美觀的媒體中心是由國務院的強化地方認同方案所資助，並由我們公司來興建。

0383 * **enhancement** [ɪn`hænsmənt]	名 強化；提升；改善 衍 **enhance** 動 強化；提升；改善 類 **improvement** 改善；改進

- subsidize 資助（參照 0302）
- local identity 地方認同

In order to make a more convincing case, your argument needs reinforcement with facts and statistical data.

為了提出更有力的說明，你的論點需要補強事實和統計數據。

0384 * **reinforcement** [ˌriɪn`forsmənt]	名 補強；增強 衍 **reinforce** 動 補強；增強；強化

- argument 論點；論證
- statistical data 統計數據

The police could not proceed with the prosecution of the suspect because there was no evidence to corroborate the witness's statement.

警方無法著手起訴嫌犯，因為沒有證據可以證實目擊者的說法。

0385 **corroborate** [kə`rɑbəˌret]	名 證實；確證 衍 **corroboration** 名 證實；確證

- proceed with 著手；進行
- prosecution 起訴
- suspect 嫌疑犯
- evidence 證據

※ 注意，別把 corroboration 跟 collaboration（合作；共同）弄混。

CheckTest

0362 ⇨ 0385

請依照文意將適當的單字填入空格中。可參考第 169 頁所提示的單字來作答。（作答時間：4 分鐘）

① Lithuania's __________ efforts for liberty were finally rewarded. The country won independence from Russia.

② Abe often scratches his neck while talking to someone; it is a nervous __________ he picked up from his father.

③ Due to the trade imbalance, our country will have to accept __________ import quotas.

④ Ms. Hart, we are sorry to tell you that your sales figures during the past three months are quite __________, and we will have to let you go.

⑤ Aircraft engineers urgently wanted. Salary __________ with experience.

⑥ I'm sending you a copy of my high school __________ and school transcripts with this application letter.

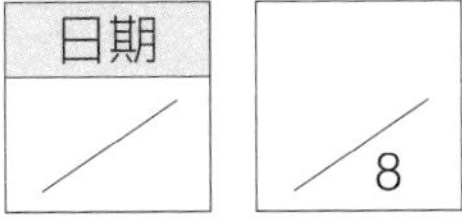

⑦ The water bill was __________ as a result of petitions filed by groups of citizens opposing the rate increase.

⑧ In order to make a more convincing case, your argument needs __________ with facts and statistical data.

參考用字

mannerism	inadequate	zealous	commensurate
annul	mandatory	diploma	reinforcement

（解答請參閱第 430 頁）

Unit 14

liable / accountable / governable

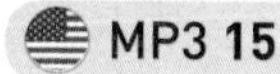

The construction company was found liable for the structural shortcomings of the building and had to pay a huge sum in compensation.

該建設公司被認定要為大樓的結構瑕疵負責，而且必須支付巨額的賠償。

0386 ** liable [ˋlaɪəbḷ]	形 應負責的；有義務的 衍 liability 名 責任；義務；債務（通常用複數） liability insurance 責任險

- structural shortcomings 結構的瑕疵
- compensation 賠償；補償

The board of a company is directly accountable to the company's shareholders.

公司的董事直接對公司的股東負責。

0387 ** accountable [əˋkaʊntəbḷ]	形 應負責的；應作解釋的 衍 account 名 帳戶；帳目；報告；記述 動 解釋；說明（後接 for）

- be accountable to ... 對……負責
- shareholder 股東

As a result of the continued widespread rioting, many people are wondering whether the country is actually governable.

由於暴動持續蔓延，有很多人都很想知道該國是否真能統治。

0388 * governable [ˋgʌvənəbḷ]	形 可統治的；可支配的 衍 govern 動 統治；治理 government 名 政府；統治

- widespread 蔓延；擴散

flexible / resilient / agile

Flexible thinking is a vital element for success in the rapidly changing world of modern business.

在變化快速的現代商業界裡，靈活的思考是成功的要素。

0389 ** **flexible** [ˋflɛksəbl̩]	形 靈活的；有彈性的；可彎曲的 衍 **flexibility** 名 靈活性；彈性；易曲性 **flexibility exercise** 增加柔韌性的運動

- vital element 要素

Our factory specializes in resilient steel products such as coils and springs.

我們的工廠專做彈性鋼鐵製品，比方線圈和彈簧。

0390 * **resilient** [rɪˋzɪlɪənt]	形 有彈性的；有韌性的 衍 **resilience** 名 彈性；韌性

- specialize in 專門從事；專攻
- coil 線圈
- spring 彈簧

Lee's agile mind quickly calculated the pros and cons of the new position offered her, and she decided to accept it on the spot.

李敏捷的頭腦很快就推算出了新職位帶給她的利弊，於是她當場就決定接受。

0391 * **agile** [ˋædʒaɪl]	形 敏捷的；機伶的；靈敏的 衍 **agility** 名 敏捷；機伶

- pros and cons 利弊；優缺點
- on the spot 當場

criticize / condemn / impeach

Just criticizing won't get us anywhere. Let's try to make our discussion more constructive so that we can work out the problem.

光批評對我們毫無用處。咱們設法讓討論更有建設性，這樣才能解決問題。

0392 ** criticize [ˋkrɪtɪˌsaɪz]	動 批判；批評；非難 衍 **critic** 名 批評者；評論家 **critical** 形 批判的；批評的；危急的 **criticism** 名 批評；批判

• won't get sb. anywhere 對某人毫無用處
• constructive 建設性的

※ in a critical condition 指「情況危急」，為常用的片語。

The man who murdered his wife for her money was condemned to life imprisonment.

為財殺妻的男子被判無期徒刑。

0393 * condemn [kənˋdɛm]	動 譴責；非難；判罪 衍 **condemnation** 名 責難；非難；定罪 類 **convict** 宣告有罪；定罪

• life imprisonment 無期徒刑

The president of the United States can be impeached if he is found to have deliberately lied to Congress.

美國總統假如被發現故意對國會說謊，就會遭到彈劾。

0394 impeach [ɪmˋpitʃ]	動 彈劾；控告；檢舉 衍 **impeachment** 名 彈劾；控告；檢舉 **impeachable** 形 可彈劾的；可檢舉的

• deliberately 故意地

incoherent / unintelligible / redundant

The witness's statement could not be used in court as it was incoherent from start to finish.

證人的供述在法庭上無法使用，因為它從頭到尾都不一致。

0395 * **incoherent** [ˌɪnko`hɪrənt]	形 不一致的；不連貫的；沒有條理的 反 **coherent** 一致的；有條理的

• from start to finish 從頭到尾

The quality of the recording was so bad that the President's remarks were mostly unintelligible.

錄音品質很糟，使得總統的談話大部分都無法聽懂。

0396 * **unintelligible** [ˌʌnɪn`tɛlədʒəbl̩]	形 難以理解的 反 **intelligible** 可理解的

TOEIC POINT unintelligible 可指「無法聽懂的」，「無法看懂或判讀的」則用 illegible 表示。

I think you could make your report shorter. You made this point earlier, so the last paragraph is redundant.

我想你可以把報告縮短。你之前就提過這點了，所以最後一段是多餘的。

0397 * **redundant** [rɪ`dʌndənt]	形 多餘的；不必要的 衍 **redundancy** 名 多餘；冗贅

• make a point 提出論點

manipulate / maneuver / dominate

The opposition party accused the government of manipulating unemployment figures to make the situation look better than it actually is.

反對黨指控政府在失業數字上動手腳，以便讓情況看起來比實際上要好。

0398 * **manipulate** [mə`nɪpjə͵let]	動 操縱；操弄 衍 **manipulation** 名 操縱；操作 **manipulative** 形 操縱的；操控的

- accuse sb. of ... 指控某人……
- unemployment figures 失業數字
- look better than it actually is 看起來比實際上要好

The pilot maneuvered the aircraft into position on the runway and waited for takeoff instructions from the control tower.

機師把飛機開到跑道的定點上，並等待塔台的起飛指示。

0399 ** **maneuver** [mə`nuvɚ]	動 操控；巧妙地移動 名 花招；伎倆；（軍隊的）調用 類 **operate** 操作；運作

- runway 跑道
- control tower（航空）塔台

World soccer is now dominated by the few clubs that are rich enough to buy the very best players.

世界足球目前是由少數幾個球團所主宰，它們錢多得足以買來最頂尖的球員。

0400 **dominate** [`dɑmə͵net]	動 占優勢；主宰；稱霸 衍 **domination** 名 控制；主宰 **dominant** 形 占優勢的；支配的；(遺傳) 顯性的 **domineering** 形 跋扈的；盛氣凌人的

※ 與帶有「以力雄人」意義的 dominate 相比，manipulate 則是有「巧妙而婉轉的操縱某人」之意。

extravagant / flamboyant / gaudy

The sightseers were awed by the extravagant architectural style of the Sagrada Famillia Church designed by Gaudi.

觀光客對聖家堂奢華的建築風格感到敬畏，它是由高第所設計。

0401 ** **extravagant** [ɪk`strævəgənt]	形 浪費的；奢侈的 衍 **extravagance** 名 浪費；奢侈 類 **wasteful** 浪費的

- be awed 感到敬畏
- architectural style 建築風格

The poster was composed of all kinds of flamboyant colors. It was certainly eye-catching.

這張海報由各種燦爛的色彩所組成。它肯定很吸睛。

0402 * **flamboyant** [flæm`bɔɪənt]	形 燦爛的；浮誇的；豔麗的 衍 **flamboyance** 名 浮誇；豔麗 類 **loud** 鮮豔的；花俏的

- be composed of ... 由……所組成
- eye-catching 吸睛的；醒目的

Useful POINT flamboyant 源自法文，原意為「冒出火焰的」。

Such gaudy clothes may be fine if you're going to a party, but they're not appropriate for the office.

假如你要去赴宴，也許可以穿這麼炫麗的衣服，但是它們不適合穿去上班。

0403 **gaudy** [`gɔdɪ]	形（文風、服飾等）華麗而俗氣的；俗豔的 類 **flashy** 俗豔的

- appropriate 適合的（參照 0269 appropriately）

absorbed / preoccupied / engrossed

I love mystery novels. Sometimes I get so absorbed in them that I forget to eat dinner.

我非常喜歡看推理小說。有時候我會入迷到忘了吃晚飯。

0404 ** **absorbed** [əb`sɔrbd]	形 入迷的；熱中的 衍 **absorb** 動 吸收（液體、氣體、光、聲等）；全神貫注 **absorbent** 形 能吸收的 名 吸收劑 **absorbing** 形 引人入勝的

Meg sounded preoccupied when I called her. I wonder if she had something on her mind.

我打電話給梅格的時候，她聽起來心不在焉的。我在想她是不是有心事。

0405 ** **preoccupied** [pri`ɑkjə͵paɪd]	形 心不在焉的；出神的 衍 **preoccupy** 動 搶先占有；盤據心頭 類 **absent-minded** 心不在焉的；魂不守舍的

• have something on one's mind 有心事

Morgan was so engrossed in the computer game that he didn't hear his little brother fall down the steps and call for help.

摩根全神貫注地在打電玩，以致於他小弟跌下樓梯在呼救時都沒聽到。

0406 * **engrossed** [ɪn`grost]	形 專心的；全神貫注的

TOEIC POINT 本例中的 hear 為「感官動詞」，其受詞後用原形動詞 fall。

susceptible / vulnerable / prone

You are susceptible to colds, so be sure to keep yourself warm when you go skating.

你很容易感冒，所以去溜冰時一定要做好保暖。

0407 ** **susceptible** [sə`sɛptəbl̩]	形 易受影響的；易受感動的 衍 **susceptibility** 名 感受性

※ 在 go 後面用 Ving 表示「去做……」，如 go hunting（去打獵）、go swimming（去游泳），go dancing（去跳舞）等。

Carol looks vulnerable to criticism, but actually she is pretty tough and can take a lot.

凱蘿看起來禁不起批評，但是她其實相當強悍，承受力很強。

0408 * **vulnerable** [`vʌlnərəbl̩]	形 脆弱的；易受傷害的 衍 **vulnerability** 名 脆弱；易受傷害

- criticism 批判；批評
- can take a lot 承受力很強

Jackie is prone to losing her self-confidence, so as her supervisor, you must remember to give her a lot of praise and encouragement.

潔琪很容易喪失自信，所以身為她的上司，你必須記得多給她讚美與鼓勵。

0409 * **prone** [pron]	形 有……的傾向；易於……

- self-confidence 自信心
- supervisor 監督者
- praise 讚美
- encouragement 鼓勵

※ prone 之後可接介系詞 to + 名詞 / 動名詞（如本例），或接不定詞 to + 原形動詞，例如：He is prone to gain weight.（他很容易發胖。）

CheckTest

0386 ⇨ 0409

請依照文意將適當的單字填入空格中。可參考第 179 頁所提示的單字來作答。（作答時間：4 分鐘）

① Lee's ________ mind quickly calculated the pros and cons of the new position offered her, and she decided to accept it on the spot.

② The opposition party accused the government of ________ unemployment figures to make the situation look better than it actually is.

③ The board of a company is directly ________ to the company's shareholders.

④ Just ________ won't get us anywhere. Let's try to make our discussion more constructive so that we can work out the problem.

⑤ The witness's statement could not be used in court as it was ________ from start to finish.

⑥ Meg sounded ________ when I called her. I wonder if she had something on her mind.

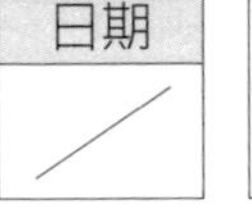

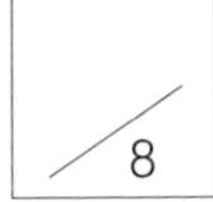

⑦ You are ________ to colds, so be sure to keep yourself warm when you go skating.

⑧ The sightseers were awed by the ________ architectural style of the Sagrada Famillia Church designed by Gaudi.

參考用字

accountable	incoherent	agile	susceptible
manipulate	extravagant	criticize	preoccupied

（解答請參閱第 430 頁）

Unit 15

superintendent / surveillance / scrutiny

MP3 16

We usually give a small gift to the superintendent of our dormitory every Christmas.

每年耶誕節我們通常都會送小禮物給我們宿舍的舍監。

0410 ** **superintendent** [ˌsupərɪnˋtɛndənt]	名 管理者；監督人；警司（英國） 衍 **superintendence** 名 監督

- dormitory 宿舍

TOEIC POINT superintendent 可簡略為 super。

The drug dealer didn't realize that he was under constant surveillance by the police.

該毒販渾然不覺自己一直被警方跟監。

0411 * **surveillance** [səˋveləns]	名 跟監；監視 衍 **surveillant** 名 監視者 形 監視用的

- drug dealer 毒販
- constant 一直的；持續的

The company's financial records were submitted to the tax inspector's scrutiny.

公司的財務記錄被交給了稅務稽查員詳查。

0412 **scrutiny** [ˋskrutṇɪ]	名 詳查；細看 衍 **scrutinize** 動 詳查；細看

- financial records 財務紀錄
- tax inspector 稅務稽查員

reference / recommendation / referral

If you have a problem using this computer system, check the reference book.

假如你不會用這套電腦系統，那就去翻翻參考書。

0413 ** **reference** [ˋrɛfərəns]	名 參考；參照；參考文獻 衍 **refer** 動 參考；查閱；提及；指涉

※ reference book 即「參考書」之意。

It's like a vicious cycle. If I don't have a recommendation, I can't get a job. But I can't get a recommendation without a job.

這就像個惡性循環。假如我沒有推薦信，我就找不到工作。但是如果我沒有工作又拿不到推薦信。

0414 ** **recommendation** [ˌrɛkəmɛnˋdeʃən]	名 推薦信；推薦 衍 **recommend** 動 推薦；提出建議

• vicious cycle 惡性循環

※「惡性循環」也可說成 vicious circle。

We don't usually advertise for staff. We've found most of our employees through referrals from our business associates.

我們通常不會登徵才廣告。我們所找的員工大部分都是透過業務夥伴的介紹。

0415 **referral** [rɪˋfɝəl]	名 轉介；推薦

• advertise 做廣告

• business associate 業務夥伴；同業

※ referral 與 reference 皆由動詞 refer 衍生而來。

abstention / mediocre / haphazard

At the board meeting, there were 5 votes for, 2 against and 1 abstention.

在董事會上，有五票贊成、兩票反對、一票棄權。

0416 * **abstention** [æb`stɛnʃən]	名 戒絕；（投票的）棄權 衍 **abstain** 動 戒絕；棄權

Useful POINT 要做某項決策時常用的說法：Who is for ？、Who is against ？、How many abstentions?，要求與會人員舉手表決。

Joe decided he would rather aim high and fail than spend his life in a mediocre job.

喬決定他寧可拉高目標而失敗，也不要把生命花在平庸的工作上。

0417 * **mediocre** [`midɪˌokɚ]	形 平庸的；中等的 衍 **mediocrity** 名 平庸 類 **ordinary** 普通的

• aim high 拉高目標

※ 本例中片語 aim high 的 aim 為「瞄準」之意，high 則為副詞用法。

Sue's boss criticized her approach to her job as haphazard, but she replied that other people just don't understand her system.

蘇的老闆批評她的工作方式雜亂無章，但她卻回答說，別人根本不懂她那一套。

0418 * **haphazard** [ˌhæp`hæzɚd]	形 雜亂無章的；偶然的；隨意的 衍 **haphazardly** 副 偶然地；隨意地 類 **disorganized** 紛亂的

• one's approach to one's job 一個人的工作方式

misfortune / mishap / adversity

Kurt had the misfortune of bearing a striking resemblance to a suspected terrorist on the international wanted list.

柯特很倒楣，他跟國際通緝名單上的恐怖分子嫌疑人長得極為相像。

0419 ** **misfortune** [mɪs`fɔrtʃən]	名 倒楣；不幸；厄運 反 **fortune** 幸運；財富

- bear a resemblance to 相像；神似
- striking 顯著的
- international wanted list 國際通緝名單

※ misfortune 的字首 mis- 與 unfortunate（不幸的）的字首 un- 皆為「否定」之意。

After the mishap of leaving her purse in the train, Laura is now very careful to keep hold of her belongings.

經過把手提包留在火車上的衰事後，蘿拉現在對隨身物品都保管得非常小心。

0420 ** **mishap** [`mɪs͵hæp]	名 衰事；小災難

- keep hold of 保管
- belongings 所有物（複數形）

TOEIC POINT purse 在英國指「小錢包」，在美國指「女用手提包」。另，「男用的皮夾」叫 wallet。

Rita overcame the adversity of growing up in poverty and went on to become one of the country's most powerful politicians.

莉塔克服了出身貧困的逆境，後來成為該國最有權勢的政治人物之一。

0421 **adversity** [əd`vɝsətɪ]	名 逆境；厄運；（經濟方面的）窘境 衍 **adverse** 形 反對的；逆向的；不利的 **adversary** 名 敵人；對手

- overcome 克服；戰勝

occasionally / intermittently / sporadically

Sam occasionally drives his family to their summer lodge in Mt. Snow.

山姆偶爾會開車載家人去雪山的避暑小屋。

0422	
** **occasionally** [ə`keʒənl̩ɪ]	副 偶爾；間或 衍 **occasion** 名 時機；場合；機會 **on occasion** 有時 **occasional** 形 偶爾的；偶然的；應景的 類 **at times / from time to time / now and then / sometimes** 偶爾；有時

• summer lodge 避暑小屋

Tomorrow's weather will be mainly sunny but we can expect light showers intermittently.

明天的天氣基本上是晴朗的，但是可以預期會有間歇性的小陣雨。

0423	
** **intermittently** [ɪntə`mɪtəntlɪ]	副 間歇地；斷續地 衍 **intermittent** 形 間歇的；斷續的 類 **on and off** 斷斷續續地

• shower 陣雨；淋浴

Albert's grades are bad because he studies only sporadically. He's in serious danger of failing to graduate.

亞伯特的成績很差，因為他完全是有一陣沒一陣地念書。他有極大的危險會畢不了業。

0424	
* **sporadically** [spə`rædɪklɪ]	副 時有時無地；零星地 衍 **sporadic** 形 時有時無的；偶發的；不經常的 類 **irregularly** 不規律的、**infrequently** 不經常的

• grade 成績

• be in serious danger 身陷極大的危險

accredit / attribute / ascribe

The school you attended is not accredited by the Department of Education, and so your degree is not recognized.

你念的學校並未經過教育部認可，所以你的學位得不到承認。

0425 ** **accredit** [ə`krɛdɪt]	動 認可；檢定為合格 衍 accreditation 名 合格鑑定；資格認定

TOEIC POINT accredit 的字根即為 credit（原意為「相信；信任」）。accredit 常以過去分詞作為形容詞使用，如：accredited school（經過認可的學校）、accredited course（經過認可的課程）、accredited member（經過認可的會員）。

Employees attribute this success to Mr. Cortez's outstanding leadership qualities.

員工們把這份成就歸功於柯提茲先生傑出的領導特質。

0426 * **attribute** [ə`trɪbjut]	動 把……歸因於；把……歸功於 名 屬性；特徵 衍 **attribution** 名 歸屬；歸因

TOEIC POINT attribute A to B 的意思為「將 A 歸因 / 功於 B」。

This passage seems to be in a different style from the rest of the book, and is usually ascribed to a different author.

這段文字的文體似乎跟書中的其他地方不同，一般被認為是出自不同作者之手。

0427 **ascribe** [ə`skraɪb]	動 把……歸因於；把……歸屬於 衍 **ascription** 名 歸因；歸屬

TOEIC POINT ascribe 的用法基本上與 attribute 相同，即 ascribe A to B。

anonymous / ambiguous / undistinguished

Joseph went to the police because he started receiving anonymous letters threatening him after the publicity in the mass media.

約瑟夫去找警察，因為在大眾媒體上成名後，他就開始收到威脅他的匿名信。

0428 * **anonymous** [ə`nɑnəməs]	形 匿名的 衍 **anonymity** 名 匿名

• threaten 威脅
• publicity 宣傳；出風頭（參照 0008）
• mass media 大眾媒體

The general idea contained in the plan is good, but the details are ambiguous.

這個計畫中所涵蓋的整體概念不錯，但是細節卻嫌含糊。

0429 * **ambiguous** [æm`bɪgjʊəs]	形 含糊不清的；模稜兩可的 衍 **ambiguity** 名 含糊；模稜兩可 類 **vague** 模糊不清的；含混的

• contain 包含

Even though she was a prize-winning student at high school, Julia's academic record at college was undistinguished.

就算高中時是獲獎學生，但是茱麗亞大學時的學業成績並不出色。

0430 * **undistinguished** [ˌʌndɪs`tɪŋgwɪʃt]	形 不出色的；平凡的 反 **distinguished** 出色的；不凡的

• academic record 學業成績

※ 勿將 undistinguished 與表示「無法區分；無法辨別」的 indistinguishable 混淆。

confidential / red tape / divulge

This information is classified as confidential. Do not communicate it to unauthorized personnel.

這則資訊被列為機密。不要向未經授權的人員透露。

0431 ** **confidential** [ˌkɑnfəˋdɛnʃəl]	形 機密的；祕密的 衍 **confidentiality** 名 機密（性）

- communicate 透露
- unauthorized 未經授權的

※ confidential 與 confident（有自信的）同源，字根 -fid- 為「信任；信賴」之意。

I finally got a working visa, but the red tape involved in the process nearly drove me crazy.

我終於拿到了工作簽證，但過程中所涉及的繁瑣程序簡直快把我搞瘋了。

0432 * **red tape** [rɛd tep]	名 繁瑣程序；繁文縟節；官樣文章 **go through the red tape** 經歷繁瑣程序

- working visa 工作簽證（也叫 work visa）
- drive someone crazy 使人發瘋

Our company deals with some patented precision instruments. Be careful not to divulge any information on our products.

我們公司經營的是一些專利精密儀器。小心別把我們產品的任何資料給洩露出去。

0433 * **divulge** [dəˋvʌldʒ]	動 洩露；暴露 衍 **divulgence** 名 洩露 關 **reveal** 動 透露；揭示 **disclose** 動 揭露；公開

- deal with 經營；處理
- patented 專利的
- precision instrument 精密儀器

Chapter 1 Unit 15

CheckTest

0410 ⇨ 0433

請依照文意將適當的單字填入空格中。可參考第 189 頁所提示的單字來作答。(作答時間：4 分鐘)

① Joe decided he would rather aim high and fail than spend his life in a ________ job.

② We usually give a small gift to the ________ of our apartment every Christmas.

③ Rita overcame the ________ of growing up in poverty and went on to become one of the country's most powerful politicians.

④ Tomorrow's weather will be mainly sunny but we can expect light showers ________.

⑤ If you have a problem using this computer system, check the ________ book.

⑥ Joseph went to the police because he started receiving ________ letters threatening him after the publicity in the mass media.

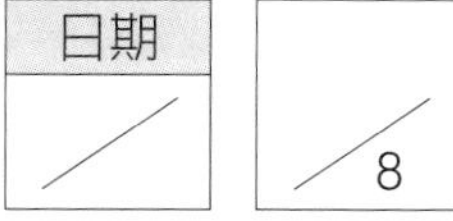

⑦ This information is classified as __________. Do not communicate it to unauthorized personnel.

⑧ Employees __________ this success to Mr. Cortez's outstanding leadership qualities.

參考用字

superintendent	attribute	reference	adversity
intermittently	mediocre	anonymous	confidential

（解答請參閱第 431 頁）

Chapter 2

Phrasal Verbs

0434 ➲ 0897

動詞片語

Unit 16

access / act

How wonderful it is to be able to access the Internet wherever you are; even in the mountains of Upstate New York where I have a little cabin.

到哪都能上網真棒；連我那間小屋所在的紐約州北邊山上也行。

0434
access the Internet 上網

- cabin 小屋；（船）客艙；（飛機）駕駛艙

Upstate New York 指紐約州北部的地區，擁有高山與白雪，是聞名的避暑聖地。

With InterTrans Corporation acting as your overseas agent, your import costs will decrease drastically.

有國際儲運公司做你的海外代理，你的進口成本將大幅降低。

0435
act as 擔任；充當

- overseas agent 海外代理
- import costs 進口成本
- drastically 大幅地；徹底地

You are going to be seven years old next month. Act your age and stop crying!

你下個月就要七歲了。什麼年紀做什麼事，別哭了！

0436
act one's age 做符合自己年紀的事

act / back

Our dog, Ben, is acting up again. He's been growling and snarling at the children. We should take him to the vet.

我們的狗狗小班又在搗蛋了。他一直對小孩子鬼吼鬼叫。我們應該帶牠去看獸醫。

0437

act up 搗蛋；調皮 類 misbehave 行為不端

- growl 咆叫
- snarl 吠
- vet 獸醫（為 veterinarian 之略）

A customer complained in a loud voice that I was trying to cheat him, but when I suggested calling the manager, he backed down and left the store.

有個顧客大聲抱怨說我想要騙他，可是當我建議說要找店長過來時，他就打退堂鼓並離開了店裡。

0438

back down 後退；放棄 類 back off 退後

- cheat someone 欺騙人

We are backing out of the public tender of the new bridge. It is too competitive and can't expect any profit.

我們要退出新橋樑的公開招標案。它太競爭了，沒有任何賺錢的希望。

0439

back out of (something) 退出（協議、計畫等）

- tender 招標；投標
- competitive 競爭的

back / balance / bear

We want to demand a 5% raise this year. Will the union back us up on this?

我們今年想要求加薪 5 %。工會會支持我們這麼做嗎？

0440
back (someone / something) **up** 支持、聲援（某人、某事）
類 support 支持；支撐

• raise 加薪

Your new job at our office is to balance the books at the end of each day.

你在我們辦公室的新工作是在每天下班前結算帳目。

0441
balance the books / accounts 結算帳目

TOEIC POINT balance 作名詞用時指「餘額」。

Bear in mind that you have only two weeks to turn in the income tax report.

記住，你只有兩個星期可以繳交所得稅申報書。

0442
bear in mind 記住；牢記在心

• income tax 所得稅

He says he is innocent, and the evidence bears out his claim.

他說自己是無辜的，證據也印證他的說法。

0443
bear out 印證；證實　類 prove to be correct 證明為正確

• claim 主張、說法

become / blow

That blouse is very becoming to you; the color matches your eyes.

那件短上衣非常適合妳；顏色跟妳的眼睛很搭。

0444
becoming to (someone) 適合（某人）

Could you please blow out the candle in front of the altar before you leave the room?

能不能麻煩你在離場前把祭壇前面的蠟燭給吹熄？

0445
blow out 吹熄；（保險絲）燒掉 類 extinguish 滅（火）

① These are inflatable boats. When you drop them into the water, they blow up automatically.

這些是充氣船。把它丟進水裡，它們就會自動充氣。

② The car parked outside the barber shop suddenly blew up and killed 3 passers-by.

停在理髮店外面的車突然爆炸，炸死了三個路人。

0446
blow up ① 膨脹；充氣 類 inflate（使）膨脹
② 爆炸 類 explode（使）爆炸

The manager blew up at us when she saw us smoking in the bathroom.

經理看到我們在洗手間抽菸，把我們罵了一頓。

0447
blow up at (someone) 責罵（某人）
類 yell at someone 對某人大吼

blow / break

Her chances for promotion blew up in her face when she made a slightly sarcastic remark to the vice president.

她對副總裁說話略帶挖苦，結果升官的機會就泡湯了。

0448
blow up in one's face 告吹 類 blow it 搞砸

• sarcastic 諷刺的；挖苦的
• vice president 副總裁

You've been talking on the phone for three hours! Are you trying to break a record?

你已經講了三小時的電話！你是想破紀錄嗎？

0449
break a record 破紀錄

Island Air had broken away from Paradise Airlines, its parent company, and became an independent entity.

島嶼航空從母公司天堂航空分割出去，成為獨立的事業體。

0450
break away 脫離

• entity 實體

Jenny broke down crying when she heard from the vet that her pet iguana had just died.

一聽到獸醫說她的寵物鬣蜥蜴剛剛死了，珍妮不禁放聲大哭。

0451
break down crying / break down in tears 放聲大哭

• ignana 鬣蜥蜴

break

You'd better get some sleep or you'll break down from exhaustion.

你最好補點眠，否則你會累倒。

0452
break down from exhaustion 累倒

If you break down the cost of your trip, 65% of it was hotel accommodations and meals. Next time, try to cut down on them.

假如你把旅費分析一下，有 65 % 是飯店住宿費和用餐費。下次試著節省一點。

0453
break down the cost 分析費用

- cut down 節省；縮減

Over time, the movement of minorities into higher level positions will break down the status quo.

慢慢地，少數族群往較高階的地位移動就會打破現狀。

0454
break down the status quo 打破現狀

- over time 慢慢地；漸漸地
- minority 少數族群
- status quo 現狀

We are not making a profit this year, but at least we're breaking even.

我們今年沒有賺錢，但是起碼打平了。

0455
break even 打平；損益兩平 類 draw 平手

break

People who want to work in Planning and Development have to break free from habitual ways of thinking.

想在企劃開發部工作的人必須跳脫習慣性的思考模式。

0456
break free from 跳脫　類 get away from 遠離

- Planning and Development 企劃開發部
- habitual way 習慣的方式

We broke the ground for the new fitness center last week.

我們上週為新健身中心進行破土。

0457
break ground 破土；開拓（新領域等）
關 groundbreaking ceremony 破土典禮

It will take at least four weeks to break in the new employees we just hired.

剛錄取的新員工至少要四週才能適應。

0458
break in (something / someone) 使（事／人）習慣、適應

The hacker broke into the sites of three banks in one night.

該駭客一個晚上就侵入了三家銀行的網站。

0459
break into 侵入、闖入；插入、打斷

TOEIC POINT break into 有時會以被動式表達。如：The store has already been broken into three times.「這個店已被小偷光顧過三次」。

break

About twenty dogs broke loose from the city dog pound and are still missing.

大約有 20 隻狗從該市的野狗收容所逃脫，至今仍然下落不明。

0460
break loose 逃脫；掙脫 類 run away / escape 逃走；脫逃

• dog pound 野狗收容所

Judy broke off her engagement to Tom when she heard about his other girlfriend.

茱蒂聽說湯姆另有女友後，便和他解除了婚約。

0461
break (something) **off** 解除（婚約等）；中止（關係等）
類 cancel / call off 撤銷；中止（參照 0499）

The United States broke off diplomatic relations with Iran over twenty years ago.

美國在 20 多年前就和伊朗斷絕了外交關係。

0462
break off with (someone)（與某人）斷絕（關係、聯絡等）

It broke my heart to have to let Ms. Simpson go. She is such a nice person, but she just couldn't keep up with her work.

必須讓辛普森小姐離職令我心碎。她是這麼好的人，但是就是無法勝任她的工作。

0463
break one's heart 令人心碎

• let someone go 讓某人離職（比 fire someone 委婉的說法）
• keep up (with)（參照 0677）

break

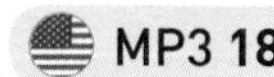

The senator broke her pledge not to raise taxes, and the voters remembered the broken promise in the next election.

該參議員違背了不加稅的承諾，選民後來在下一次的選舉時都記得她不守信用。

0464
break one's pledge 違背承諾

Even though the peace treaty had been signed, little skirmishes continued to break out here and there in the city.

雖然簽了和平條約，在該市還是持續爆發小規模的衝突。

0465
break out 爆發；突然發生

- treaty 條約
- skirmish 小衝突；小規模戰鬥

Every time I eat raw crab, I break out in a rash. I'm allergic to it.

每次吃生螃蟹，我就會起疹子。我對它過敏。

0466
break out in a rash 起疹子

- allergic to something 對某事物過敏

Three prisoners broke out of the prison this morning and are considered armed and dangerous.

今天早上有三個犯人越獄，據信他們有攜械，而且很危險。

0467
break out of （從某處）逃脫 類 escape from（從某處）脫逃

- armed 武裝的；攜械的

break

Mr. Worth helped his employees break the smoking habit by quitting smoking himself.

靠著自己戒菸，沃斯先生也幫助員工戒掉了抽菸的習慣。

0468
break the habit 戒掉習慣

TOEIC POINT 本句的 help 為使役動詞用法，故其後動詞用原形。另注意，quit 之後可用名詞或動名詞。

The farewell luncheon for Lenny proceeded rather drearily until Patrick broke the ice by telling one of his crazy jokes.

藍尼的送別餐會進行得相當沉悶，直到派屈克講了一個他的瘋狂笑話，這才打破了僵局。

0469
break the ice 破冰；打破僵局

- farewell luncheon 送別餐會
- drearily 沉悶地

※ icebreaker 指「打破僵局的事物；破冰船」。

E-mail marketers are breaking the law if they attempt to hide or disguise their identity when they send an e-mail to a potential customer.

電子郵件的行銷人員在寄發電子郵件給潛在顧客時，假如企圖隱匿或偽裝自己的身分，那就是違法。

0470
break the law 違法

- marketer 行銷人員
- attempt to 企圖
- disguise one's identity 偽裝身分
- potential customer 潛在顧客

break

Nobody wanted to break the news to Mrs. Jones that her son was arrested by the police.

沒有人想透露消息給瓊斯太太說，她兒子遭到了警方逮捕。

0471
break the news 告訴（某人）壞消息

• arrest 逮捕

At 11:46 this morning, our museum broke the one millionth visitor mark.

今天早上 11 點 46 分時，我們的博物館突破了第一百萬參觀者的大關。

0472
break the (one millionth) **visitor mark** 突破（第一百萬）參觀者的大關

※ 要注意 the one millionth 為序數。另，mark 指「標靶」

Last month we had record sales of $459,388. Let's break the record again this month and try for $500,000!

上個月我們創下了 45 萬 9,388 元的銷售紀錄。這個月讓我們再度打破紀錄，朝 50 萬元邁進！

0473
break the record 打破紀錄

• record sales 銷售紀錄

break

Giving micro-loans to underprivileged women who want to start a small business is an attempt to break the vicious cycle of poverty.

提供小額貸款給想要做小生意的弱勢婦女是為了打破貧窮的惡性循環。

0474
break the vicious cycle 打破惡性循環

- micro-loans 小額貸款
- underprivileged 貧困的

TOEIC POINT vicious cycle 或 vicious circle 的意思為「惡性循環」。

Our overseas operations have grown tremendously in the past five years. Last year we broke through the $35,000,000 mark in sales.

我們的海外業務在過去五年中大幅成長。去年我們的營業額突破了 3,500 萬元的大關。

0475
break through 突破；克服（困難等）

- overseas operation 海外業務
- tremendously 極大地；大幅地

The federal government's decision to break up large construction contracts into smaller components was helpful to small, local businesses wishing to make a bid.

聯邦政府決定把大型的營建合約分拆成比較小的單位，這對有意競標的小型地方企業有所助益。

0476
break up 分拆；拆解；解散

- small component 小單位
- make a bid 競標

※ component 為「成分；零件」之意。

break / bring

Johnson had been Getz's partner in a law firm for over two decades before he broke up with her.

強森原本是蓋茲在法律事務所超過 20 年的合夥人，後來他跟她拆夥了。

0477
break up with (someone) 跟（某人）拆夥、分手

※ decade 指「10 年」。

Bill is smart enough to bring about change without upsetting people.

比爾聰明到能不得罪人而推行變革。

0478
bring about 引起；造成；導致

• upset 得罪；惹惱

It was forty years ago when I visited the Grand Canyon, but this photo brings back memories.

我是在 40 年前去大峽谷的，但是這張照片勾起了回憶。

0479
bring back memories 勾起回憶

• the Grand Canyon 大峽谷

One of the four gas stations on Main Street brought down its prices last week. Consequently, the other three brought theirs down in order to compete.

緬恩街上的四家加油站中，有一家在上星期調降了價格。結果為了競爭，其他三家也跟著調降。

0480
bring down 降低（物價等）；使垮台

• consequently 結果；因此

bring

His humorous act and mimicry brought down the house.

他詼諧的演出和模仿搏得了滿堂采。

0481
bring down the house 搏得滿堂采；引起哄堂大笑

• mimicry 模仿

If you think Mr. Sanders is guilty of embezzlement, you will need to bring forward the evidence in court.

假如你認為桑德斯先生犯了侵吞公款的罪行，那你就得在法庭上提出證據。

0482
bring forward 提出（議案、問題等）；舉出（證據等）

• embezzlement 挪用公款；侵吞（公款）

I didn't think the building designs offered by H&H Architectural Studio were very practical, so I brought in a new architect on the project.

我認為 H&H 建築工作室所提出的建築設計不是非常實用，所以我在這個案子上找了一位新建築師。

0483
bring in 找來（協助者等）；引進、採用（新流行等）
類 introduce 引入；引進；引介

I understand that you feel underpaid, but I think you are lucky to have a job and be able to bring in a paycheck regularly.

我知道你覺得你的薪資偏低，但是我認為你有工作，而且能固定領到薪水，這樣就很幸運了。

0484
bring in a paycheck 賺得薪水

• underpaid 薪水偏低的

※ paycheck 可指「薪水」或「支付薪資的支票」。

bring

Hurricane Laurence is expected to bring in heavy rain from the south.

羅倫斯颶風預計將從南邊帶來豪雨。

0485
bring in heavy rain 帶來豪雨

- hurricance 颶風

① Dr. Veli's shocking new theory brought on attacks from other scientists.

維利博士令人震撼的新理論招致了其他科學家的攻擊。

② Inhalation of exhaust fumes in Bangkok brought on my asthma attack.

在曼谷吸到排放的廢氣導致我氣喘發作。

0486
bring on attack(s) ① 招致攻擊 ② 導致發作

- inhalation 吸入
- exhaust fumes（汽、機車等排放的）廢氣
- asthma 氣喘

Our new boss brings out the best in her employees by identifying their interests.

我們的新老闆靠找出員工的興趣來激發出他們的最佳表現。

0487
bring out the best in (someome) 激發（某人）最佳的表現

- identify 識別；確認（參照 0110）

bring

If you have a major concern about our proposed budget for the new plant, please bring it into the open at tomorrow's meeting so that we can discuss it.

假如你對我們所提議的新廠預算有很大的疑慮，請在明天開會時當衆說明，這樣我們才能討論。

0488
bring (something) **into the open** 當衆說明（某事）

• major concern 重大的疑慮
• proposed budget 提議的預算

Bringing up children in today's world requires parents to be able to monitor their children's use of communication technologies such as text messaging and the Internet.

在現今的世界裡，父母在養育子女時，必須要能監督子女對通訊科技的使用，比方像傳簡訊和上網。

0489
bring up (someone) 養育（某人）

• text messaging 傳簡訊

TOEIC POINT 「養育人」的動詞可用 bring up 或 raise，「飼養動物」的動詞用 keep，而「種植植物」則用 grow。另注意，bring up 也可指「提出」，如 bring up an issue（提出一個議題）。

CHAPTER 2 UNIT 16

CheckTest

0434 ⇨ 0489

請依照文意將適當的動詞片語填入空格中。可參考第 210 頁所提示的片語來作答。（作答時間：7 分 30 秒）

① Our dog, Ben, is ________________ again. He's been growling and snarling at the children. We should take him to the vet.

② He says he is innocent, and the evidence ________________ his claim.

③ You are going to be seven years old next month. ________________ and stop crying!

④ Island Air had ________________ from Paradise Airlines, its parent company, and became an independent entity.

⑤ It will take at least four weeks to ________________ the new employees we just hired.

⑥ We want to demand a 5% raise this year. Will the union ________________ on this?

⑦ Nobody wanted to ________________ to Mrs. Jones that her son was arrested by the police.

⑧ ________________ children in today's world requires parents to be able to monitor their children's use of communication technologies such as text messaging and the Internet.

⑨ The manager ________________ us when she saw us smoking in the bathroom.

⑩ Every time I eat raw crab, I ________________. I'm allergic to it.

⑪ His humorous act and mimicry ________________.

⑫ The farewell luncheon for Lenny proceeded rather drearily until Patrick ________________ by telling one of his crazy jokes.

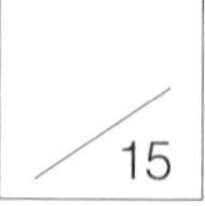

⑬ Mr. Worth helped his employees __________ smoking __________ by quitting smoking himself.

⑭ Our overseas operations have grown tremendously in the past five years. Last year we ____________________ the $35,000,000 mark in sales.

⑮ Johnson had been Getz's partner in a law firm for over two decades before he ____________________ her.

參考用字

act one's age	break in	act up
back someone up	blow up at	break away
bring down the house	bear out	break up with
break the habit	break the news	bring up
break out in a rash	break through	break the ice

（解答請參閱第 431 頁）

Unit 17

burn

Can you burn a DVD of the sales presentation you did yesterday so I can take it with me to the Chicago Office?

你能不能把你昨天的業務簡報燒成 DVD，好讓我可以帶去芝加哥辦事處？

0490
burn a DVD 燒一張 DVD

- sales presentation 業務簡報

Our warehouse burned down last June, and we lost a lot of inventory in the fire.

我們的倉庫去年六月燒毀了，在該場火災中我們損失了很多存貨。

0491
burn down 燒毀；焚燬

- warehouse 倉庫
- inventory 存貨；一覽表

Practicing hula dance is a fun way to burn off calories.

練習草裙舞是一種有趣的燃燒熱量方式。

0492
burn off calories 燃燒熱量 類 burn fat 燃燒脂肪

If you're feeling burned out at your job, you might consider taking a break from work and going back to school for a professional degree.

假如你覺得倦勤，不妨考慮停止工作一陣子，並回學校拿個專業學位。

0493
(be) burned out （人）耗盡筋力的；（燈泡、機械等）燒壞
類 (be) exhausted 筋疲力盡、(be) spent 覺得非常疲累

- professional degree 專業學位

As the space shuttle roared into the sky, the booster rockets fell off and burned up in the atmosphere.

太空梭轟隆一飛沖天，推進火箭也隨之掉落，並在大氣層中燃燒殆盡。

0494
burn up 燃燒殆盡

• space shuttle 太空梭 • roar 發出持續的轟鳴聲；呼喊 • atmosphere 大氣層

Jeff is burned up because you forgot to call him back.

傑夫氣炸了，因為你忘了回電給他。

0495
(be) burned up 氣炸了 類 be furious 大發雷霆

TOEIC POINT 表「非常生氣」時，burn up 亦可使用主動式，例如：She burns up at the mention of his name.（一聽到他的名字，她就火大。）

The marketing division wants to call a meeting to discuss our display at the upcoming convention in San Diego.

針對即將在聖地牙哥舉行的大會，行銷部想召開會議來討論我們的展示。

0496
call a meeting 召開會議

• division 部門 • display 展示 • upcoming 即將來臨的；將屆的

The president called for education reforms after he learned of the nationwide decline in reading scores.

在總統得知全國的閱讀能力下滑後，便呼籲要教育改革。

0497
call for 呼籲；要求

• nationwide 全國的 • decline 下滑；下降；衰退 • scores 分數

call

Wow! It's already 8:30. We've accomplished a lot, so let's call it a day, shall we?

哇！已經八點半了。我們完成了不少，那就到此為止吧，好嗎？

0498
call it a day 今天到此為止

• accomplish 完成；達到

Our reforestation project in Malaysia was called off due to the lack of funding and volunteers.

我們在馬來西亞的重新造林案撤銷了，因為缺乏金援和志工。

0499
call off 取消；終止 　類 cancel 取消；廢止

• reforestation 重新造林 　• funding 金援；資金

It was childish of you to call him names. You should apologize.

你竟然幼稚到去罵他。你應該要道歉。

0500
call someone names 辱罵某人

• childish 幼稚的；稚氣的
※ 注意，勿將 childish 與 childlike（如孩童般地無邪與純真）混淆。

The chair called the meeting to order exactly at 9:00 a.m.

主席在早上九點整宣布開議。

0501
call the meeting to order 宣布開議

TOEIC POINT the chair 指「（不論性別）主席」，為 chairperson 之略。有時也會使用 chairman（男）或 chairwoman（女），但需注意勿造成性別歧視的誤會。

Attendance is supposed to be perfect today because the teacher forgot to call the roll at the beginning of class.

今天的出席率應該很理想，因為老師在一上課時忘了點名。

0502
call the roll 唱名；點名 類 take attendance 點名

Show your enthusiasm for the product you are selling, but don't get too carried away. Too much enthusiasm could scare away potential customers.

對於你所賣的產品，要把熱忱表現出來，但是不要太忘我。熱情過頭可能會把潛在顧客給嚇跑。

0503
get carried away 得意忘形的 類 overdo something 將某事做過頭

- enthusiasm 熱忱；熱情
- potential customer 潛在顧客

Speeding in a school zone carries a fine of up to $500.

在學校區超速可罰款到 500 美元。

0504
carry a fine 受罰款

- up to 可達（某數量）

The motion to accept the amended budget was carried unanimously.

接受修正預算的動議獲得了無異議通過。

0505
carry a motion 通過動議（通常用被動式）

- amended budget 修正預算
- unanimously 無異議地；全體一致地

TOEIC POINT 採多數決進行會議時，主席可宣布 the motion is carried（此動議通過），或 the motion is denied（此動議遭否決）。

carry

Don't stop the discussion because of me. Carry on.

不要因為我而把討論停下來。請繼續。

0506
carry on 繼續（做某事） 類 continue 繼續；持續

Ms. Kim needs an assistant who can carry out simple instructions quickly and efficiently.

金小姐需要一個能迅速而有效率地完成簡單指示的助理。

0507
carry out 完成、執行（計畫、任務等）

Unused vacation days may be carried over into the next fiscal year.

沒有用完的休假可以留到下個會計年度。

0508
carry over 將……留用；使……延續

- fiscal year 會計年度

Thank you for serving as Master of Ceremonies at our golden wedding anniversary last night. You carried it off with style.

謝謝你昨天晚上擔任我們金婚週年紀念日的司儀。你主持得很有風格。

0509
carry something off 成功地應付某事；獲得（獎賞、榮譽等）

- Master of Ceremonies 司儀；節目主持人（常用字母縮寫 MC 表示）
- golden wedding 金婚；結婚 50 週年紀念

I want to thank you for setting up and running the seminar. You really carried the day.

我要謝謝你籌備並主辦了這場研討會。你真的辦得很成功。

0510

carry the day 成功；獲得勝利

• run 經營；管理；主辦 • seminar 研討會

It was a great idea to invite Patty on stage to sing and dance. She carried the show.

邀請佩蒂上台表演歌舞真是個好主意。她風靡了全場。

0511

carry the show 風靡全場；主導全局

• stage 舞台

A senior executive's opinion usually carries more weight than a secretary's.

資深主管的意見通常比祕書的意見更有分量。

0512

carry weight 有分量；有影響力

類 be convincing 有說服力的、be influential 有影響力的

• senior executive 資深主管

I am going to catch it when the accounting office hears about the $35 error I made on the daily sales report.

等會計室知道我的每日銷售報表錯了 35 美元，我就要挨罵了。

0513

catch it 挨罵；受罰 關 be scolded 受到責罵、be reprimanded 受到訓斥；be punished 受到處罰

• error 錯誤 • daily sales report 每日銷售報表

catch

Green tea is catching on very quickly all over the U.S. now, so we need to develop a line of green tea beverages without delay if we want to take advantage of this trend.

綠茶現在在全美各地風行得非常快，所以假如我們想利用這股風潮，就要趕緊開發出一系列綠茶飲料。

0514
catch on 風行；走紅 類 become popular

• a line of 一系列的 • beverage 飲料 • take advantage of 利用（參照 0839）

The new photocopy machine is quite user-friendly, so most of the staff has already caught on to it.

新的影印機相當好上手，所以大部分的人員已經會用了。

0515
catch on to 理解；搞懂 類 begin to understand 開始了解

• user-friendly 好用的

I sometimes catch myself yawning when the manager talks about all of his grandchildren's school achievements.

當經理在一一細數他孫子在學校的成就時，我有時候會發現自己在打呵欠。

0516
catch oneself doing 發現自己在……
類 notice oneself doing 注意到自己在……

• yawn 打呵欠 • achievement 成就；達成

I'm sorry to answer the door in my pajamas. You caught me off guard.

抱歉我穿著睡衣就來應門了。你讓我措手不及。

0517
catch someone off guard 使某人措手不及；使某人猝不及防

The thief was caught red-handed. I opened the door to my office, and there she was looking through my desk drawers.

小偷被逮個正著。我開門進辦公室就看到她正在翻我的書桌抽屜。

0518
(be) caught red-handed 被逮個正著；當場被抓到
類 catch someone in the act

• look through 識破；翻查

Sean and I meet for coffee once a month to catch up with each other's lives.

我和尚恩一個月會見面喝一次咖啡，以掌握彼此的生活近況。

0519
catch up with (something / someone) 得知最新的情報、訊息；趕上（人、進度等）

• meet for coffee 見面喝咖啡

Robert caused quite a commotion last night when he came home drunk.

羅勃昨天晚上喝醉酒回到家時，引起了很大的騷動。

0520
cause a commotion 引起騷動

• come home drunk 喝醉酒回家

I don't mean to cause a fuss, but I'm afraid you've spelled my name wrong on the program.

我不是要找碴，但是我在程序表中的名字恐怕拼錯了。

0521
cause a fuss 小題大做；找碴 類 cause trouble 造成麻煩

• don't mean to 無意要……

chip / come

The trouble with my supervisor is that he chips away at everyone's confidence and we feel demoralized.

我的上司的問題是，他會打擊大家的信心，使我們覺得氣餒。

0522
chip away 打擊；削弱

• the trouble with someone is 某人的問題是 • demoralize 使氣餒；使士氣低落

Boss's Day is coming up. Shall we all chip in on a gift?

老闆日要到了。我們要不要全體合送個禮物？

0523
chip in on (something) 集資、湊錢、買（禮物等）

10 月 16 日為美國的 Boss's Day（老闆 / 上司日），可接受來自屬下的禮物。此乃為了與 4 月的第四個星期三的 Secretary's Day（祕書日）抗衡才衍生的節日。

How did it come about that Yoko grew up in Australia?

洋子怎麼會是在澳洲長大的？

0524
come about（事情）發生 類 happen 發生

If you come across the new Paul Auster novel I was looking for, let me know.

假如你剛好發現我在找的那本保羅．奧斯特的新小說，跟我說一聲。

0525
come across 偶然發現或遇見
類 happen to see / meet 恰好看到 / 碰面

※ 另，come across as 指「給人留下……的印象」，例如：He comes across as very arrogant.（他給人留下非常自大的印象。）

come

Sid doesn't agree with your plan now, but he will eventually come around to it.

席德現在不同意你的計畫，但是他終究會回心轉意的。

0526
come around to it 回心轉意
類 will finally understand / agree 最終會了解／同意

I always advise job seekers to come clean on a resume.

我總是建議求職者在履歷上要一切坦白。

0527
come clean 一切坦白；和盤托出 類 tell the truth 說實話

- advise 向……提出建議；忠告
- job seeker 求職者

Jennifer came close to getting the job, but they finally decided to hire Kevin instead.

珍妮佛差一點就得到那份工作，但是他們最後卻決定錄取凱文。

0528
come close to 差一點就……

come close to 中的 to 是介系詞而不是不定詞，所以後面必須接名詞或動名詞。

You came down on your assistant pretty hard. She was only two minutes late, and it wasn't her fault.

你訓斥你的助理真凶啊。她只不過遲到了兩分鐘，而且也不是她的錯。

0529
come down on (someone) 訓斥（某人）
類 scold (someone) 責罵（某人）

come

I feel chilly and achy all over my body. I think I'm coming down with a cold.

我覺得全身又冷又痛。我想我得到了感冒。

0530
come down with (something) 得到、染上（感冒、病等）

- chilly 冷的
- achy 痛的

come down with 一般不用於由醫生診斷的重病，如 cancer（癌症）、diabetes（糖尿病）等。

Many Americans who came of age in the 1960s protested the Vietnam War and became conscientious objectors.

在 1960 年代成年的美國人有很多都反對越戰，並成為基於反戰而拒絕服兵役者。

0531
come of age 成年；成熟　類 become an adult 變成大人

- protest 抗議；反對
- the Vietnam War 越戰
- conscientious objector 基於反暴力、反戰之道德信念而拒服兵役者

Would you please let me know if my meeting with the sales rep tomorrow is going to come off or not?

可不可以麻煩你告訴我，我明天跟業務代表的會議要開還是不要開？

0532
come off 舉行；成功　類 take place 發生、succeed 成功

- sales rep 業務代表（為 sales representative 之略）

Tony comes off as a nice guy in person, but I don't trust him after the way he talked about me behind my back.

湯尼本人讓人覺得是個好人，但是在得知他在背後這麼講我後，我就不相信他了。

0533
come off as 讓人覺得……

• talk behind someone's back 在某人背後講閒話

Ms. Higgins came on too strong in her sales pitch, and scared away a would-be client.

辛吉絲小姐的銷售話術太過咄咄逼人，嚇跑了可能的客戶。

0534
come on strong 咄咄逼人

• would-be client 可能的客戶

The price of cattle feed has gone up. To come out ahead, dairy farmers will have to raise milk prices starting next month.

牛飼料漲價了。為了賺錢，酪農只好從下個月開始調高牛奶的售價。

0535
come out ahead 賺錢；盈利；取得優勢
類 make a profit 獲利、get the upper hand 占優勢

• cattle feed 牛飼料　• dairy farmer 酪農

He got away with sexual harassment until his victims came out in the open and confronted him.

他躲過了性騷擾的罪名，直到受害者公開出面跟他對質為止。

0536
come out in the open 公開出面

• get away with（做壞事但卻）躲過（懲罰）　• confront 對質

come

Come out with it. Who took my brand-new Parker pen from my desk this morning?

說。今天早上是誰拿了我書桌上全新的派克鋼筆？

0537
come out with (something) 說出（某事）
類 make (something) public 公開（某事）

• brand-new 全新的

After the four-hour operation, Mark came to in the recovery room.

經過四個小時的手術後，馬克在恢復室裡醒了過來。

0538
come to 甦醒；恢復知覺 類 regain consciousness 恢復意識
反 pass out 昏倒（參照 0726）、become unconscious 變得無意識、lose consciousness 失去意識

• operation 手術；運作

The total bill for dinner is 124 dollars, which, divided by four, comes to 31 dollars per person.

晚餐的帳單一共是 124 美元，四個人來分，換算下來是每人 31 元。

0539
come to ... 合計是…… 類 amounts to ... 總計是……

The hostility between Taylor and Martin finally came to a showdown, and Taylor resigned.

泰勒和馬丁之間的敵對終於攤牌，泰勒辭職了。

0540
come to a showdown 攤牌；一翻兩瞪眼

• hostility 敵對

come

I ordered an expensive espresso machine that I didn't really need, but then I came to my senses and canceled the order.

我原本訂購了一台昂貴卻並不是真正需要的濃縮咖啡機，但是後來我恢復理智，於是把訂單取消了。

0541
come to one's senses 恢復理智；醒悟過來
類 become reasonable 變得理智

After so many years of blaming himself for his son's accident, Ned finally came to terms with his feelings when he saw his son receiving a doctorate in a wheelchair.

為兒子的意外自責了這麼多年後，當他看到兒子坐著輪椅拿到博士學位時，奈德總算平復了內心的情緒。

0542
come to terms with (one's feelings) 平復（心情、情緒）

- doctorate 博士學位
- wheelchair 輪椅

Management finally came to terms with the factory workers' demand for better working conditions, and made a number of improvements.

對於工廠的勞工要求改善勞動條件，管理階層總算和他們達成了協議，並做了一些改進。

0543
come to terms with (someone)（與某人）達成協議、和解
類 make an agreement with (someone)（與某人）達成協議
end an argument with (someone) 終止（與某人的）爭端

- management 管理階層
- factory worker 工廠的勞工
- demand 要求
- working conditions 勞動條件

come

Five years ago, we dreamed of opening a new store in the heart of town, and today, our dream has come true.

五年前，我們夢想要在市中心開一家新的店，如今我們的夢想成真了。

0544
come true （夢想、願望、預言）成真 類 become reality 實現

The developers of a condominium project at Black Sand Beach came up against opposition from environmental groups concerned about endangering nesting sea turtles.

黑沙灘集合住宅案的開發商遭到了環保團體的反對，因為他們擔心會危害到築巢的海龜。

0545
come up against 遭到、面對（困難、問題等）

- eopposition 反對
- environmental group 環保團體
- nesting sea turtle 築巢的海龜

Can you come up with an eye-catching name for this new line of lipstick?

你能不能為這款新口紅想個引人注目的名稱？

0546
come up with （針對問題等）想出；提出
類 think up 構思、think of 想出

- eye-catching 引人注目；搶眼的

comply / count

Kitchen staff is reminded to comply with public health regulations.

廚房人員被提醒要遵守公共衛生規範。

0547
comply with 遵守（規則） 類 obey 聽從

- staff 全體職員；員工
- remind 提醒
- public health regulations 公共衛生規範

You'll be meeting the CEO and his wife at the Plaza Hotel and accompanying them to the reception. I'm counting on you to make them feel welcome.

你要在廣場飯店跟執行長伉儷碰面，並陪同他們前往接待會。要讓他們覺得賓至如歸，一切就靠你了。

0548
count on (someone) 依靠；指望
類 rely on 倚靠、depond on 依靠

- CEO 執行長（= chief executive officer）
- accompany 陪同；伴隨
- make someone feel welcome 讓人覺得賓至如歸

If you are still looking for people to join the Community Improvement Committee, count me in. I am very much interested.

假如你還在找人加入社區改善委員會，算我一份。我非常有興趣。

0549
count (someone) **in** 算（某人）一份；把（某人）算入
反 count someone out 不要算（某人）一份

- Community Improvement Committee 社區改善委員會

CheckTest

0490 ⇨ 0549

請依照文意將適當的動詞片語填入空格中。可參考第 229 頁所提示的片語來作答。(作答時間:7 分 30 秒)

① If you're feeling ______________ at your job, you might consider taking a break from work and going back to school for a professional degree.

② The president ______________ education reforms after he learned of the nationwide decline in reading scores.

③ Our warehouse ______________ last June, and we lost a lot of inventory in the fire.

④ Our reforestation project in Malaysia was ______________ due to the lack of funding and volunteers.

⑤ Unused vacation days may be ______________ into the next fiscal year.

⑥ Management finally ______________ the factory workers' demand for better working conditions, and made a number of improvements.

⑦ Practicing hula dance is a fun way to ______________.

⑧ Wow! It's already 8:30. We've accomplished a lot, so let's ____________________, shall we?

⑨ Show your enthusiasm for the product you are selling, but don't __________ too __________. Too much enthusiasm could scare away potential customers.

⑩ If you ____________________ the new Paul Auster novel I was looking for, let me know.

⑪ The new photocopy machine is quite user-friendly, so most of the staff has already ____________________ it.

⑫ Kitchen staff is reminded to ____________________ public health regulations.

⑬ You'll be meeting the CEO and his wife at the Plaza Hotel and accompanying them to the reception. I'm ____________________ you to make them feel welcome.

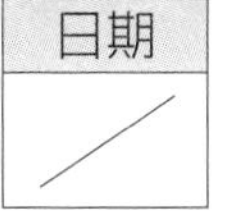

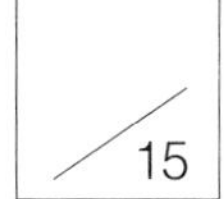

⑭ Speeding in a school zone ________________ of up to $500.

⑮ Would you please let me know if my meeting with the sales rep tomorrow is going to ________________ or not?

参考用字

burn off calories	burn down	call for
burn out	get carried away	call it a day
call off	carry over	come to terms with
come off	count on	carry a fine
catch on to	come across	comply with

（解答請參閱第 431 頁）

Unit 18

cut

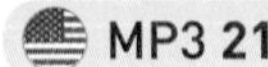

You can cut down on paper if you send out your 80-page report by e-mail instead of printing out copies.

假如你把你那 80 頁的報告用電子郵件寄出，而不要印成紙本，就能節省用紙。

0550
cut down on (something) 節省、減少（某事物）
類 cut back on (something) 削減（某事物）

Excuse me for cutting in, but the floor supervisor would like to speak with you.

抱歉打斷你的話，樓層主管有話要跟你說。

0551
cut in 突然插進（別人的談話）；打斷（別人的話） 類 interrupt 打斷

- floor supervisor 樓層主管

One ingredient of our health supplement formula comes from a country with an unstable government, so we run a risk of having our supplies cut off in the event of a coup.

我們的健康補充配方中有一樣成分是來自一個政府不穩定的國家，所以萬一發生政變，我們就會面臨供應中斷的風險。

0552
cut off 中斷；停止；切除
類 stop 停止、discontinue 中止、separate 分離

- ingredient 成分；原料
- supplement 補充
- formula 配方；公式
- unstable 不穩定的
- run a risk 冒風險
- coup 政變 (= coup d'etat)

cut

After our competitor cut out doing ads on prime time TV, their sales went down by 40%.

我們的競爭對手停止在電視的黃金時段打廣告之後，業績就掉了四成。

0553
cut out 停止做、說（某事）；刪除　類 stop 停止、remove 移除

- competitor 競爭者
- doing ads 打廣告
- prime time 黃金時段

There were several complaints about your publicist's handling of news releases. Perhaps she is not cut out for public relations after all.

你們的公關人員所發的新聞稿被抱怨了好幾次。或許她根本不適合做公關。

0554
cut out for 適合做……（常用於否定句）

- complaint 抱怨
- publicist 公關人員
- news release 新聞稿
- public relations 公關（複數形，可略為 PR）
- after all 畢竟；到底

Joe Brown wants to leave us and go play for the other team, so buy out his contract and cut him loose.

喬·布朗想要離開我們去別隊效力，那就買斷他的合約，把他釋出吧。

0555
cut (someone / something) **loose** 將（某人／某物）放開、鬆綁
類 release (someone / something) 釋放（某人／某物）

Well, I don't want to deprive you of your sleep, so let's continue this conversation tomorrow. Good night!

嗯，我可不想剝奪你的睡眠，所以我們明天再繼續這段談話吧。晚安！

0556
deprive a person of (something) 剝奪一個人的（資格、權利等）
類 take (something) away from a person 除去一個人的（資格、權利等）

Thank you for taking on the Farwell contract. You did a very good job.

謝謝你接下了法威的合約。你表現得非常出色。

0557
do a good job 表現出色

• take on 承接；承擔

TOEIC POINT job 為可數名詞，故前需加冠詞 a。另，注意同義的 work 則為不可數名詞，前面不需加上冠詞，在使用上要多加注意。

Let's do away with protocols. I would like to hear your candid opinion on this.

咱們別客套了。我想聽聽你對這件事的真心話。

0558
do away with 去掉……；捨棄……
類 get rid of 去除……；擺脫……

• candid 真心的；坦白的

Our company does all the business on the Internet.

我們公司所有生意都在網路上做。

0559
do business 做生意

• on the Internet 在網際網路上

do

We have to get together and do some brainstorming for the September issue of the company newsletter.

我們必須聚在一起為九月號的公司通訊做點腦力激盪。

0560
do brainstorming 做腦力激盪

• issue 刊號
• company newsletter 公司通訊

Congratulations on your promotion, Jim. I brought some champagne. Allow me to do the honors.

恭喜你升官了，吉姆。我帶了一些香檳來。且容我盡一下主人之誼。

0561
do the honors 盡主人之誼

• allow me 容許我
※ 注意 honors 在此片語中須用複數形。

We'll be in New York City for one night, so let's do the town — have dinner out and maybe catch a Broadway show.

我們會在紐約市待一晚，所以我們在城裡玩樂一番吧——去外面吃個晚餐，也許去百老匯看場秀。

0562
do the town 在城裡玩樂一番

• catch a show 看場秀

do / draw

Just ten years ago, hardly anyone had a cell phone, but nowadays it seems we can't do without them.

在不過 10 年前，幾乎沒有人有行動電話，但是如今看起來，我們卻是沒有它不行。

0563

do without 沒有……也可以

- nowadays 現今；時下（注意，字尾有 s）
- hardly 幾乎不

The results of the environmental assessment for the forestry project are so contradictory that it is impossible to draw a conclusion.

林業案的環評結果十分矛盾，根本無法做出結論。

0564

draw a conclusion 做出結論

- environmental assessment 環境評估
- forestry 林業
- contradictory 矛盾的

Taka's art gallery is a little difficult to find from the station, so I'll draw you a map.

從車站要找到塔卡的畫廊有點困難，所以我會畫張地圖給你。

0565

draw a map 畫地圖

- art gallery 畫廊

draw

Our engineers draw high salaries because they are all graduates of highly reputable schools.

我們的工程師之所以領高薪是因為他們全都畢業於很有名望的學校。

0566
draw high salaries 領高薪

• highly reputable 很有名望的

And now it is time to draw our program to a close. We want to thank you all for coming.

現在我們的節目到了該結束的時候了。我們要感謝各位的蒞臨。

0567
draw (something) **to a close** 結束（某事）
類 end / finish something 把某事告一段落

We are fairly tolerant of employees' smoking and drinking outside of work, but we draw the line at hard drugs such as cocaine and heroin.

對於員工在下班後抽菸喝酒，我們相當寬容，但是我們嚴禁重毒品，比如古柯鹼和海洛因。

0568
draw the line at 堅持反對；絕不接受

• tolerant 寬容的；容忍的

draw / drive

Before you can ask venture capitalists to invest in your business, you need to draw up a good plan.

你要先制訂一套好的計畫，才能請創投者投資你的事業。

0569
draw up a plan 制訂計畫　類 make a plan 擬訂計畫

• venture capitalist 創投者

Rogers is a ruthless buyer who drives such a hard bargain that nobody can make a profit.

羅傑斯是個無情的買主，態度強硬，根本沒人賺得了錢。

0570
drive a hard bargain（談判時）態度強硬

• ruthless 殘忍的；無情的
• make a profit 獲利；賺錢

You keep talking about how nice Paris is around this time of year. Come on. What are you driving at?

你開口閉口都在說巴黎每年這個時候有多美。說吧！你到底想講什麼？

0571
drive at 想講；想要　類 mean to say or do 想說或做

That cackling voice of Aunt Nellie is driving me crazy. She never stops talking and her voice is so loud.

奈麗伯母那種咯咯咯的聲音快把我逼瘋了。她講話從來沒停過，音量又那麼大。

0572
drive a person crazy / mad 把人逼瘋；令人抓狂

• cackling voice（像母雞叫般）咯咯咯的聲音

drive / eat

The small grocery store in the neighborhood was driven out of business by the opening of a huge new supermarket.

新的大型超市一開幕，街坊的小雜貨店就被逼到了走投無路。

0573
drive (someone) **out of**
將（某人）逼出、趕出〔本句中為被動用法〕

Sorry to eat and run like this, but I have an appointment in 10 minutes.

很抱歉像這樣一吃完就閃人，但是我 10 分鐘後有個約會。

0574
eat and run 一吃完就閃人

Don't let your worries eat away at you. Take a relaxing vacation at our five-star resort and forget your troubles.

不要讓煩惱折磨你。到我們的五星級度假中心來度個輕鬆的假，把麻煩給忘掉。

0575
eat away at 折磨；侵蝕

• five-star hotel 五星級飯店

Kristi eats like a bird. Yesterday she ate nothing but a small salad and two crackers.

克利絲堤跟小鳥一樣吃得很少。昨天她只吃了一小份沙拉和兩塊餅乾。

0576
eat like a bird 吃得跟小鳥一樣少 類 eat very little

• eat nothing but 只有吃……

以動物來比喻吃相的說法還有 eat like a pig（像豬一樣貪婪地吃）、eat like a horse（像馬一樣食量很大）。另外，drink like a fish 指「有好酒量」。

eat

MP3 22

I know my answer is correct. If it isn't, I'll eat my hat.

我知道我的答案是對的。假如不對的話，我就把帽子吞了。

0577
eat one's hat 把帽子吞了

※ I'll eat ny hat. 用於表示說話者對某事很有把握時。

Working overtime on the Hartfield contract last week, I ate out every single night, so I'd like to cook at home tonight.

上星期加班處理哈菲德的合約，我每天晚上都在外面吃，所以今天晚上我想在家做飯。

0578
eat out 在外面吃 反 eat in / eat at home 在家裡吃

My old car really eats up gas, so I'm going to trade it in for a newer, more economical model.

我的老爺車非常耗油，所以我要把它賣掉換個較新、較省油的車款。

0579
eat up gas 耗油

• economical 經濟的；省錢的

eat / end / fall

A: Wow! Look at this view! They gave you the best office on the 10th floor!
B: I know, I know! Eat your heart out.

A: 哇！你看這個景色！他們給了你 10 樓最棒的辦公室！
B: 我知道，我知道！羨慕死你吧！

0580
eat your heart out 羨慕死你吧

After Tim pleaded with me for two hours, I ended up lending him 50 dollars, which he will probably lose on a slot machine in a wink.

在提姆跟我哀求了兩個小時後，我最後借給他 50 美元，他大概一轉眼就會在吃角子老虎上輸掉了吧。

0581
end up doing 結果落得……；以……收場

- plead 懇求
- slot machine 吃角子老虎
- in a wink 一轉眼

When negotiations between management and the union fell apart, two hundred and fifty workers were laid off.

勞資雙方談判破裂後，有 250 名員工就被解雇。

0582
fall apart 破裂；失敗

- negotiation 談判；協商
- union 工會
- lay off 解雇

※ 在本例中 the union 指代表勞方的工會。

fall

As our business grew and competition fell away, we became the leading women's shoe manufacturer.

隨著我們業績的成長與競爭對手的衰微，我們成了最大的女鞋製造商。

0583
fall away 逐漸下降；衰微

- competition 競爭（者）
- manufacturer 製造者；廠商

MAT Phone Company fell behind because they did not keep up with new innovations in technology.

MAT 電話公司之所以落後是因為他們沒有跟上新的科技創新。

0584
fall behind 落後；拖欠

- keep up with 掌握；跟上（參照 0677）
- innovation 創新（參照 0043）

Dickinson was very nervous and didn't speak well, so his presentation fell flat, and his proposal was rejected.

因為狄金森很緊張，話也說不清楚，所以他的簡報做得一場糊塗，提案也被否決了。

0585
fall flat 徹底失敗　類 fail completely 完全失敗

- nervous 緊張的
- presentation 簡報
- reject 拒絕；駁回；否決

fall

I don't understand how you could fall for such an obvious scam?

我不懂你怎麼會對這麼明顯的騙局信以為真。

0586
fall for 上……的當；受……的騙；對……信以為真

- scam 詐騙；欺詐

Teenagers easily fall into a vicious cycle of paying off one credit card using another credit card, piling up debts compounded by interest.

青少年很容易陷入以卡養卡的惡性循環，並被利上加利搞得債台高築。

0587
fall into a vicious cycle 陷入惡性循環

- pay off one credit card using another credit card 以卡養卡
- pile up debts 債台高築
- compounded by interest 利上加利

When Rosa announced her engagement to a rock musician, her father almost fell off his chair.

當羅莎宣布跟一名搖滾樂手訂婚時，她老爸差一點就從椅子上摔下來。

0588
fall off one's chair 從椅子上摔下來

※ fall off one's chair 指「非常吃驚」。

Leadership responsibilities fell on the assistant manager when the manager was away.

經理不在時，領導責任就落到了副理身上。

0589
fall on someone 落在某人身上；由某人承擔

Soon after falling out with the board of directors, the CEO resigned.

跟董事會鬧翻後沒多久，執行長就辭職了。

0590
fall out with (someone) （與某人）吵架、鬧翻

The book deal fell through because the publisher wanted a book that would reach a younger audience.

出書案告吹了，因為出版社要的是以年輕讀者群為對象的書。

0591
fall through （計畫、安排）失敗；告吹
類 fail 失敗 反 come off 成功

• publisher 出版商；出版社 • younger audience 年輕讀者群

You will feel awkward standing on the stage in front of an audience of two hundred, so be sure to wear an outfit that gives you a boost in confidence.

站在台上面對 200 名觀衆，你會覺得很不自在，所以一定要穿上能讓你提振信心的服裝。

0592
feel awkward 感覺尷尬、不自在
關 feel nervous 覺得緊張、feel uncomfortable 覺得不舒適、feel out of place 覺得不自在

• outfit 全套服裝 • give a boost 提振

feel

I felt disgusted at the deceit and hypocrisy of Wilson's business dealings and decided to cut off all ties with him.

威爾森經營手法的欺詐與偽善令我感到作嘔，所以我決定跟他斷絕所有的往來。

0593
feel disgusted at ... 對……感到作嘔

• deceit 欺詐；詐騙　• hypocrisy 偽善　• tie 關係；聯繫

Do you feel like going to a movie after work tonight?

今天晚上下班後，想不想去看場電影？

0594
feel like doing something 覺得想做……

※ feel like something 指「想要」某物，例如：I feel like a cup of tea.（我想喝杯茶。）

The message in our ad for diamond rings is that receiving a gift of diamonds will make you feel loved.

我們鑽戒廣告中所要傳達的訊息是，收到鑽石當禮物會讓你感覺到被愛。

0595
feel loved 感覺到被愛

• message 信息；訊息

There is no dress code at our company. Just dress professionally on the first day and then feel it out from there.

我們公司沒有著裝規定。只要第一天穿得專業，接下來再慢慢摸索就好了。

0596
feel it out 慢慢摸索

• dress code 著裝規定　• dress professionally 穿得專業

feel / get

I know you've been home with a cold, but if you feel up to it, I'd like to e-mail you some work that you can do at home.

我知道你感冒在家，但是如果你覺得可以的話，我想用電子郵件寄一些工作給你，讓你可以在家裡做。

0597

feel up to (something) 覺得可以擔當（某事）

Under the new city ordinance, businesses will get a break on taxes when they donate to a local charity.

根據新的市政條例，捐款給當地慈善機構的企業可在稅賦上享有優惠。

0598

get a break on taxes 享有稅賦優惠

- ordinance 法令；條例
- donate 捐贈；捐款
- local 當地的；地方的
- charity 慈善（機構）

Congratulate me! I just had my annual physical, and got a clean bill of health.

恭喜我吧！我剛剛做完年度健檢，獲得了健康證明。

0599

get a clean bill of health 獲得健康證明

- annual physical (check-up) 年度健檢

get

Before you venture into a market overseas, it's essential that you get a firm grasp of consumer needs in the other culture.

在你進軍海外市場前，一定要先確實了解他國文化的消費者需求。

0600

get a grasp of (something) 了解、掌握（某事）

- venture into 冒險進入（市場、行業等）
- firm 確實的

Big Box Store got a head start on competing stores and stocked the newest digital cameras before anyone else did.

大箱子商店比競爭的商店搶先一步，在別人都還來不及之前，就進了最新的數位相機。

0601

get a head start on ... 比……搶先一步

- stock 進貨
- digital camera 數位相機

The office assistants are getting a real kick out of the joke books you brought in the other day.

你前幾天帶來的笑話集讓辦公室的助理們愛不釋手。

0602

get a kick out of (something) 從（某事物）中得到興趣或快感；非常喜愛（某事物）

- joke book 笑話集

get / go

Don't worry — you'll get the knack of the new filing system in no time. It just takes a little practice.

別擔心，你很快就會掌握到新建檔系統的訣竅。只要多練習一下就行了。

0603
get the knack of (something) 掌握到（某事物的）訣竅

- in no time 很快地

No, I'm afraid I can't make an exception for you but have to go by the rules. Your rent was due two weeks ago.

不行，恐怕我不能為你破例，而必須照規矩走。你的房租兩週前就到期了。

0604
go by the rules 照規矩走

- make an exception 破例
- due 到期的；應支付的；預定的

My winery went down the drain after a serious drought destroyed the vineyards.

在嚴重的乾旱把葡萄園摧毀後，我的釀酒廠也付諸流水了。

0605
go down the drain 前功盡棄；付諸流水

- winery 釀酒廠
- drought（參照 0331 arid）
- vineyard 葡萄園

類似 go down the drain 的說法還有 go down the toilet、go down the tube。

go

Maya expected that Peter would treat her to lunch, but she was shocked when he suggested they go fifty-fifty.

瑪雅以為彼得會請她吃午飯，但是當他建議各出一半時，她相當震驚。

0606
go fifty-fifty（費用）各出一半　類 split the bill 分攤費用

• shocked 震驚的；驚愕的

※ go Dutch 是「各付各的」的意思，但是現在已經很少這樣使用，因為 Dutch 含有對荷蘭人歧視的意味。

The law abolishing the death penalty went into effect a year after he had been executed.

廢除死刑的法律在他被處決一年後才生效。

0607
go into effect（法律或規定）生效
類 implement 實施；實行（參照 0279）

• abolish 廢除
• death penalty 死刑
• execute 處決；執行

CheckTest

0550 ⇨ 0607

請依照文意將適當的動詞片語填入空格中。可參考第 250 頁所提示的片語來作答。(作答時間：7 分 30 秒)

① We have to get together and ________________ for the September issue of the company newsletter.

② You can ________________ paper if you send out your 80-page report by e-mail instead of printing out copies.

③ There were several complaints about your publicist's handling of news releases. Perhaps she is not ________________ public relations after all.

④ We'll be in New York City for one night, so let's ________ ________ — have dinner out and maybe catch a Broadway show.

⑤ Well, I don't want to ________________ your sleep, so let's continue this conversation tomorrow. Good night!

⑥ We are fairly tolerant of employees' smoking and drinking outside of work, but we ________________ hard drugs such as cocaine and heroin.

⑦ Excuse me for ____________________, but the floor supervisor would like to speak with you.

⑧ My winery ____________________ after a serious drought destroyed the vineyards.

⑨ The book deal ____________________ because the publisher wanted a book that would reach a younger audience.

⑩ You keep talking about how nice Paris is around this time of year. Come on. What are you ____________________?

⑪ After Tim pleaded with me for two hours, I ____________________ him 50 dollars, which he will probably lose on a slot machine in a wink.

⑫ The law abolishing the death penalty ____________________ a year after he had been executed.

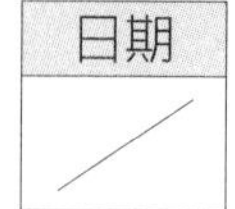

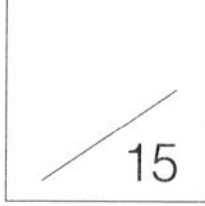

⑬ Under the new city ordinance, businesses will ____________ on taxes when they donate to a local charity.

⑭ Teenagers easily ____________ of paying off one credit card using another credit card, piling up debts compounded by interest.

⑮ When negotiations between management and the union ____________, two hundred and fifty workers were laid off.

参考用字

deprive someone of	cut out for	end up doing
cut down on	do brainstorming	cut in
do the town	fall into a vicious cycle	draw the line at
drive at	fall apart	get a break
fall through	go down the drain	go into effect

（解答請參閱第 431 頁）

Unit 19

go

MP3 23

Home sales are going nowhere, and real estate agents are getting nervous.

房屋銷量不見起色，房仲業者緊張了。

0608
go nowhere 不見起色；毫無進展 類 be / get stuck 停滯；卡住

I especially want to thank the members of the hospitality committee for going out of their way to make my stay in the city of Denver a most pleasant one.

我尤其要謝謝接待委員會的委員竭盡全力，使我待在丹佛市的這段期間非常愉快。

0609
go out of one's way to 竭盡全力；特地

• hospitality committee 接待委員會 • pleasant 令人愉快的

Thanks for attending the tryout. Now let's go over the dance number from the beginning.

謝謝各位參加選拔。現在我們把舞曲從頭復習一遍。

0610
go over (something) 復習、查看（某事物） 類 review 復習

• tryout 選拔；試演 • dance number 舞曲

As you go over the auditor's report, please make note of any results that look significant to you.

你在審閱稽查員的報告時，請把任何你覺得重要的結果都記下來。

0611
go over the report 審閱報告

• auditor 稽查員 • make note of something 將某事記錄下來 • significant 重要的

I sent my assistant out to buy one floral bouquet for the conference room, but she went overboard and came back with seven potted orchids.

我派我的助理去替會議室買一束花，但是她卻做過了頭，買了七盆蘭花回來。

0612
go overboard 衝過頭；做得太過火 類 go too far 太過分

- floral bouquet 花束
- conference room 會議室
- potted orchid 盆栽蘭花

Nick was accepted to every university he applied to. That young man is going to go places.

尼克所申請的每所大學都錄取了他。這個年輕人將會出人頭地。

0613
go places 出人頭地；到處旅行
類 go up the ladder of success 順著成功的階梯往上爬

Until they went public in 1997, Pico Cola was a struggling start-up. Now their stock is soaring.

在 1997 年公開發行前，匹克可樂只是家掙扎的新創公司。如今他們的股價則是扶搖直上。

0614
go public 公開發行；把祕密公開

- struggling 掙扎的；奮鬥的、努力的
- start-up 新創公司
- soar 高飛；飆漲

go

I'm sorry that you had to go through such a rough performance evaluation. I think your boss was a little insensitive.

很抱歉你必須經歷這麼不留情面的績效考核。我想你的老闆有點遲鈍。

0615
go through 經歷；舉行；討論

- rough 粗糙的；粗魯的
- performance evaluation 績效考核
- insensitive 遲鈍的

Bernie went to pieces when he found out that his best friend had been killed in a car accident.

得知他最好的朋友在車禍中喪生，柏尼崩潰了。

0616
go to pieces 崩潰；垮掉 類 be devastated 極為震驚；身心交瘁

I think the government went too far when they completely banned liquor ads on TV.

政府完全禁止酒類廣告在電視上播放，我認為太過分了。

0617
go too far 過分

- ban 禁止
- liquor 酒類；烈酒

You might not like soy milk the first time you try it, but the taste grows on you.

第一次嘗到豆漿時，你可能會不喜歡，但是你會逐漸喜愛那種味道。

0618
grow on (someone) 逐漸被（某人）喜愛

soy milk 指「豆漿」。事實上，soy（大豆、黃豆）在國外 vegetarian（素食主義者）之間相當有人氣。soy sauce（醬油）與 soy paste（味噌）也可說成 shoyu 以及 miso。最近 Starbucks 這類連鎖咖啡店也推出了豆漿口味的咖啡與冰淇淋。

Does your child grow out of shoes as fast as you buy them? Why not try Flex Shoe? Flex Shoe expands as your little one's feet grow!

你的小孩是不是長得快到讓你來不及買鞋？何不試試「彈性鞋」？「彈性鞋」會隨著你的小朋友的腳長大而撐大！

0619
grow out of (something) 因長大而穿不下（衣服等）

- as fast as ... 和……一樣快
- expand 擴展

The procedures for quality control were handed down from company headquarters, and we have to follow them to the letter.

公司總部把品管程序交代下來了，我們必須嚴格遵守。

0620
hand down 交代；傳達下來

- procedure 程序；手續
- quality control (QC) 品管
- headquarters 總部（複數形）
- follow something to the letter 嚴格地遵守某事

hand / hang

All section heads are reminded to hand in their pay roll sheets by 4:00 Friday afternoon.

各課的課長都接獲提醒，星期五下午四前點要繳交薪資表。

0621
hand in 繳交　類 submit 遞交

TOEIC POINT section head 指一課地位最高的人，即「課長」，但這並不是一種職稱，使用上要多加注意。正式的職稱為 section manager、section chief。

I've got to hand it to you. I didn't think you would ever be able to close on the Mega Golf Resort deal. Good job!

我得好好誇你一下。我沒想到你竟然能拿下梅嘉高爾夫度假村的案子。幹得好！

0622
hand it to (someone) 誇讚（人）；讚美（人）

• close a deal 敲定一筆交易

I'm not quite ready to go. Can you hang around the office while I finish up this report?

我還沒辦法馬上走。在我把這份報告完成前，你能不能在辦公室附近晃晃？

0623
hang around 閒晃；閒逛

I'm sorry to hear you're having such a hard time finding a job. But hang in there and keep sending out those resumes.

很遺憾聽說你找工作這麼不順利。但是請撐下去，繼續把那些履歷寄出去。

0624
hang in 撐下去

TOEIC POINT have a hard time Ving（動名詞）指「為了做某事而歷經辛苦」的意思。

hang / have

I've got to hang on to this job even though the working hours are so irregular. I have five kids to support.

就算工時這麼不固定，我還是得牢牢把握這份工作。我有五個小孩要養。

0625
hang on to something 牢牢抓住某事物 類 retain 保持；保留

• irregular 不規律的

Nancy's problem is that she gets hung up on details and doesn't see the big picture.

南西的問題在於，她對細節斤斤計較而不看大局。

0626
(get) **hung up on** (something) 過度專注於（某事）
類 (be) obsessed by (something) 著迷於、執著於（某事物）

TOEIC POINT 指「吊掛」時 hang 的過去式與過去分詞皆為 hung，但指「吊死」時過去式與過去分詞則為 hanged，如：be hanged to death（處以絞刑）和 hanged oneself（上吊自殺）。

The interns had a ball setting up the holiday window display. They said it was the "funnest" job we'd given them yet.

實習生開心地布置過節的櫥窗展示。他們說那是我們給他們做過「最好玩」的工作。

0627
have a ball 玩得開心

• intern 實習生
• window display 櫥窗展示

TOEIC POINT 事實上並沒有 funnest 這個單字。例句中為了表現 fun（歡樂）的「最高級」，才造出這個單字。

have

It's getting close to 1:00. Shall we go have a bite to eat and then finish up this project after lunch?

快要一點了。我們要不要去隨便吃點東西，等午餐後再把這個案子做完？

0628
have a bite to eat 隨便吃點東西
㊖ eat and run 一吃完就閃人（參照 0574）

※ 注意，本例中的 bite 為名詞。

The reason Jeff has a chip on his shoulder is that he wasn't promoted to assistant manager, so now he thinks everyone is against him.

傑夫火氣很大的原因是，他沒有被晉升為副理，所以現在他覺得大家都在跟他作對。

0629
have a chip on one's shoulder 動不動就生氣

If you have a clean conscience, there is no need for you to respond to accusations regarding your behavior. So remain calm.

假如你問心無愧，你就不必回應別人指控你的所作所為。所以要保持冷靜。

0630
have a clean conscience 問心無愧；心安理得

- accusation 指控
- regarding 有關；關於
- remain calm 保持冷靜

The reporters had a field day when they found out about the royal divorce.

探聽到王室的離婚消息讓記者欣喜狂若。

0631
have a field day 非常愉快

have

I can't seem to get the lid off this jar of jam. Could you have a go at it?

我似乎沒辦法把這罐果醬的蓋子打開。你可不可以試一下？

0632
have a go at (something) 試一下（某事）
類 try at (something) 試試看（某事）

• lid 蓋子 • a jar of jam 一罐果醬

Although he is a recent college graduate, Mr. Suzuki has a good command of English and is qualified for a number of entry-level jobs in our international division.

雖然大學畢業不久，但鈴木先生精通英語，足以在我們的國際部擔任一些基層職務。

0633
have a good command of (something) 精通（外語等）
類 have a good knowledge of something 對……瞭若指掌

• be qualified for 足以；有資格 • entry-level job 基層職務

Let Becky be in charge of taking care of the office plants. She's the only one here who has a green thumb.

讓貝琪來負責照顧辦公室的花草。她是這裡唯一懂園藝的人。

0634
have a green thumb 擅長園藝

I'm just going down to the coffee shop to have a pick-me-up. I'll be back in fifteen minutes.

我只是要到咖啡店去喝杯咖啡提提神。15 分鐘就回來了。

0635
have a pick-me-up 喝杯提神的飲料

※ pick-me-up 指「提神的飲料」，如咖啡。

have

The nurses should have a say in all decisions regarding patients' medication schedules.

與病患用藥時程相關的所有決定，護士都應該要有發言權。

0636
have a say in something 對某事有發言權
類 have the right to say something 有權利發言

- medication schedule 用藥時程

At a buffet, people have eyes bigger than their stomachs, so they will pile their plates high with food and then leave it half uneaten.

在吃自助餐時，人都是眼睛大、胃口小，所以會把食物在盤子上堆得老高，然後只吃完一半。

0637
have eyes bigger than one's stomach
眼睛大、胃口小；貪心不足蛇吞象

- pile high 堆得很高
- half eaten 只吃了一半

That pounding construction noise has been going on outside my office window all morning, and I have had it up to here. Who can I complain to about it?

我辦公室窗外建築工地震耳欲聾的噪音吵了一整個早上，我真是受夠了。我可以向誰投訴？

0638
have had it up to here 受夠了
類 can't stand it anymore 再也受不了了

- pounding 重擊聲

TOEIC POINT Who can I complain to ... 亦可說成 To whom can I complain ...。

I'm sorry. I had no business getting involved in your argument with Samantha. Please forgive me.

抱歉，我沒有資格介入你和莎曼珊的紛爭。請見諒。

0639
have no business doing (something) 沒有資格做（某事）
類 have no right to do (something) 無權做（某事）

• get involved in 介入；捲入

There's the new dean of the College of Foreign Languages. See her? She has on a blue dress and a white hat.

外語學院的新院長在那裡。看到了嗎？她穿著藍裙、戴著白帽。

0640
have on (something) 穿戴

• dean 院長

put on 是「穿上」的意思，have on 則指「穿著」。

I finally got a job as a receptionist at the movie studio. It's a low-pay job, but at least I have my foot in the door now.

我總算在電影公司找到了一份接待員的工作。它是個低薪工作，但是起碼我現在跨進門了。

0641
have one's foot in the door 跨進門；得到機會

• receptionist 接待員
• movie studio 電影公司
※ studio 可用來指藝術家的「工作室」或電視台的「攝影棚」。

have

The actress had her nose in the air as she walked by me, and appeared not to hear my polite request for her autograph.

那個女演員目中無人地從我旁邊走過，我客氣地請她簽名，她似乎充耳不聞。

0642
have one's nose in the air 目中無人；自視甚高
類 put on airs 擺架子

- appear not to 似乎不
- request 要求；請求

TOEIC POINT autograph 是指名人的簽名。sign 或 signature 則是某些文件上的簽名，使用時不要混淆。

Now that I've read bad reviews of this book, I'm having second thoughts about buying it.

我既然看過了這本書的惡評，這會兒要重新考慮是不是要買。

0643
have second thoughts about something 對某事重新考慮

- now that ... 既然
- review 評論

※ book review 指「書評」。

I would say your briefcase has seen better days. Why don't you buy a new one?

我會說你的公事包真是今非昔比。你為什麼不買個新的？

0644
have seen better days 今非昔比；大不如前

- briefcase 公事包

have / hit / hold

At an intersection with no traffic signs, the car on your right has the right-of-way.

在沒有交通號誌的十字路口，右側的來車擁有優先通行權。

0645
have the right-of-way 擁有優先通行權

- intersection 十字路口 • traffic sign 交通號誌

The stock market hit a new high this week, and confidence in the economy surged.

股市本週創下新高，對經濟的信心也節節高升。

0646
hit a new high 創下新高

- surge 激增

The minute Ray met his new boss, they hit it off right away.

雷一見到新老闆，雙方立刻一見如故。

0647
hit it off 一見如故；一拍即合

- the minute 一……（就）

Sid holds a grudge against me because I was promoted to branch manager, which was the job he wanted.

席德對我懷恨在心，因為我被升任為分店店長，而那正是他所想要的職務。

0648
hold a grudge against (someone) 對（某人）懷恨在心
類 bear a grudge against (someone) 對（某人）懷有怨恨、惡意

- branch manager 分店店長；分公司經理

hold

Be honest with your doctor. Don't hold back information about your bad habits.

對醫生要實話實說。對於你的壞習慣，不要隱瞞相關的資訊。

0649
hold back 隱瞞；壓抑；退縮

I didn't get the job I wanted because the company said they have decided to hold back on hiring until next year.

我並沒有錄取我所想要的工作，因為那家公司說他們決定到明年遇缺都不補。

0650
hold back on (something) 暫停（某事）
類 withhold (something) 抑制、阻擋（某事）

The movie was so sad that I just couldn't hold back my tears.

這部電影真哀傷，我就是止不住淚水。

0651
hold back one's tears 忍住不掉淚

A poor boy growing up in an impoverished part of town, Mike held fast to his dream to go to college.

麥克是個在市內貧民區長大的窮小子，但是他堅持追求上大學的夢想。

0652
hold fast to (something) 堅持追求（某事物）
類 hold firm on / to (something) 堅守、固守（某事物）

• impoverished 赤貧的

※ 注意，本例中的 fast 用來指「牢固地」。另，fast asleep 可用來形容「睡得很熟」。

hold

Hold it right there! Only authorized personnel are allowed through that door.

原地止步！只有經許可之人員才能進那道門。

0653
hold it 止步；別動

• authorized personnel 經授權、許可之人員

A: Hello, Marie. It's Jack. Is Nick there?
B: Yes, but he's in the outer office. Hold on, please.

A: 喂，梅莉。我是傑克。尼克在不在？
B: 在，可是他在外面的辦公室。請等一下。

0654
hold on 不要掛；等一下 類 hold the line 稍候；別掛斷電話

You should hold on to this money. It will be useful for a rainy day.

你應該把這筆錢留下來。它可以應付急用。

0655
hold on to (something) 抓住；保留（某事物）

• for a rainy day 以備不時之需

Ms. Hogue knew her boss was cheating on his taxes, but she held her tongue in the interest of keeping the peace.

霍格小姐知道老闆漏稅，但是為了維持和協，她保持緘默。

0656
hold one's tongue 默不作聲；保持緘默
類 keep one's mouth shut 閉嘴；保持沉默

• cheat on one's taxes 逃漏稅
• keep peace 維持和平

hold

The company operated in the red the first two years, but they held out and finally turned a profit in the third year.

公司營運的頭兩年都是赤字，但是他們堅持不懈，到第三年時終於轉虧為盈。

0657
hold out 堅持不懈　類 stand firm 屹立不搖

Without your holding out a helping hand, he would have gone down with the company.

要不是你出手相助，他就和公司一起垮了。

0658
hold out a hand 出手相助；伸出援手

• go down 落下；沉沒；垮台

Mr. Simpson is here again with his lawyer and insists on seeing you. Shall I hold him off?

辛普森先生又帶著律師來了，並堅持要見您。要不要我把他擋下來？

0659
hold someone off 阻擋某人

• insist on ... 堅持……

※ hold off doing something 指「拖延做某事」。

Hold still, everyone. I want to take one more group picture.

大家不要動。我要再拍一張團體照。

0660
hold still 不要動　類 keep still 保持不動

• group picture 團體照

hold / impose

This mattress is holding up well. We've used it for 10 years.

這個床墊很耐用。我們已經用了 10 年了。

0661
hold up 維持良好狀態；支撐　類 be durable 經久耐用的

※ hold up 亦可作「搶劫」解，例如：Three armed robbers held up the bank.（三個攜帶槍械的強匪搶了那家銀行。）

We've got to hold up on shoe production. The leather hasn't arrived yet.

我們必須停止做鞋。皮革還沒有到。

0662
hold up on (something) 停止、中斷（某事）

• leather 皮革

The President imposed a freeze on all the prices in order to curb runaway inflation.

總統凍結了所有的物價，以遏止失控的通貨膨脹。

0663
impose a freeze on (something) 凍結（某事）

• curb 遏止；抑制　• runaway 失控的　• inflation 通貨膨脹

The county has imposed a vending machine tax which will go into effect in April.

該郡開徵了自動販賣機稅，將在 4 月份生效。

0664
impose a tax 課稅

• vending machine 自動販賣機　• go into effect 生效；實行

impose

I hope I'm not imposing on you dropping in like this without an appointment.

我沒有約好就這樣來拜訪，希望沒有打擾到你。

0665
impose on 打擾

- drop in 順利拜訪

The state government imposed so many regulations on businesses that some companies moved to other states.

州政府針對企業強制實施了一大堆規定，於是有些公司便搬到別州去了。

0666
impose (something) **on / upon ...** 把（某事物）強加於……

CHAPTER 2 UNIT 19

CheckTest

0608 ⇨ 0666

請依照文意將適當的動詞片語填入空格中。可參考第 270 頁所提示的片語來作答。（作答時間：7 分 30 秒）

① You might not like soy milk the first time you try it, but the taste ____________________.

② I think the government ____________________ when they completely banned liquor ads on TV.

③ I'm sorry to hear you're having such a hard time finding a job. But ____________________ there and keep sending out those resumes.

④ Nick was accepted to every university he applied to. That young man is going to ____________________.

⑤ Although he is a recent college graduate, Mr. Suzuki ____________________ English and is qualified for a number of entry-level jobs in our international division.

⑥ Until they ____________________ in 1997, Pico Cola was a struggling start-up. Now their stock is soaring.

⑦ That pounding construction noise has been going on outside my office window all morning, and I ____________________. Who can I complain to about it?

⑧ Nancy's problem is that she ____________________ details and doesn't see the big picture.

⑨ The stock market ____________________ this week, and confidence in the economy surged.

⑩ This mattress is ____________________ well. We've used it for 10 years.

⑪ I'm sorry. I ____________________ getting involved in your argument with Samantha. Please forgive me.

⑫ I hope I'm not ____________________ you dropping in like this without an appointment.

⑬ Now that I've read bad reviews of this book, I'm ____________________ buying it.

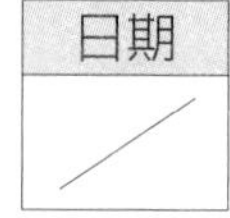

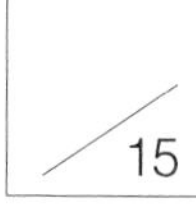

⑭ A poor boy growing up in an impoverished part of town, Mike ____________ his dream to go to college.

⑮ Mr. Simpson is here again with his lawyer and insists on seeing you. Shall I ____________?

参考用字

have had it up to here	go places	go public
grow on someone	hang in	have no business
have a good command of	go too far	get hung up on
have second thoughts about	hold fast to	hit a new high
hold someone off	impose on	hold up

（解答請參閱第 431 頁）

Unit 20

Keep

MP3 25

As a private detective, Mr. Summers has to keep a low profile.

身為私家偵探，桑默斯先生必須保持低調。

0667
keep a low profile 保持低調

• private detective 保持低調
※ profile 的原意為「側影」、「側寫」，延伸指一個人的「姿態」、「形象」。

Everyone tried hard to keep a straight face when Henry walked into the room wearing a pink polka-dot tie and a red shirt.

當亨利打著粉紅色的圓點領帶、穿著紅襯衫走進場內時，大家都想盡辦法忍住不笑。

0668
keep a straight face 保持嚴肅；忍住不笑

Walter boasts that he always keeps company with some of the wealthiest entrepreneurs in Europe.

華特自誇說他向來都是與歐洲一些最有錢的企業家為伍。

0669
keep company with (someone) 與（某人）為伍；相伴

• boast 自誇；吹噓　• entrepreneur 企業家

Hugh tries to keep fit by running every day and eating macrobiotic food.

修努力健身，每天都跑步並吃養生食物。

0670
keep fit 保持健康　類 keep in shape 維持身體狀況良好

• macrobiotic food 養生食物（參照 0013）

TOEIC POINT get in shape 指「把身體練好」的意思。另，be out of shape 則指「體態不佳、身體狀況不好」。

keep

Would you please put up a "Keep Off the Grass" sign on the lawn near the front entrance?

能不能麻煩你在前門附近的草地上立個「請勿踐踏草坪」的牌子？

0671
keep off (something) 避開（某物）

• lawn 草地；草坪　• front entrance 前面的入口；前門

I hope it snows tonight so we can open our ski slope tomorrow. Keep your fingers crossed.

希望今天晚上會下雪，這樣明天滑雪坡才能開放。求求老天吧！

0672
keep one's fingers crossed 祈求好運

TOEIC POINT cross one's fingers 是指將食指與中指交叉，藉此作出十字架的形狀，動作的用意是驅魔，常用在會話裡。

Warning! This is private property! Keep out!

警告！此為私有地！禁止進入！

0673
keep out 禁止進入

• private property 私人地產

The police kept the drunk in custody until he was sober enough to get home on his own.

警方拘留了這名醉漢，直到他清醒到可以自行返家為止。

0674
keep (someone) **in custody** 拘留（某人）

• sober 清醒的

keep / know

Watch out! Our manager is keeping track of how long we are away on our lunch hour.

注意！經理正在追蹤我們午餐時間外出了多久。

0675
keep track of (something) 追蹤（某事物）；掌握（訊息等）
反 lose track of (something) 沒留意到（某事物）；未能掌握（訊息等）

Your report on the soybean crop in the Southeast region was excellent. Keep up the good work.

你對東南區大豆收穫量的報告寫得很棒！好表現繼續保持下去。

0676
keep up (something) 把（某事）保持下去

• soybean crop 大豆收穫量 • region 區域

I subscribe to movie magazines because I want to keep up with the latest trends in the film industry.

我訂閱電影雜誌，因為我想掌握電影業的最新趨勢。

0677
keep up with (something) 跟上（人、時代潮流等）
類 catch up with（參照 0519）

• latest trend 最新趨勢

Mel has been a telephone repairman for twenty-six years, so he knows the job backwards and forwards.

梅爾當電話維修員已經 26 年了，所以他對這份工作瞭若指掌。

0678
know (something) **backwards and forwards**（對某事物）瞭若指掌 類 know something inside out 徹底了解（某事物）

※ read someone like a book 指「對某人知之甚詳」。

For our tour guide training program, we've paired each new employee with an experienced tour guide who knows the ropes.

以我們的導遊訓練課程來說，每位新進員工都搭配一位內行的老經驗導遊。

0679
know the ropes 熟知內情；懂得訣竅

① Why do hens make so much noise when they lay an egg?

母雞在下蛋的時候，為什麼會叫這麼大聲？

② Gerald sang beautifully in the first act, but in the second act of the opera, he laid an egg and was booed off the stage.

傑洛德在第一幕唱得很好聽，但是到了劇中的第二幕，他卻荒腔走板，並被噓下了台。

0680
lay an egg ① 下蛋 ② 荒腔走板；失敗

- opera 歌劇
- be booed off 被噓下來

Somebody left this umbrella in the office last week, but nobody has laid claim to it, so I guess it's OK if I use it.

上星期有人把這把傘遺忘在辦公室，但是卻沒有人來認領，所以我想我拿來用應該沒關係。

0681
lay claim to (something) 對（某物）提出權利要求

lay

Employees were taking longer and longer coffee breaks until the manager laid down the law and limited them to ten minutes.

員工休息喝咖啡的時間愈來愈久，於是經理便下令限縮為 10 分鐘。

0682
lay down the law 發號施令

- employee 員工
- coffee break（工作期間的）休息（喝咖啡）時間

I can hardly wait to lay hands on the new laptop. It's being delivered directly to my office this afternoon.

我簡直等不及要用用看新筆電了。它今天下午直接送到了我的辦公室。

0683
lay hands on (something) 動手試試（某物）；取得（某物）

That company laid off half of its middle management personnel and went bankrupt shortly thereafter.

那家公司資遣了半數的中階管理人員，隨後旋即破產。

0684
lay off 資遣；解雇

TOEIC POINT lay（放置、下蛋）的動詞變化形為 lay-laid-laid。注意，勿與不及物動詞指「躺下來」的 lie-lay-lain，混淆。

When are you going to lay out a marketing plan for our new cell phone?

你什麼時候會為我們的新手機訂出行銷計畫？

0685
lay out 訂出；安排；展示；攤開

- marketing plan 行銷計畫

lay / leave

If you are willing to lay over in Portland on Saturday night, you can save $250 on the fare.

假如你願意星期六晚上在波特蘭短暫停留的話，票價就可以省下 250 美元。

0686
lay over 中途在……短暫停留 類 stop over 中途停留

• fare 車費；船費；飛機票價

I want to buy this suit, but I can't pay for it today. May I lay it away?

我要買這套西裝，但是沒辦法今天付款。我可以先寄著嗎？

0687
lay (something) **away** 把（某物）擱置、儲存起來
類 put (something) aside（將商品等）延後取件

The hotel was in a lovely location, but the room and the food left a lot to be desired.

那家飯店的地點不錯，但是房間和菜色大有改善的空間。

0688
leave a lot to be desired 大有改善的空間

• location 地點

Police left no stone unturned in their search for the missing child.

警方盡一切辦法尋找這個失蹤兒童。

0689
leave no stone unturned 盡一切辦法；不遺餘力

• missing 失蹤的

leave

My dream is to develop a pesticide that kills insects but leaves no trace of harmful residue.

我的夢想是要開發出能殺死蟲子但是不遺留有害殘留物的殺蟲劑。

0690
leave no trace 不遺留任何痕跡

• pesticide 殺蟲劑 • residue 殘留物

Barbara's colleagues left her out in the cold after she spread nasty rumors about one of them.

芭芭拉遭到了同事排擠，因為她散布了關於其中一人的惡意謠言。

0691
leave (someone) **out in the cold** 排擠、孤立（某人）

• colleague 同事 • nasty 污穢的；惡意的；卑鄙的

The customer left out her phone number on this form, so I can't call her.

這位顧客漏填了這張表格上的電話號碼，所以我沒辦法打電話給她。

0692
leave (something) **out** 遺漏（某事物）

• customer 顧客 • form 表格

Treat each client with courtesy and respect, and you will leave the door open for future business with that person.

對待每位客戶都要禮貌而尊敬，以便將來能有機會跟那個人做生意。

0693
leave the door open for 保留機會
類 leave some possibility for ... 為……保留一些可能性

• treat 對待

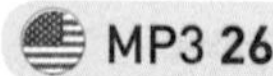

We have the most reliable delivery business in town. We won't let you down!

我們的配送業務是市內最可靠的。我們不會讓您失望的。

0694
let (someone) **down** 讓（某人）失望

The police officer let Jane off the hook this time, but if she gets caught for reckless driving again, she'll go to jail.

那位警官這次放了珍一馬，但是假如她又被抓到危險駕駛，她就要去坐牢了。

0695
let (someone) **off the hook** 放（某人）一馬；饒過（某人）

• reckless 危險的 • go to jail 入獄

The birthday party for Kim was supposed to be a surprise. Who let the cat out of the bag?

金的慶生會原本是要來個驚喜的。是誰洩了密？

0696
let the cat out of the bag 洩漏祕密
類 let a secret slip 洩漏祕密

spill the beans（把豆子灑出來）也可用來指「洩漏機密」。另，open a can of worms（打開蟲罐），則指「製造麻煩」。

Your daughter is old enough to choose her friends without your interfering. Live and let live.

你女兒夠大了，你不用干涉她交朋友。讓大家都好過吧。

0697
live and let live 自己活，也讓別人活；讓大家都好過

• interfere 干涉；干預

live

The poor, struggling painter lived from hand to mouth until her work was discovered by a wealthy collector.

那位貧窮且掙扎的畫家過得很拮据，直到她的作品被一位有錢的收藏家發掘。

0698
live from hand to mouth 僅能餬口；過得很拮据

• struggling 掙扎的；奮鬥的
• collector 收藏家

We have a little money left over in the party fund, so let's live it up.

我們的歡樂基金裡還剩一點錢，所以咱們盡情享受一下。

0699
live it up 盡情玩樂
類 have a ball 興高采烈；樂不思蜀（參照 0627）

• party fund 歡樂基金

The whole family lives off the little grocery store.

全家人都靠這家小雜貨店過日子。

0700
live off (something) 靠（某物）過日子

• grocery store 雜貨店

Now that we are number one in the electrical appliance industry, we have to live up to our reputation.

既然我們是電器業的龍頭，我們就必須不枉我們的名聲。

0701
live up to (something) 符合（期望、名聲等）
類 measure up to (something) 符合、達到（希望、標準等）

look

A number of assembly line workers have complained to me that their supervisor looks down on them.

有些組裝線工人跟我投訴說，他們的領班瞧不起他們。

0702

look down on / upon (someone) 瞧不起、輕視（某人）

類 depise (someone) 鄙視、看不起（某人）

反 look up to someone 尊敬某人

• assembly line 組裝線

We are looking into the possibility of building three more greenhouses, and we would like you to do a cost analysis.

我們正在研究多蓋三座溫室的可能性，並希望你做個成本分析。

0703

look into (something) 調查；檢視

• greenhouse 溫室 • cost analysis 成本分析

Look out for dishonest business offers. If it sounds too good to be true, it probably is.

當心騙人的生意手段。假如聽起來太好而不像是真的，那八成就不是真的了。

0704

look out for (something) 當心、留意（某物）

類 watch out for (something) 密切注意（某物）

I sent my assistant home because he looked pale and said he felt sick.

我送我助理回家了，因為他看起來臉色蒼白，而且他說覺得想吐。

0705

look pale 臉色蒼白

注意，look 為「連綴動詞」，其後應直接用形容詞作為主詞補語，如 You look angry.（你看起來很生氣），不可說成 You look like angry。

look / lose

I don't think your spelling is correct. Would you please look it up in the dictionary?

我想你拼得不太對。能不能麻煩你查一下字典？

0706
look (something) **up in ...** 在……查閱（單字、人名等）

Don't talk to me; I'll lose count.

不要跟我說話；我會忘記算到哪裡。

0707
lose count 忘記數、算到哪裡

Jack often loses his temper because his workers are so incompetent.

傑克常常發脾氣，因為他的員工十分無能。

0708
lose one's temper 發脾氣；發怒
關 keep one's temper 按捺住脾氣；不發怒

• incompetent 無能的

I was on the Internet and lost track of the time. I apologize for being late.

我在上網，沒留意到時間。我為遲到致歉。

0709
lose track of (something)
沒留意到（某事物）；失去（某事物）的線索
反 keep track of (something) 掌握（某事物）的線索

• apologize 致歉

make

Our competitor **makes a big deal about** how cheap its products are, but they aren't really any cheaper than ours.

我們的競爭對手拿自己的產品有多便宜來大作文章，但是其實他們的東西一點都不比我們的便宜。

0710
make a big deal about (something)
針對（某事）大作文章；小題大作
類 make a federal case out of (something) 對（某事）大驚小怪；誇大其事

Jason **made a fool out of** the visiting speaker when he asked him a difficult question he couldn't answer.

傑森讓來訪的講者出了洋相，問了他一個他答不出來的困難問題。

0711
make a fool out of (someone) 讓（某人）出洋相
類 humiliate someone 羞辱某人

Governor Bartlett **made a name for himself** by eliminating the state sales tax on food and clothing.

巴列特州長因為廢除了食品與衣服的州營業稅而聲名大噪。

0712
make a name for oneself 聲名大噪；打響名號
類 become famous 成名

• eliminate 排除；淘汰

The angry customer **made a scene** and demanded to see the store manager.

怒氣沖沖的顧客當衆發飆，並要求店長出面。

0713
make a scene 當衆大吵大鬧

make

Heather made a real spectacle of herself last night after she drank too much and began strip dancing.

海瑟昨天晚上喝得太多而開始跳脫衣舞，真是出盡了洋相。

0714
make a spectacle of oneself 出盡洋相
類 make a scene 當眾大吵大鬧（參照 0713）

In firing Stella for arriving at work late, Ms. Jasper made an example of her as a warning to the other employees.

傑斯帕女士以上班遲到為由開除了史黛拉，並拿她殺雞儆猴，以警告其他的員工。

0715
make an example of (someone) 懲戒（某人）以儆戒他人；拿（某人）來殺雞儆猴

Don't make a big issue of his behavior. He is still too young. Give him a chance.

不要拿他的行為來小題大作。他還太年輕。給他個機會。

0716
make an issue of (something) **...** 拿（某事）來作文章
類 make a big deal about (something) 針對（某事）大作文章

Tom got stuck in traffic on the way to church and almost didn't make it to his own wedding.

在去教堂的路上，湯姆被卡在車陣中，差一點沒趕上自己的婚禮。

0717
make it 趕上；成功 類 be in time 及時

- get stuck 被卡住
- almost didn't ... 差一點沒……

make

I make it a rule to make sure all the doors and windows are locked before going to bed.

我養成習慣會確定所有的門窗都鎖好了才去睡覺。

0718

make it a rule 養成習慣；形成規則　類 make it a habit 養成習慣

I think it makes sense to pay off one debt before incurring another.

我想，先還掉一筆債再借另一筆才合情理。

0719

make sense 有道理；合情理；有意義

- incur 招致

If you have a mixer at home, you can make nutritious baby food from scratch.

假如你家有攪拌器，就可以用原料自製營養的嬰兒食品。

0720

make (something) **from scratch** 用原料自製（某物）

- mixer 攪拌器
- nutritious 營養的

※ from scratch 的原意為「從零開始」。

I tried to make something out of the peculiar handwriting but I couldn't.

我試圖辨識這個獨特的筆跡，但是無能為力。

0721

make something out of ... 從……中看出（某物）

- peculiar 獨特的；奇異的
- handwriting 筆跡

make

I can't believe the statistics in our competitor's ad. I think they made them up.

我無法相信對手廣告裡的統計數字。我想他們那些數字是捏造出來的。

0722
make (something) **up** 捏造、虛構（某事物）

- statistics 統計數字

I have to make up for the delay by doing overtime tonight.

我今天晚上必須加班趕工，以彌補延誤。

0723
make up for (something) 彌補（某事物）

注意，do / work overtime 指「加班」，而 overwork 指「過勞」。

CheckTest

0667 ⇨ 0723

請依照文意將適當的動詞片語填入空格中。可參考第 288 頁所提示的片語來作答。（作答時間：7 分 30 秒）

① That company ______________ half of its middle management personnel and went bankrupt shortly thereafter.

② Warning! This is private property! ______________!

③ Watch out! Our manager is ______________ how long we are away on our lunch hour.

④ Walter boasts that he always ______________ some of the wealthiest entrepreneurs in Europe.

⑤ Somebody left this umbrella in the office last week, but nobody has ______________ it, so I guess it's OK if I use it.

⑥ If you are willing to ______________ in Portland on Saturday night, you can save $250 on the fare.

⑦ For our tour guide training program, we've paired each new employee with an experienced tour guide who ______________.

⑧ I can hardly wait to ________________ the new laptop. It's being delivered directly to my office this afternoon.

⑨ We are ________________ the possibility of building three more greenhouses, and we would like you to do a cost analysis.

⑩ Don't ________ big ________ his behavior. He is still too young. Give him a chance.

⑪ If you have a mixer at home, you can ________ nutritious baby food ________.

⑫ I have to ________________ the delay by doing overtime tonight.

⑬ Now that we are number one in the electrical appliance industry, we have to ________________ our reputation.

⑭ Tom got stuck in traffic on the way to church and almost didn't ________________ to his own wedding.

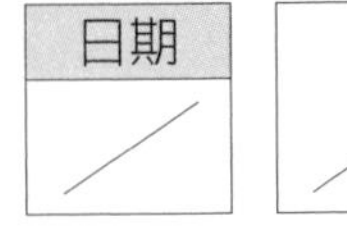

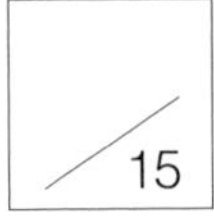

⑮ Jack often ______________________ because his workers are so incompetent.

參考用字

keep company with	keep out	lay off
keep track of	know the ropes	lay claim to
look into	lay hands on	lay over
lose one's temper	live up to	make an issue of
make ... from scratch	make up for	make it

（解答請參閱第 432 頁）

Unit 21

manage / pass

MP3 27

It was a difficult meeting, but Carter somehow managed to come up with a solution to satisfy both parties.

這是場難開的會議，但是卡特不知怎麼地就是有辦法提出解決方案來讓雙方滿意。

0724
manage to 設法做；勉強做到

• solution 解決（方案）

Ted McCorey, former CEO of Marvelous Toy Company, passed away yesterday at the age of 91.

非凡玩具公司的前任執行長泰德．麥可瑞昨天過世了，享壽 91 歲。

0725
pass away 過世；去世

• marvelous 非常好的；絕妙的

When the air conditioning system broke down, two people in our office passed out from heat exhaustion.

空調系統故障時，我們辦公室有兩個人因為熱衰竭而昏倒了。

0726
pass out 昏倒 類 faint 暈倒、black out 昏厥

• break down 故障
• heat exhaustion 熱衰竭

We passed the hat and collected $103 for next week's office party.

我們為下星期的辦公室派對募捐，並募得了 103 美元。

0727
pass the hat 募捐

※ 用到 pass 這個動詞的片語還有指「推諉責任」的 pass the buck。

I carry a little notebook so I can jot down ideas as they pass through my mind.

我都隨身帶著小筆記本，以便在有想法閃過腦海時，可以隨手記下來。

0728
pass through one's mind 閃過腦海
類 cross one's mind 掠過心頭

• jot down 草草寫下；快速記下

I ended up paying an arm and a leg just to get our fence repaired.

我到最後花了一大筆錢，只為了把圍籬修好。

0729
pay an arm and a leg 花大錢；所費不貲

• end up 最後……（參照 0581）
• fence 圍籬

When Loretta discovered Smith's illegal scheme, he paid her off, and she promised never to tell anyone.

在羅瑞塔發現史密斯的違法陰謀時，他買通了她，她則答應絕對不告訴任何人。

0730
pay (someone) off 買通（某人） 類 buy (someone) off 收買（某人）

• illegal scheme 違法陰謀

pay / pick

The letter from the card company said if I don't pay up they'll send a collection agency after me.

信用卡公司的信上說，假如我不把錢付清，他們就會請討債公司來找我。

0731
pay up 付清欠債

• collection agency 討債公司

Never pick a fight with your boss. You could find yourself out of a job.

千萬不要跟老闆對槓。你可能會發現自己丟了飯碗。

0732
pick a fight 尋釁；挑戰

The other kids like to pick on him because he has a funny-sounding name.

其他的小孩喜歡找他麻煩，因為他的名字聽起來很好笑。

0733
pick on (someone) 找（某人）的碴；刁難（某人）

• funny-sounding 聽起來很好笑的

Can I pick your brain for a minute? I want to know what you think of my idea for a new e-business.

我能請教你一下嗎？我想知道對於我提出的新電子商務構想你有什麼看法。

0734
pick someone's brain 請教某人；徵詢某人的意見

Picking out reliable information from the enormous amount of material on the Internet is painstaking work.

從網路上多如牛毛的素材中挑選出可靠的資訊是件費力的事。

0735
pick out 挑選出；辨認出

• enormous 龐大的；巨大的
• painstaking 費力的；辛苦的

The police dog picked up the faint scent of the criminal.

警犬嗅出了該犯人微弱的氣味。

0736
pick up 嗅出；拾起；學會；得到；收到；（用車）接人

• faint 微弱的

Five of us had dinner at the hotel restaurant, and Jerry generously picked up the tab.

我們五個人在飯店的餐廳吃晚餐，傑瑞很大方地埋單。

0737
pick up the tab 埋單　類 treat someone 請客

※ tab 指「餐廳的」帳單。美式英文常用 check 表示。

If we all pitch in, I think we can get Room 100 cleaned up in time for the meeting.

假如我們一起動手，我想我們就能在開會前把 100 號房及時清理好。

0738
pitch in 參與；出力　類 cooperate 合作

• in time 及時

pitch / play

Life pitched Herman a curve ball when he was diagnosed with an incurable disease.

生命對賀曼開了個大玩笑，他被診斷出得了絕症。

0739

pitch (someone) a curve ball 讓（某人）措手不及

• diagnose 診斷 • incurable disease 絕症

※ pitch a curve ball 原意為「投出曲球」。

The man who hacked into our system played cat and mouse with the authorities for a year before they caught him.

駭入我們系統的人跟有關當局玩了一年的貓捉老鼠才被逮到。

0740

play cat and mouse 玩貓捉老鼠；鬥智

• hack into 駭入 • authorities 有關當局（複數形）

This movie theater chain plays for keeps. They intend to drive every local theater out of business.

這家連鎖戲院是玩真的。他們打算讓在地的每家戲院都關門大吉。

0741

play for keeps 玩真的

• intend to 打算；意圖 • drive someone out of ... 把某人逼出、趕出……（參照 0573）

※ for keeps 可指「永久地」。

The buyer from Fashion City is playing hard to get. She wants us to lower our prices.

時尚城市的買主在故作姿態。她想要我們降價。

0742

play hard to get 故作姿態

play

I don't know what Mr. Thornton will want to do after he arrives here. Let's play it by ear.

我不曉得索頓先生到這裡後想做什麼。我們到時候再說吧！

0743
play it by ear 到時候再說；權宜行事

※ play by ear 指「不看樂譜彈奏」。

Worried about security on the Internet? Play it safe with our newest firewall.

擔心網路安全嗎？用我們最新的防火牆來買個保險吧！

0744
play it safe 小心行事；買個保險

We need a decision from Big Ocean about the sale, but they haven't returned our calls. I think they're playing possum.

我們需要大洋公司決定到底做不做這筆生意，但是他們卻不回我們的電話。我想他們在裝傻。

0745
play possum 裝死；裝作毫不知情

※ possum 為「負鼠」，在受生命威脅時負鼠會裝死。

Although the candidate was generally popular, his opponent played him down by calling him a liar.

雖然這個候選人人氣很旺，但是他的對手貶損他，說他是個騙子。

0746
play (someone) **down** 貶損（某人）
反 play up to (someone) 討好（某人）（參照 0750）

• opponent 對手

play

Don't play me for an imbecile! I know you've been cheating on me all along.

不要把我當白癡。我知道你一直對我不忠。

0747
play (someone) **for an imbecile** 把（某人）當白癡
類 play (someone) for a fool 把（某人）當傻子

• cheat on someone 對某人不忠
※ idiot、moron 也常被用來指「白痴」、「笨蛋」。

My financial advisor says the safest way to play the market is to diversify my investments.

我的理財顧問說，做股票最保險的方法就是分散投資。

0748
play the market 做股票；投機

• financial advisor 理財顧問
• diversify 多樣化；多角化
• investment 投資
※ 本句中的 market 指的就是 stock market（股市）。

Do you see that shiny object floating in the sky, or are my eyes playing tricks on me?

你有沒有看到那個飄在空中亮晶晶的東西，還是我被我的眼睛給騙了？

0749
play tricks on (someone) 矇騙（某人）

Cathy is constantly playing up to her boss. She really wants the promotion.

凱西一直在討好她的老闆。她真的很想升官。

0750
play up to (someone) 討好（某人）
類 flatter someone 奉承某人；拍某人馬屁

Norah was possessed by the idea of one day building her own school for orphans in a developing country.

諾拉滿腦子的想法都是，有朝一日要在一個開發中國家為孤兒蓋一所她自己的學校。

0751
possessed by (something) 滿腦子都是……；執迷於……

TOEIC POINT possessed by 不一定都是負面的意思，而 obsessed by 則常指「被……附身；被……纏住」，含有否定的意味。

You want to call the fire department as a joke? You can go to jail if you pull a stunt like that.

你要打電話去開消防隊的玩笑？玩笑開這麼大是會讓你坐牢的。

0752
pull a stunt 搞噱頭；耍特技

Useful POINT pull a publicity stunt 是指「為了變得有名（引人目光）而搞噱頭」。

A trick that magazine companies often pull is to give a new subscriber a deep discount on the first year, and then raise the rate the following year.

那家雜誌社經常耍的花招是，第一年給新訂戶很大的折扣，然後隔年就調高費率。

0753
pull a trick 耍花招；耍手段

• subscriber 訂戶 • a deep discount 很大的折扣 • rate 費率

pull

Our packaging division redesigned these zipper-lock plastic bags after customers complained that they were too hard to pull apart.

在顧客抱怨太硬而拉不開後，我們的包裝部重新設計了這些可封口的塑膠袋。

0754
pull apart 拉開

- packaging division 包裝部
- zipper-lock plastic bag 可封口的塑膠袋

TOEIC POINT pull apart 指「拉開」，需要受詞；fall apart 則是「四分五裂」的意思，不需要受詞。勿將二者搞混。

We need volunteers who will set up and pull down the convention decorations.

我們需要志工來架設並拆除大會的布置。

0755
pull down (something) 拆除（房屋等）

- set up 架設；樹立；裝配
- decoration 裝飾（品）

Look at this e-mail. It says there is 100,000 euros deposited in my bank account. Someone is pulling my leg.

你看這封電子郵件。它說我的銀行戶頭裡存了 10 萬歐元。有人在開我玩笑。

0756
pull one's leg 開人玩笑；逗弄人
類 play tricks on someone 開某人玩笑

pull

Frank was upset by the way the press was treating him, but he managed to pull himself together for the next interview.

法蘭克被新聞界對待他的方式搞得心煩意亂，但是他還是勉強打起精神接受下一場訪問。

0757
pull oneself together 打起精神；振作起來

• upset 心煩意亂 • manage to 勉強做（參照 0724） • interview 訪問；面談

Get Swinhart to sign the agreement before he changes his mind and tries to pull out of the deal.

在史文哈特改變心意、想退出交易之前讓他在協議書上簽字。

0758
pull out of ... 從……退出、抽身 類 retreat from 從……撤退

TOEIC POINT pull something out of ... 是「將某物從……拉出來」的意思。

Could you just pull over to the curb, please? I'll get out right here. Thank you very much for the ride.

能不能麻煩你靠邊停就好？我要在這裡下車。非常謝謝你載我一程。

0759
pull over to the curb（把車）靠邊停

• curb 路緣 • ride 便車

Congratulations for pulling off the Greenwood Mall deal.

恭喜你拿下格林伍德賣場的案子。

0760
pull (something) off 成功做成（某事）
類 accomplish (something) 完成（某事）

pull / put

Our tourist industry nearly collapsed after the terrorist attack, but we pulled through the crisis and are thriving once again.

在恐怖攻擊後，我們的觀光業差一點就垮了，但是我們度過了危機，並再次蓬勃發展。

0761
pull through (something) 度過（危機或難關）

• collapse 垮台；崩潰 • thrive 蓬勃發展

※ 不接受詞時，pull through 指「恢復健康」，例如：I'm sure your father is going to pull through.（我確信你爸爸會康復）

A long, white limousine pulled up to the hotel entrance, and the CEO and his wife emerged.

一輛很長的白色豪華轎車在飯店門口停了下來，就看見執行長夫婦二人現身。

0762
pull up to the entrance 停在入口處

• emerge 出現 • limousine 豪華大轎車

How much of your paycheck were you able to put away in savings last month?

上個月你從薪水中攢下多少積蓄？

0763
put away (money) 存下（錢） 類 save money 存錢

• savings 存款（複數形）

We'll have to put away the marketing plan temporarily until all the side effects of this drug are cleared.

我們必須把行銷計畫暫時擱置，直到這款藥品的副作用消除為止。

0764
put away (something) 擱置（某事）；將（某物）放回原處

put

The complete failure of negotiations with the contractor put us back to square one with a new builder.

由於和包商談判全面失敗，我們只好找新的建築業者從頭來過。

0765
put (someone) back to square one 使（某人）回到起點

- negotiation 談判
- contractor 包商

Our old cat suffered great pain, so we sadly took him to the vet to have him put down.

我們的老貓非常痛苦，於是我們哀傷地帶他去找獸醫，讓他安樂死。

0766
put down (an animal) 使（動物）安樂死
類 put (an animal) to sleep 讓（動物）安樂死

- vet 獸醫（為 veterinarian 之略）

This morning, we put down $250,000 to hold our offer on Fern Meadows Golf Course.

今天早上我們繳交了 25 萬美元，以保有我們購買蕨草高爾夫球場的權利。

0767
put down (some money) 支付（部分費用）
類 deposit (some money) 付（訂金）

- offer 出價

put

I'm applying for a job at your company. Would you put in a good word for me?

我要應徵你們公司的工作。你能幫我美言幾句嗎？

0768
put in a good word for (someone) 幫（某人）美言幾句

• apply for 申請

No cash? No worry. Put it on your Gold Card and pay later!

沒帶現金？別擔心。用您的金卡來刷，事後再付款！

0769
put it on a card 用信用卡支付

Useful POINT Can I put it on my card?（可以使用信用卡嗎？）、I maxed out my card（信用卡的額度超過了）都是很常用的說法。

I have a popcorn popper that I have never used. I think I'll put it on eBay.

我有個爆米花鍋從來沒用過。我想我會拿去 eBay 上賣。

0770
put it on eBay 拿到 eBay 上賣

I'd rather not see Ms. Wikoff now. Could you put her off?

我現在並不想見魏科夫小姐。你能不能拖延她一下？

0771
put off (something / someone) 拖延（某事／某人）
類 hold (someone / something) off 阻擋（某人；某事）（參照 0659）

put

Carrie claims to be friends with many famous people in Hollywood, but she's just putting on airs.

凱莉自稱是許多好萊塢名人的朋友，但是她只是在裝腔作勢。

0772
put on airs 裝腔作勢；擺架子

• claim 宣稱；主張

The suspect's story doesn't hold water. I think he is putting on an act.

嫌犯的說詞站不住腳。我想他在裝模作樣。

0773
put on an act 裝模作樣

• hold water 站得住腳；合情合理

Put on your coat, and let's go out for a walk.

把外套穿上，我們到外面去散個步。

0774
put on (something) 穿上；戴上；塗抹（在身上）

• go for a walk 去散步

Webster has put on a little weight since I last saw him fifteen years ago.

跟 15 年前我最後一次看到他時比起來，韋布斯特變胖了一點。

0775
put on weight 增加體重　反 lose weight 減重

put

Try to put yourself in my shoes. Wouldn't you have done the same thing as I did?

試著站在我的立場想想。你不會跟我做一樣的事嗎？

0776
put oneself in someone's shoes 站在某人的立場

Pleasant Press wants to put out a book on etiquette especially for teens.

「愉悅出版社」想出版一本專為青少年所寫的禮儀書。

0777
put out a book 出版、發行一本書 類 publish a book 出版一本書

- pleasant 令人愉快的
- etiquette 禮儀；禮節

The vice-president put out a statement denying all allegations of corruption.

副總統發表一則聲明，否認一切貪污收賄的指控。

0778
put out a statement 發表一則聲明

- corruption 腐化；收賄

As manager of a Las Vegas casino, I spent most of my time putting out fires. There was just one crisis after another.

身為拉斯維加斯賭場的經理，我大部分的時間都在救火。危機總是接踵而來。

0779
put out fires 救火；化解事端

- casino 賭場
- one after another 一個接一個

put

Environmentalists are putting pressure on the oil refinery to reduce their pollutants.

環保人士正在對煉油廠施壓，要他們減少製造污染物。

0780
put pressure on (someone) 對（某人）施壓

- environmentalist 環保人士
- refinery 煉油廠
- pollutant 污染物

Dr. Pak put me in the picture about how my heart is malfunctioning.

帕克醫生對我解說了我的心臟哪裡有毛病。

0781
put (someone) **in the picture** 把情況告訴（某人）

- malfunction 故障；失靈

You can't be over 50 years old! You are putting me on.

你不可能有 50 多歲！你在唬哢我。

0782
put (someone) **on** 唬哢、耍騙（某人）

I don't want to put you out, but would you be able to stay a half hour longer today?

我不想造成你的不便，但是你今天能不能多留個半小時？

0783
put (someone) **out** 造成（某人）的不便；麻煩（某人）

CheckTest

0728 ➪ 0783

請依照文意將適當的動詞片語填入空格中。可參考第 307 頁所提示的片語來作答。（作答時間：7 分 30 秒）

① We ____________ and collected $103 for next week's office party.

② When Loretta discovered Smith's illegal scheme, he ________ her ________, and she promised never to tell anyone.

③ Five of us had dinner at the hotel restaurant, and Jerry generously ____________.

④ It was a difficult meeting, but Carter somehow ________ come up with a solution to satisfy both parties.

⑤ Worried about security on the Internet? ____________ with our newest firewall.

⑥ When the air conditioning system broke down, two people in our office ____________ from heat exhaustion.

⑦ If we all ____________, I think we can get Room 100 cleaned up in time for the meeting.

⑧ The other kids like to ____________________ him because he has a funny-sounding name.

⑨ Congratulations for ____________________ the Greenwood Mall deal.

⑩ I don't know what Mr. Thornton will want to do after he arrives here. Let's ____________________.

⑪ You want to call the fire department as a joke? You can go to jail if you ____________________ like that.

⑫ Our old cat suffered great pain, so we sadly took him to the vet to have him ____________________.

⑬ I don't want to __________ you __________, but would you be able to stay a half hour longer today?

⑭ Frank was upset by the way the press was treating him, but he managed to ____________________ for the next interview.

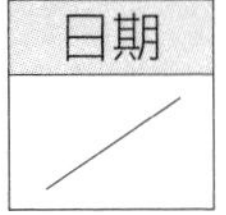

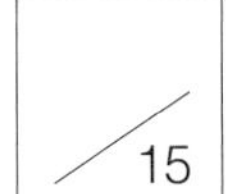

⑮ We'll have to ________________ the marketing plan temporarily until all the side effects of this drug are cleared.

參考用字

pass the hat	pass out	pay someone off
pick on	pick up the tab	manage to
play it safe	play it by ear	pitch in
pull oneself together	pull a stunt	put down
put someone out	put away	pull off

（解答請參閱第 432 頁）

Unit 22

put

MP3 29

Let me put it down before I forget. Those e-mail addresses are really hard to remember.

讓我把它寫下來，以免忘掉。這些電子郵件地址真是難記。

0784
put (something) **down** 將（地址、號碼等）寫下來

Nicholas decided to close his pub and put it up for sale.

尼可拉斯決定收掉他的酒吧，把它賣出去。

0785
put (something) **up for sale** 出售（某物）

If our product doesn't sell, we can put the blame on poor advertising.

假如我們的產品賣不好，我們可以歸咎於宣傳不力。

0786
put the blame on (something / someone) 歸咎於（某事）；怪罪（某人）

They're putting up a twenty-five-story building next to ours, so it's been very noisy.

他們正在我們隔壁蓋一棟 25 層的大樓，所以吵得不得了。

0787
put up 建造；豎立；架設 類 build 興建

If the farm workers don't get a raise, the union is going to put up a fight.

假如農場工人沒有獲得調薪，工會就會發動抗爭。

0788
put up a fight 發動抗爭

put

Mr. Eaton puts up a good front when he's with customers, but back in the office, he's hostile and unfriendly to co-workers.

伊頓先生在顧客面前裝出一副好人的樣子，但是回到辦公室對同事卻心懷敵意而不友善。

0789
put up a front 裝出一副樣子

- hostile 不利的；懷敵意的；敵對的（參照 0249）
- co-worker 同事

It's a cute little house, but there's no place to put up a guest for the night.

這是間可愛的小房子，但是沒有地方可以讓客人夜晚留宿。

0790
put up a guest 留宿客人
類 accommodate someone 容納某人；留宿某人

To get started in your business, you need to put up a website right away.

為了展開你的事業，你必須立刻架設網站。

0791
put up a website 架設網站

Why put up with annoying pop-up ads? Install NO-POP software today! Free 30-day trial offer!

為什麼要忍受煩人的彈出式廣告？今天就安裝 NO-POP 軟體！免費提供試用 30 天！

0792
put up with (someone / something) ... 忍受（某人／某事）

- annoying 煩人的
- pop-up ad（電腦）彈出式廣告
- trial offer 提供試用

So sorry to hear about the flood. If your property was damaged, you should raise a claim with the insurance company.

十分遺憾聽到水災的消息。假如你的房子有受損，你應該要向保險公司申請理賠。

0793
raise a claim 申請理賠

• flood 洪水；水災 • damage 損害 • insurance campany 保險公司

The customer threatened to raise a racket if our store didn't refund her money.

假如我們店裡不退她錢的話，那位顧客威脅要把事情鬧大。

0794
raise a racket 把事情鬧大

• threaten 威脅 • refund 退錢（參照 0170）

※ racket 的原意為「吵鬧聲」。另，相同拼法的 racket 也可指「網球拍」。

I attended the town meeting on transportation in order to raise the issue of safety for cyclists.

為了提出單車騎士的安全問題我出席了鎮民交通大會。

0795
raise an issue 提出問題

• transportation 運輸；交通 • issue 問題；課題（參照 0215） • cyclist 單車騎士

For guests who like to rough it, there is a campground a little ways from the main lodge.

如果有客人喜歡回歸自然，離主屋不遠的地方有個營地。

0796
rough it 回歸自然

※ 複數形的 ways 常用來表「距離」或「時間」。

rub / run

You don't have to tell me again and again. I know I've made a stupid mistake. Don't rub it in!

你不用跟我一講再講。我知道我犯了個愚蠢的錯誤。不要碎碎念了！

0797
rub it in 嘮叨地說不愉快的事；揭人瘡疤

I can't explain why I don't like the new assistant. His personality just rubs me the wrong way.

我說不出來為什麼我不喜歡那個新助理。他的個性就是讓我不爽！

0798
rub (someone) **the wrong way** 讓（某人）不爽；惹惱（某人）

• personality 個性；性格

Cheryl is running a fever and feels sick to her stomach, so she is leaving work early.

雪莉發燒並覺得反胃，所以她要提早下班。

0799
run a fever / temperature 發燒

• sick to one's stomach 反胃

My cell phone battery has run way down. I'll have to recharge it tonight.

我的手機電池已經沒電了。我今天晚上必須充電。

0800
run down （電池、機器等）耗盡（電力、能源等）

• recharge 充電

在此例句中的 way 為副詞，用來強調，如 way over 指「相當遙遠」、way up 指「相當高、相當貴」、way back 則為「相當後面、相當早期」的意思。

run

Technology skills run in the family. My brothers and I all have jobs working with computers.

科技長才是家族遺傳。我和我幾個哥哥都從事電腦方面的工作。

0801
run in the family 家族遺傳

• technology skill 科技長才

Hybrid cars run on gasoline and electricity.

油電混合車以汽油和電力為動能。

0802
run on (something) 以（某物）為動能

• hybrid car 油電混合車
※ hybrid 的原意為「混種」、「雜種」。

There are no service stations on Cedar Mountain Road, so fill up before you go, or you may run out of gas.

雪松山路沒有加油站，所以去之前要把油加滿，否則你可能會把油用光。

0803
run out of (something) 把（某物）用光

• service station 加油站
※ 在美國「加油站」多用 gas station 表示。

We ran short of storage space, so we built another warehouse on the waterfront.

我們的儲存空間不夠用，所以在濱水區又蓋了一座倉庫。

0804
run short 不夠用；剩不多

• storage space 儲存空間 • warehouse 倉庫 • waterfront 濱水區

run / save

If you invest all of your money in one stock, you run the risk of losing everything.

假如你把錢全部砸在一支股票上，就要承擔賠光的風險。

0805
run the risk of (something) 承擔（某事）的風險

• stock 股票

I'm still confused about how this machine works. Would you please run through the instructions again?

我還是搞不懂這部機器要怎麼操作。能不能麻煩你很快地再講解一次用法？

0806
run through (something) 迅速說明、查看（某事物）

• instruction(s) 指示（常用複數）

Save your breath. It's no use talking to John.

不要浪費唇舌了。跟約翰講也沒有用。

0807
save one's breath 不要浪費唇舌

※ 注意，在 no use 之後須用動名詞。

Thank you for not telling my boss about my traffic violation. You saved my neck.

謝謝你沒把我交通違規的事告訴我老闆。你救了我一命。

0808
save one's neck / skin 救人一命

• traffic violation 交通違規

scare / see / set

Don't ever come out of the dark suddenly like that! You scared the wits out of me.

別再那樣突然從暗處跑出來了！你把我嚇壞了！

0809
scare the wits out of (someone) 把（某人）嚇壞
類 scare someone to death 嚇死某人

※ 注意，本例中的 dark 為名詞用法，指「黑暗（處）」。

Herman quit his job because he did not see eye to eye with his boss on most issues.

賀曼辭掉了工作，因為他跟老闆在大部分的問題上看法都不一致。

0810
see eye to eye with (someone) 跟（某人）看法一致
類 have the same point of view / opinion 看法／見解一致

• quit 辭職；停止

Willie has been seeing things since he suffered from a concussion in a car accident.

自從在車禍中腦震盪之後，威利就產生了幻覺。

0811
see things 產生幻覺 類 hear things 幻聽

• suffer from ... 受……之苦 • concussion 腦震盪

We hope that this all solar-housing development will set a precedent for future developments in the city.

我希望這些全太陽能住宅開發案能為市內將來的開發案創下先例。

0812
set a precedent 創下先例

• solar-housing 太陽能住宅的

set

Mr. Tinker set off to the Imperial Plaza in the company car to meet with a client over lunch.

汀克先生搭公司用車前往帝國廣場，去跟一位客戶共進午餐。

0813
set off 動身；出發 類 set out 啓程；動身

- imperial 帝國的
- plaza 廣場
- client 客戶

The income tax set her back $2,000 this year.

所得稅今年讓她失血 2,000 美元。

0814
set (someone) **back** (some money) 讓（某人）花費（一筆錢）

After her divorce, Sharon's friends set her on her feet with her first job.

雪倫離婚後，朋友幫她謀得了第一份工作，使她得以自立。

0815
set (someone) **on one's feet** 使（某人）自立

- divorce 離婚

① I think Megan set me up. She said she was going to double my money and disappeared with it two weeks ago.

我想梅根擺了我一道。她說她會還我兩倍的錢，結果兩個星期前居然拿著錢跑了。

② Evan's father set him up with his own car dealership.

艾凡的父親資助他開了自己的汽車經銷店。

0816

set (someone) up ① 陷害（某人）② 資助（某人）

- double the money 給兩倍的錢
- car dealership 汽車經銷店

TOEIC POINT 請注意 set someone up 這兩個幾乎相反的用法。整句話的意思必須依前後文來判斷。

Sally was badly shaken up after her car collided with a tree, but fortunately she wasn't hurt.

車子撞樹後，莎莉被嚇壞了，但是所幸她並沒有受傷。

0817

(be) shaken up 受到驚嚇

TOEIC POINT (be) shook up 這個說法在會話中也很常用。

I have nothing to show off to my guests except my three beautiful dogs. They are my family as well as my guardian angels.

除了三隻漂亮的狗之外，我沒有什麼東西可以對客人炫耀的。牠們既是我的家人，也是我的守護天使。

0818

show (something) off 炫耀（某物）

- guardian angel 守護天使

show / sit

Marlin showed up one hour late to her meeting and still managed to close a deal with the client. I wonder what her secret weapon is.

瑪琳開會遲到了一個小時才現身，但是還是有辦法拿下客戶的案子。真不知道她有什麼祕密武器。

0819
show up 現身；出現；出席

- close a deal 完成一筆交易
- secret weapon 祕密武器

You can't just sit back and watch our money go down the drain in the stock market. Do something!

你不能只是坐在那裡，看著我們的錢在股市裡付諸東流。想點辦法啊！

0820
sit back 坐著不行動；袖手旁觀

- go down the drain 付諸東流

The manager can't attend the briefing, so the assistant manager is sitting in for her.

經理沒辦法出席簡報，所以副理代替她。

0821
sit in for (someone) 代替（某人）
類 substitute for (someone) 替代（某人）

- briefing 簡報

I don't feel like playing another game of tennis. I'll sit the next one out.

我不想再打一場網球賽了。下一場我就坐在一邊。

0822
sit (something) **out** 坐在一邊；不加入

On Sundays I always sleep in. Sometimes I don't get up until noon.

星期天我總是會睡懶覺。有時候我睡到中午才起床。

0823
sleep in 睡懶覺 類 sleep late 晚起來

※ 注意，「晚睡」是 go to bed late ，不是 sleep late。

I can't give you an answer right now. Can I sleep on it and let you know in the morning?

我沒辦法馬上給你答案。我能不能考慮一個晚上，等早上再告訴你？

0824
sleep on (something) 考慮（某事）一個晚上

Phil drank too much last night, and he's sleeping it off now.

菲爾昨天晚上喝得太多，現在還在睡覺消除宿醉。

0825
sleep (something) **off** 以睡眠解除（宿醉等不適）

At the shareholders' meeting, many people spoke out against the nominee for chairman, so his name was dropped.

在股東大會上，有很多人發言公開反對董事長的被提名人，所以他的名字就被剔除了。

0826
speak against (someone) 發言反對（某人）

• nominee 被提名人

※ speak ill of someone 指「說某人的壞話」。

speak

① The result speaks for itself. You need to study much harder.

結果不證自明。你還得更加用功。

② A: Pink coffee mugs? Who will buy them? Nobody likes pink.
B: Speak for yourself. I like pink.

A: 粉紅色的咖啡杯？誰會買啊？沒有人會喜歡粉紅色。
B: 那是你說的。我就喜歡粉紅色。

0827
speak for oneself ① 不證自明；不言而喻
類 be self-explanatory 再清楚不過的
② 那是你說的；那是你的想法

※ speak for oneself 的意思取決於主詞。

Animal rights' activists spoke out strongly against the use of monkeys in clinical trials.

動物權倡導人士大聲疾呼，強烈反對把猴子用於臨床試驗。

0828
speak out 大聲疾呼

- animal rights' activist 動物權倡導人士
- clinical trial 臨床試驗

We can't hear you at the back. Speak up, please!

我們在後面聽不到你說的話。請說大聲點。

0829
speak up 大聲說；大膽地說

I'm afraid that seat is already spoken for, but there's a free place over there by the window.

那個位子恐怕已經有人坐了，但是那邊窗戶旁還有空位。

0830
(be) spoken for 為某人留下的；為某人所有的
類 be already taken 已經有人坐了

I can lift this business out of bankruptcy. I will spit in the eye of anyone who tells me to give up.

我有辦法把這家企業從破產中解救出來。有哪個人叫我放棄，我就唾棄他。

0831
spit in someone's eye 唾棄某人

※ spit 是「吐口水」的意思。

Come on. Spit it out. Who gave you that kind of money?

快點。從實招來。那筆錢是誰給你的？

0832
spit it out 從實招來 類 confess 招認

This latest model printing machine spits out 100 copies per minute.

這款最新的印刷機每分鐘可印 100 張。

0833
spit out 吐出；產出

- model 機型；模特兒
- printing machine 印刷機
- per mimute 每一分鐘

stand

Don't worry about our new competitor. They don't stand a chance against us.

不用擔心我們的新對手。他們是沒機會贏我們的。

0834
stand a chance 有機會（成功、獲勝等）

Two-car accident on 44th and Maple Street. Stand by, please.

44 號和楓樹街街口有兩輛車發生事故。請待命。

0835
stand by 待命 類 be ready and wait 準備好等待

My name is Georgina Lee. I'm standing in for Mr. Barth who couldn't be here today.

我叫喬吉娜・李。我代理今天不能來的巴爾斯先生。

0836
stand in for (someone) 代理（某人）
類 substitute for (someone) 代替某人（參照 0243）

I'm sorry to see you leave the company, but I won't stand in your way if this is what you want.

很遺憾看到你離開公司，但是假如這就是你要的，我不會阻止你。

0837
stand in one's way 阻止；妨礙

take

Thanks for asking me out, but I already have plans for tonight. Can I take a rain check?

謝謝你約我出去，但是我今晚已經有計畫了。可以改天嗎？

0838
take a rain check 改天

TOEIC POINT rain check 原指棒球比賽因雨取消，大會給在場觀眾下次入場的票。

Take advantage of our great offer! Two DVDs for the price of one!

好好把握我們的難得優惠！一片的價格買兩片 DVD ！

0839
take advantage of (something / someone) 利用（某事）；占（某人）便宜

Pam takes after her father in her love for animals. Maybe she'll come to work in his veterinary practice some day.

潘跟她爸很像，都喜愛動物。也許有朝一日她會來他的獸醫診所上班。

0840
take after (someone) 像（某人）

• veterinary practice 獸醫診所

TOEIC POINT take after 只能用來形容同一家族的成員。要說明與第三者之間長相相似則要用 look like / resemble。

Even if you didn't win the game, don't take it out on me!

就算你沒有打贏比賽，也不要把氣出在我身上。

0841
take it out on (someone) 把氣出在（某人）身上

take

The plane is taking off in a few minutes. Is there anything else you want me to do before I leave?

飛機再幾分鐘就要起飛了。在我離開前，你還有沒有什麼要我做的事？

0842
take off（飛機）起飛

※ take off 亦可指「脫掉（衣物）」，例如：He took off his coat.（他把大衣脫掉。）

Never take your customers for granted. Treat them well, or they may take their business elsewhere.

千萬不要把顧客視為理所當然。要善待他們，否則他們就會把生意交給別人做。

0843
take ... for granted 把……視為理所當然

I took the liberty of ordering coffee and doughnuts for the meeting. It's on me.

我自作主張為會議訂了咖啡和甜甜圈。我請客。

0844
take the liberty of doing ... 擅自或冒昧做……

TOEIC POINT 注意，liberty 指「因努力而得來的自由」，freedom 則為「天賦之自由」，兩者之間在意思上有些許差異。

CheckTest

0784 ⇨ 0844

請依照文意將適當的動詞片語填入空格中。可參考第 326 頁所提示的片語來作答。（作答時間：7 分 30 秒）

① Let me ________ it ________ before I forget. Those e-mail addresses are really hard to remember.

② You don't have to tell me again and again. I know I've made a stupid mistake. Don't ________________!

③ If our product doesn't sell, we can ________________ poor advertising.

④ The income tax ________ her ________ $2000 this year.

⑤ Why ________________ annoying pop-up ads? Install NO-POP software today! Free 30-day trial offer!

⑥ If you invest all of your money in one stock, you ________________ losing everything.

⑦ The customer threatened to ________________ if our store didn't refund her money.

⑧ Technology skills ________________. My brothers and I all have jobs working with computers.

⑨ I ________________ ordering coffee and doughnuts for the meeting. It's on me.

⑩ This latest model printing machine ________________ 100 copies per minute.

⑪ The manager can't attend the briefing, so the assistant manager is ________________ her.

⑫ I think Megan ________________. She said she was going to double my money and disappeared with it two weeks ago.

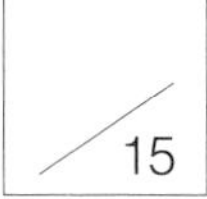

⑬ Never __________ your customers __________. Treat them well, or they may take their business elsewhere.

⑭ ____________________ our great offer! Two DVDs for the price of one!

⑮ I'm afraid that seat __________ already __________, but there's a free place over there by the window.

參考用字

put the blame on	put up with	rub it in
put something down	raise a racket	take the liberty of
set someone back	run in the family	run the risk of
spit out	set someone up	be spoken for
sit in for someone	take ... for granted	take advantage of

（解答請參閱第 432 頁）

Unit 23

take / talk

I taught my daughter to fly, and she really took to it. Now she's a commercial pilot.

我教我女兒開飛機，結果她愛得不得了。現在她是個民航機師。

0845
take to (something) 喜愛（某事物）
類 take a liking to (something) 喜歡（某事物）

• commercial pilot 民航機師

The man I sat next to on the plane talked my ear off for three hours about his divorce.

在飛機上坐我隔壁的那個男人，喋喋不休地跟我講了三小時他離婚的事。

0846
talk someone's ear off 喋喋不休地跟某人講

When Barry started his business, he talked his head off about it to everyone he met. That was his first advertising campaign.

貝瑞在創業時，遇到每個人都把它說得天花亂墜。那就是他一開始的廣告宣傳。

0847
talk one's head off 說得口沫橫飛

• advertising campaign 廣告宣傳

talk one's head off 的 head 是指「說話者本身的腦袋」，但 talk someone's ear off 的 ear 卻是指「聽話者的耳朵」，例如：Emma talked her head off. vs. Emma talked my ear off. 要多加注意兩者之間的差別。

talk / think

Helen was able to talk her client into making a big down payment on a luxury yacht.

海倫說服了客戶為豪華遊艇付出大筆的頭期款。

0848
talk (someone) **into doing** (something)
說服（某人）做（某事）

• down payment 頭期款
• luxury yacht 豪華遊艇

Tina's boss talked her out of resigning by promising her a big raise.

提娜的老闆說服她打消辭意，並保證替她加薪。

0849
talk (someone) **out of** (something) 說服（某人）不做（某事）

• resign 辭職

Please don't mind what I've just said. I'm just thinking out loud.

請不要介意我剛剛說的話。我只是在自言自語。

0850
think out loud 自言自語

The exorbitant price of the new fax machine made me think twice about buying it.

新傳真機的價格過高，我還在慎重考慮要不要買。

0851
think twice 慎重考慮 類 think over 仔細考慮

• exorbitant 過高的；不合理的

throw

I don't like working with Janey because her uncle is the CEO, and she throws his name around all the time to make herself look important.

我不喜歡跟詹妮共事，因為她叔叔是執行長，所以她老是搬出他的名號，好讓自己顯得重要。

0852
throw someone's name around 搬出某人的名號
類 put on airs 裝腔作勢；擺架子（參照 0772）

Our guest of honor threw us a curve when she told us on the morning of the luncheon that she was a strict vegetarian.

我們的貴賓讓我們措手不及，因為她到午餐會的早上才告訴我們她吃純素。

0853
throw (someone) **a curve** 讓（某人）措手不及

• strict vegetarian 吃純素者

Do you want to keep this old sweater or throw it away?

你要留下這件舊毛衣還是把它丟掉？

0854
throw (something) **away** 丟棄、扔掉（某物）
類 throw (something) away 扔掉（某物）

Please don't throw out today's newspaper. I haven't read it yet.

請不要把今天的報紙扔掉。我還沒看。

0855
throw (something) **out** 扔掉（某物）

※ throw someone out 指「把某人趕出去」。

My dog **threw up** on my car seat and I have to clean it up.

我的狗吐在我的車椅上，我必須把它清乾淨。

0856
throw up 嘔吐　類 vomit 嘔吐

※ feel sick 指「感到反胃；想吐」。

My computer screen is still frozen. I **tried turning** it **off**, but it won't go off. Shall I try unplugging it?

我的電腦螢幕還是動不了。我試過把它關掉，但是卻關不掉。我是不是該試試拔掉插頭？

0857
try doing (something) 試做（某事）

• freeze（使）結冰；使螢幕不動（freeze-froze-frozen）

Ma'am, would you like to **try on** that dress in the fitting room?

小姐，您要不要去試衣間試穿一下那件洋裝？

0858
try (something) **on** 試穿（衣服、鞋子等）

※ ma'am 為口語，是對不知名女性的禮貌稱呼，念做 [mæm]。

Try out Vitamin X! If you aren't 100% satisfied, you pay nothing!

請試用維他命 X！假如您沒有 100% 滿意，就不用付錢！

0859
try (something / someone) **out** 試用（某物 / 某人）

※ 注意，try on 指「試穿」，try out 指「試用」。

try / turn

Try to talk to Cathy again. We can't afford to lose her expertise on DTP.

試著再跟凱西說說看。我們禁不起失去她在排版方面的專長。

0860
try to do (something) 嘗試去做（某事）

• DTP 利用電腦進行整本書的編輯與版面設計的技術 (= desktop publishing)

TOEIC POINT try doing 指「試做某事」，try to do something 指「嘗試去做某事」。二者的意思不盡相同，須注意。

Steve wanted to buy the property adjacent to his horse farm, but his offer was turned down by the owner.

史提夫想要買緊鄰他自己馬場的那塊地，但是他的提議被地主拒絕了。

0861
turn (someone / something) **down** 拒絕、回絕（某人 / 某事）

• adjacent 緊鄰的 ※ 另，turn up / down 指「調高 / 低；調大 / 小」。

An inexperienced teacher may turn off his students with an overly exaggerated manner.

缺乏經驗的老師可能會因為過度誇大的態度而澆熄學生的興趣。

0862
turn (someone) **off** 澆熄（某人）的興趣
反 turn (someone) on 引起（某人）的興趣

• inexperienced 缺乏經驗的 • exaggerated 誇大的；誇張的

The FBI turned the criminal over to the police.

聯邦調查局把該罪犯交給警方。

0863
turn (someone) **over to ...** 把（某人）移交給……

• FBI 聯邦調查局（= Federal Burean of Investigation）

① Over 1,000 people turned out at the funeral of Ken Kierney, the great singer who died young.

有一千多人參加了英年早逝的偉大歌手肯・基爾尼的葬禮。

② The quality of the coffee crop this year turned out to be better than expected.

今年咖啡收成的品質竟然比預期中要好。

0864
turn out ①參加；出席 ②結果是；結果為

I feel we have finally turned the corner on this excavating project.

在這個開挖案上，我覺得我們總算度過難關了。

0865
turn the corner 度過難關；好轉

• excavate 挖掘（古物）

I can't find that note from Judy. If it turns up, let me know.

我找不到茱蒂寫的那張便條。假如它出現的話，告訴我一聲。

0866
turn up 出現；發生

People kept walking off with the pen at the reception counter, so we had to attach it to a clipboard.

人們老是把接待櫃台上的筆順手拿走，我們只好把它固定在帶夾的寫字板上。

0867
walk off with (something) 順手拿走（某物）
類 walk away with something 帶走（某物）

• clipboard 帶夾寫字版

walk / wash

Sonia walked out on her partners and started her own cosmetics business.

桑妮亞棄合夥人而去，並開創了自己的化妝品事業。

0868
walk out on (someone) 棄（某人）而去

• cosmetics 化妝品（複數形）

Don't forget to walk the dog and feed him while I'm gone.

我不在的時候，別忘了遛狗並餵牠吃飯。

0869
walk the dog 遛狗

※ walk the dog 是「遛狗」的意思，這裡的 walk 是及物動詞。其他如 I'll walk you to the station.（我會走路送你到車站。）中的 walk 也是類似的及物用法。

Will's been working between fifty and sixty hours a week recently. No wonder he looks washed out.

威爾近來每週工作 50 到 60 個小時。難怪他臉色蒼白，一副很累的樣子。

0870
washed out 臉色蒼白的；筋疲力盡的
類 worn out、exhausted、tired out 筋疲力盡

Benson is all washed up at our company. I don't think he deserves another chance.

班森在我們公司完全不行。我認為不該再給他機會了。

0871
(be) washed up 徹底失敗

• deserve 應得；應受

 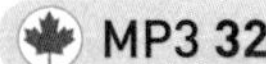

Emma's enthusiasm for collecting stamps wore off as she grew up.

艾瑪長大之後對集郵的熱情逐漸消退。

0872
wear off（情緒、疼痛等）漸趨平緩；（藥效等）逐漸消退

- enthusiasm 熱情；熱愛

Ken needs to rest, or he will wear himself out.

肯需要休息，否則他會累垮。

0873
wear oneself out 累垮

After a bribery scandal, the government failed to win a confidence vote.

經過賄賂醜聞後，政府得不到信任票。

0874
win a confidence vote 得到信任票

- bribery 賄賂

※「收受賄賂」說成 take a bribe。

Jon Lorenz won a reputation as an excellent arbitrator in labor-management disputes.

瓊·勞倫茲贏得「勞資爭議絕佳調解人」之美譽。

0875
win a reputation 贏得美譽

- arbitrator 調解人；仲裁者
- labor-management dispute 勞資爭議

win / wipe

Ms. Jones won the election by a hair, and her opponent demanded a recount of the ballots.

瓊斯女士在選舉中險勝，她的對手要求驗票。

0876
win by a hair 險勝　反 win by a big margin 大勝

• recount 重新計算　• ballot 選票（參照 0261）

When the opposing team failed to show up for the game, the home team won by default.

由於客隊不克出賽，主隊不戰而勝。

0877
win by default 因對手缺席而獲勝

• show up 出現；現身（參照 0819）
※ default 可指「缺席」、「違約」，亦可用來指電腦的「預設值」。

Don't forget to wipe off the dust before you turn on the projector.

別忘了先抹掉灰塵，再把投影機打開。

0878
wipe off 擦去；抹去

TOEIC POINT 類似的說法 wipe up 指「(用布）擦乾，例如：Wipe up the floor.（把地板擦乾。)」。

The lava flow from the volcano wiped out the entire neighborhood.

從火山流出的熔岩吞沒了整個鄰近地區。

0879
wipe out 徹底摧毀

• lava flow 熔岩流　※「山崩」為 landslide，「土石流」則為 mudslide。

work

Quincy has worked for Echo Electronics as an engineer for eight years.

昆西服務於艾柯電子公司，當了八年的工程師。

0880
work for (a company) 服務於（某公司）

work for 有「被某家公司雇用」的意思，work at 則指「在某處（地點）工作」。例如：I work for safe Insurance and I work at their Chicago branch.（我服務於安全保險公司，在他們的芝加哥分公司上班。）

Brian lost both arms in an accident and can no longer work for a living.

布萊恩在一場意外中失去了雙臂，再也無法靠工作謀生。

0881
work for a living 靠工作謀生

Janna works for world peace by teaching a seminar on conflict resolution.

珍娜以在研討會中教人化解衝突的方式，努力推展世界和平。

0882
work for world peace 努力推展世界和平

- seminar 研討會
- conflict solution 化解衝突

I enjoy working in customer relations because I love helping people.

我喜歡處理顧客關係，因為我熱愛助人。

0883
work in 處理；從事

- customer relations 顧客關係

※ 注意，在 enjoy 後用動名詞。

work

The Children's Health Project works in collaboration with City Hospital.

兒童健康計畫跟市立醫院攜手合作。

0884
work in collaboration 攜手合作

※ 注意，勿將 collaboration 與 corroboration（確證）混淆。

Ladies! Work off excess fat in just twenty easy minutes a day with Wanda's Workout DVD!

各位女士！旺妲的健身 DVD 讓您一天只要輕輕鬆鬆的花 20 分鐘，就能消除多餘的脂肪！

0885
work off excess fat 消除多餘的脂肪

※ excess 指「多餘的」，excessive 指「過度的」。

When the housing market declined, we shut down our lumber mill and worked off excess inventory for a few weeks.

房市下滑時，我們收掉了木材工廠，並花了好幾週打消多餘的庫存。

0886
work off excess inventory 打消多餘的庫存

- housing market 房市
- shut down 關閉
- lumber mill 木材工廠

Our company is building a fitness center so employees can work off steam after work.

我們公司正在蓋一個健身中心，好讓員工在下班後能放鬆一下身心。

0887
work off steam 發洩精力、悶氣

work

The dentist is working on a patient just now. May I give him a message?

牙醫師正在替病人看診。要我留個話給他嗎？

0888
work on a patient 替病人看診 類 treat a patient 治療病人

I can't persuade Brown to help finance our start-up business. Can you work on him?

我說服不了布朗幫忙金援我們的新創事業。你能不能勸勸他？

0889
work on (someone) 努力說動（某人）

• persuade 說服

Sorry to hear things didn't work out between you and Dean.

很遺憾聽說你和狄恩之間的事業不順利。

0890
work out（人與人的關係或計畫等）順利；練身體；解決（問題）

Sam works the night shift at the plant, so he hardly ever sees his wife.

山姆在工廠上的是晚班，所以幾乎看不到他太太。

0891
work the day / night shift 上白天 / 夜班

※「大夜班」叫 graveyard shift。(graveyard 原指「墓地」)

work / write

He went for a long walk to work up an appetite.

他散很久的步以激起食慾。

0892
work up 激發；激起

- appetite 食慾

Joy's anti-aging cream works wonders for your skin!

喬依的抗老化乳液對妳的皮膚有奇效！

0893
work wonders 有奇效

- anti-aging 抗老化的

You can write off your car as a business expense as long as it is registered and insured as a commercial vehicle.

只要你的車子是以營業用車來登記與投保，就可以把它當作營業支出來打銷。

0894
write off (something) 打銷……；勾銷……

- business expense 營業支出 • register 登記
- insure 投保 • commercial vehicle 營業用車

Jane's music teacher wrote her off as a failure, but she went on to become a successful opera singer.

珍的音樂老師認為她不行而把她淘汰，但是她後來卻成了一位成功的歌劇演唱家。

0895
write (someone) **off** 認為（某人）不行而將（某人）淘汰、除名

※ 注意，failure 可作可數或不可數名詞用。

write

I bought a fax machine for my home business and wrote it off my taxes.

我為我的家庭事業買了一台傳真機，並用它來抵稅。

0896
write (something) **off one's taxes** 用（某物）來抵稅

- fax machine 傳真機

The details are written out in the lease for the benefit of both landlord and tenant.

細節都詳列在租約中，以保障房東與房客雙方的權益。

0897
write out 詳細寫出 類 spell out

- detail 細節
- lease 租約
- landlord 房東
- tenant 房客

CHAPTER 2 UNIT 23

CheckTest

0845 ⇨ 0897

請依照文意將適當的動詞片語填入空格中。可參考第 343 頁所提示的片語來作答。（作答時間：7 分 30 秒）

① The exorbitant price of the new fax machine made me ________________ about buying it.

② ________________ to Cathy again. We can't afford to lose her expertise on DTP.

③ The man I sat next to on the plane ________________ for three hours about his divorce.

④ The FBI ________ the criminal ________ the police.

⑤ Helen was able to ________ her client ________ a big down payment on a luxury yacht.

⑥ Over 1,000 people ________________ at the funeral of Ken Kierney, the great singer who died young.

⑦ ________________ Vitamin X! If you aren't 100% satisfied, you pay nothing!

⑧ Please don't ________________ today's newspaper. I haven't read it yet.

⑨ The lava flow from the volcano ________________ the entire neighborhood.

⑩ Emma's enthusiasm for collecting stamps ________________ as she grew up.

⑪ People kept ________________ the pen at the reception counter until we attached it to a clipboard.

⑫ I bought a fax machine for my home business and ________________ my taxes.

⑬ Ken needs to rest, or he will ________________.

⑭ Ladies! ________________ excess fat in just twenty easy minutes a day with Wanda's Workout DVD!

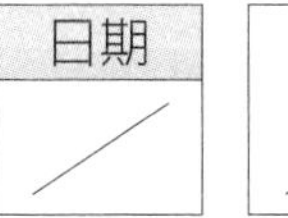

⑮ When the opposing team failed to show up for the game, the home team ____________________.

參考用字

talk someone into doing something		think twice
talk one's ear off	try out	throw out
turn someone over to	turn out	try to do something
write something off	wear oneself out	walk off with
win by default	wipe out	wear off
work off		

（解答請參閱第 432 頁）

Chapter 3

Adjectival, Adverbial
and Prepositional Phrases
0898 ➲ 0985

形容詞・副詞・介系詞片語

Unit 24

I can't believe I forgot my reading glasses. I've become so absent-minded lately.

我不敢相信自己忘了帶老花眼鏡。我最近變得超健忘。

0898
absent-minded 心不在焉的 類 forgetful 健忘的；疏忽的

• reading glasses 老花眼鏡；閱讀用眼鏡

The union of electrical workers is demanding a 5% across-the-board pay raise for all its members this year.

電機工會要求今年所有的會員要全面加薪 5%。

0899
across-the-board 全面的；全盤的

• electrical 與電有關的
• pay raise 加薪

We offer an all-inclusive tour of one full week in Hawaii for only 599 dollars.

我們提供夏威夷一整週的統包式旅遊，只要 599 美元。

0900
all-inclusive 統包式的；涵蓋一切的

• tour 觀光；旅遊

Even if I needed to borrow money, I would ask my friends only as a last resort.

就算我要借錢，我也只會在迫不得已時才向朋友開口。

0901
as a last resort（在迫不得已時）當作最後手段

※ resort 可指「名勝」，如 a summer resort（避暑勝地）。

As a token of our appreciation, on behalf of everyone in the company I would like to present Greg Hollister with the Employee of the Year Award.

為了表示我們的肯定，我要代表公司全體人員頒發年度最佳員工獎給葛瑞格 · 霍里斯特。

0902
as a token of ... 為了表示……；藉以表示……

• on behalf of ... 代表…… • Employee of the Year 年度最佳員工

I understand your desire to work hard and succeed, but you shouldn't do so at the expense of your family.

我明白你很想努力工作並成功，但你不該為了這麼做而犧牲家庭。

0903
at the expense of (someone) 以犧牲（某人）為代價

Before I knew it, a car had run a stop signal at the intersection and almost crashed into me.

我還不知道是怎麼回事，有一輛車就闖過路口的停車號誌，差一點就把我給撞了。

0904
before someone knows it（某人）還不知道是怎麼回事

• run a stop signal 闖過停車號誌 • intersection 路口
• crash 碰撞；（飛機）墜毀；垮台

If the guilt of the defendant cannot be established beyond a reasonable doubt, the court has no choice but to let him go free.

假如被告的罪行無法證明是殆無疑義，法庭就只好把他放了。

0905
beyond a reasonable doubt 殆無疑義

• defendant 被告 • court 法庭 • have no choice but ... 只好……

I don't believe it! My brand-new jacket already has a tear in it.

我不相信！我全新的外套上已經有裂縫了。

0906

brand-new 全新的；嶄新的

• tear [tɛr] 裂縫（與「眼淚」trear [tɪr] 的拼字相同，但發音卻不同，發音上要多加注意。）

I'm going to be working in my study all afternoon, so by all means use my car to drive to the mall.

我整個下午都要在書房工作，所以儘管把我的車開去賣場。

0907

by all means 當然（表示歡迎對方採取行動）；一定

By and large, Americans are much friendlier on first meeting than British people.

總的來說，美國人在第一次見面時，比英國人要親切得多。

0908

by and large 總的來說

• on first meeting 第一次見面

Larry is not very popular with his colleagues because he gives them the impression that he is willing to get to the top by any means.

賴瑞不是非常受同事歡迎，因為他給他們的印象是，他會不擇手段取得高位。

0909

by any means 不擇手段；無論如何

• impression 印象

• the top 最高位置

The costumes for tonight's play were made available by courtesy of Fitzgerald Theater.

今晚演出的戲服承蒙費茲傑羅劇院提供。

0910
by courtesy of (someone) 承蒙（某人）提供

- costume 戲服
- available 可取得的；有空的

For all I know, my boss could be secretly planning to sell the company.

就我所知，我老闆可能在暗中計畫把公司賣掉。

0911
for all I know 就我所知 類 as far as I know 據我所知

For better or worse I'm going to sign the contract. This may be my last chance to stay in show business.

不管怎樣，我都要簽約。這可能是我留在演藝圈的最後機會了。

0912
for better or worse 不管怎樣；無論好壞

- sign a contract 簽合約
- show business 演藝界

Marilyn was so tired of the fast pace of New York that she decided to leave for good and start a new life in a small town.

瑪麗蓮對於紐約的快步調深感厭倦，所以決定永遠離開，並在小鎮展開新生活。

0913
for good 永遠；永久地 類 forever 永遠、permanently 永久地

- fast pace 快步調

Peter decided to turn down the offer of a professorship in another state for his parents' sake.

為了父母，彼得決定婉拒另一州所提供的教授職。

0914
for one's sake 因為某人的緣故

• turn down 婉拒；拒絕（參照 0861）
• professorship 教授之職位

Are you going to join the Peace Corps for real?

你當真要加入和平部隊？

0915
for real 當真；真實地

• Peace Corps 和平部隊（注意，Corps 的發音為 [kɔr]）

Shelley was hands down the best golfer in the competition, and fully deserved to win.

雪莉無疑是比賽中最強的高球選手，獲勝完全是應該的。

0916
hands down 無疑地；輕而易舉地

• deserve 應得；應受

Kenny is by nature a shy person and feels ill at ease when he has to attend social gatherings.

肯尼天生就是個害羞的人，當他必須參加社交聚會時，他就會覺得不自在。

0917
ill at ease 不自在；彆扭

• by nature 天生 • attend 參加；照料 • social gathering 社交聚會

When Joanna heard her child crying, she ran down the stairs in a flash to see what was wrong.

喬安娜一聽到孩子在哭，立刻就跑下樓去看出了什麼事。

0918
in a flash 立刻；瞬間

• run down the stairs 由樓梯往下跑

Zelda is in a jam. She borrowed money from a loan shark that charges 30%

佐爾妲麻煩大了。她用三分利跟一個放高利貸的人借了錢。

0919
in a jam 陷入困境 類 in a bind、in a fix 陷入困境

• loan shark 放高利貸者

Stay here. I'll be back in a jiffy.

待在這裡。我馬上就回來。

0920
in a jiffy 馬上 類 in a wink 一轉眼；一瞬間

There was an explosion, and in a split second, the previously calm street had become a scene of chaos.

發生爆炸後，剎那之間，原本平靜的街頭就陷入了混亂的景象。

0921
in a split second 剎那之間

• previously 先前
• scene 景象；景色
• chaos 混亂；混沌（參照 0340）

You can take your vacation in accordance with company regulations on employee leave.

你可以依照公司的員工請假規定來休假。

0922
in accordance with 依照　關 according to 根據

In consequence of the company reorganization, the research division moved to a new laboratory in a different part of the country.

由於公司重組，研究部遷往了國內一個不同地區的新實驗室。

0923
in consequence of (something) 由於

• reorganization 重組　• laboratory 實驗室

In consideration of the continuing growth of electronic communications, the publishing company decided to launch a computer-based learning system.

考量到電子通訊的持續成長，出版社決定推出電腦化學習系統。

0924
in consideration of (something) 考量到（某事）

• launch 推出　• computer-based 以電腦為主的

TOEIC POINT communication 為不可數名詞，意思為「傳達」、「溝通」，但如果當成可數名詞使用，並以複數形態出現，單字意義就轉換成「通訊」的意思。

After the collapse of oil prices, the country's economy was in crisis.

油價暴跌後，該國的經濟便陷入了危機。

0925
in crisis 陷入危機

• collapse 瓦解；崩潰；暴跌

Look at those black clouds up there. It looks like we're in for some nasty weather.

你看天上那些烏雲。看來我們即將面臨若干惡劣的天候。

0926
(be) in for (something) 即將經歷（某事）

• nasty 惡劣的；下流的；令人不快的

The Bergdorf Award for Clinical Research was created in honor of Dr. Julius F. Bergdorf, the former director of the Metropolitan Hospital.

柏格多夫臨床研究獎的設立是為了紀念大都會醫院的前院長朱利斯．柏格多夫博士。

0927
in honor of (someone) 紀念（某人）；向（某人）致敬

• clinical research 臨床研究 • former 前任的 • metropolitan 大都會的

In lieu of a pay raise, the company offered the staff an extra week's paid leave each year.

公司給了員工每年多一星期的有薪假，以代替加薪。

0928
in lieu of (something) 代替（某事物）
類 instead of (something) 替代（某事物）

The proverb says you can't make an omelette without breaking eggs. In other words, you can't create something new without destroying something old.

俗話說，不打蛋就做不了煎蛋餅。換句話說，不破壞舊東西，就做不了新東西。

0929
in other words 換句話說；換言之

• proverb 諺語 • omelette 煎蛋餅

In round figures, it will probably cost you at least $300,000 to buy a two-bedroom apartment in the downtown area.

以整數來算，要在市中心區買一間兩房的公寓，你大概起碼要花掉 30 萬美元。

0930
in round figures / numbers 以整數來算

- two-bedroom apartment 兩層的公寓
- downtown area 市中心區

※ 注意，本例中的 two-bedroom 為形容詞，room 不可用複數。

Doctors are worried because fresh water is in short supply in the earthquake affected area.

醫生們很擔心，因為地震受災區的淡水供應短缺。

0931
in short supply 供應短缺

- earthquake affected 被地震影響的

Terry played baseball in spite of his doctor's advice to rest, and ended up making his injury worse.

泰瑞不顧醫生要他休息的建議，照樣打棒球，結果到最後使傷勢加劇。

0932
in spite of 不管；儘管

- end up ... 結果……（參照 0581）

In terms of historical interest, Rome is one of the world's greatest cities.

從具歷史趣味性的角度來看，羅馬是世界上最偉大的城市之一。

0933
in terms of ... 從……的角度來看

After long years of recession, many analysts say they feel a new sense of business confidence in the air.

經過多年的衰退後，有很多分析師說，他們察覺到處都散發出一股新的企業信心。

0934
in the air 處處散發出

• recession 衰退；不景氣 • analyst 分析師 • business confidence 企業信心

The CEO told the board members not to worry because the deal to acquire their main rival was in the bag.

執行長請董事們不要擔心，因為收購主要對手的案子已十拿九穩。

0935
in the bag 十拿九穩的

• acquire 獲得；收購

Some business leaders love being in the limelight, while others prefer to work behind the scenes.

有的企業領導人很愛出風頭，有的則寧可在幕後操盤。

0936
in the limelight / spot light 出風頭；為眾人所矚目
反 behind the scenes 在幕後；祕密地

The coffee machine in our office is not in working order. Let's go to Starbucks on the corner.

我們辦公室的咖啡機運作不太正常。我們去街角的星巴克吧！

0937
in working order （機器等）運作正常

• coffee machine 咖啡機 • on the corner 在拐彎處
※ 注意，「在角落裡」為 in the corner。

Fred was really embarrassed when he discovered he had been wearing his sweater inside out the whole day.

佛瑞德真是尷尬，因為他發現自己整天毛衣都是反穿的。

0938
inside out 內裡朝外

• embarrassed 尷尬的；丟臉的
• the whole day 一整天

I go to the gym off and on, but I really need to exercise more regularly if I want to lose weight.

我不時會上健身房，但是假如我要減肥的話，就真的要更規律運動才行。

0939
off and on 不時；斷斷續續地
類 sometimes 有時、occasionally 間或

George is really convinced that his economic forecast for next year is accurate, but I think he's a long way off base.

喬治深信他對於明年經濟的預測很準，但是我認為他錯得離譜。

0940
off base 不對；不正確

• forecast 預測
• accurate 準確的
• a long way 很遠

The finance minister thought he was speaking to reporters off the record, and so he was shocked to see his words quoted in the following day's newspapers.

財政部長以為自己是跟記者私下談話，所以隔天在報紙上看到他的話被引述時，他很震驚。

0941
off the record 私下的；不公開的 反 on the record 公開的；正式的

- finance minister 財政部長；財務大臣
- shocked 震驚的
- quote 引用；引述

The per capita income of the region has increased enormously since oil was discovered there five years ago.

自從那個地區在五年前發現石油之後，當地的每人平均所得就大幅增加。

0942
per capita 每人平均

- income 收入
- region 地區；區域
- enormously 巨大地；非常地

CheckTest

0898 ⇨ 0942

請依照文意將適當的片語填入空格中。可參考第 360 頁的提示來作答。(作答時間：7 分 30 秒)

① ____________ our appreciation, on behalf of everyone in the company I would like to present Greg Hollister with the Employee of the Year Award.

② Are you going to join the Peace Corps ____________?

③ ____________ the company reorganization, the research division moved to a new laboratory in a different part of the country.

④ After the collapse of oil prices, the country's economy was ____________.

⑤ The union of electrical workers is demanding a 5% ____________ pay raise for all its members this year.

⑥ Marilyn was so tired of the fast pace of New York that she decided to leave ____________ and start a new life in a small town.

⑦ I don't believe it! My ____________ jacket already has a tear in it.

⑧ Zelda is ____________________. She borrowed money from a loan shark that charges 30% interest.

⑨ The proverb says you can't make an omelette without breaking eggs. ____________________, you can't create something new without destroying something old.

⑩ The ____________________ income of the region has increased enormously since oil was discovered there five years ago.

⑪ Look at those black clouds up there. It looks like we're ____________________ some nasty weather.

⑫ ____________________ the continuing growth of electronic communications, the publishing company decided to launch a computer-based learning system.

⑬ ____________________ historical interest, Rome is one of the world's greatest cities.

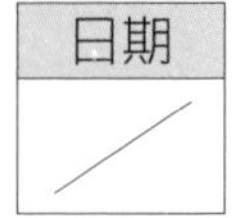

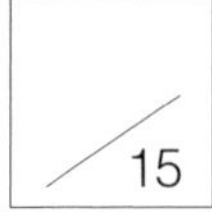

⑭ Doctors are worried because fresh water is ____________ in the earthquake affected area.

⑮ I go to the gym ____________, but I really need to exercise more regularly if I want to lose weight.

參考用字

across-the-board	brand-new	as a token of
in consequence of	for real	in a jam
in consideration of	in crisis	in for
in other words	in short supply	for good
off and on	in terms of	per capita

（解答請參閱第 432 頁）

MP3 35

Vera was down on all fours in the bathroom looking for the contact lens she dropped.

薇拉趴在浴室裡找她掉的隱形眼鏡。

0943
on all fours 趴著；爬著

• contact lens 隱形眼鏡

On behalf of all the members of the department, I'd like to congratulate Harriet on being awarded a Ph. D.

我想代表全系上下恭賀哈里特獲頒博士學位。

0944
on behalf of (someone) 代表（某人）

• department 系；部門 • award 授予 • Ph. D. 博士學位（= Doctor of Philosophy）

Tom was feeling on edge because his boss said he wanted to see him to discuss his performance appraisal.

湯姆覺得很緊張，因為老闆說要見他，以討論他的績效考核。

0945
on edge 緊張的；不安的

• performance appraisal 績效考核

I'm on good terms with everyone in the office except for Robert. For some reason, he doesn't seem to like me.

我跟辦公室裡的每個人都很要好，除了羅勃之外。基於某種理由，他似乎不喜歡我。

0946
on good terms with (someone) 跟（某人）關係良好

• except for ... 除了……之外

I wanted to buy the pirated DVD because it was so cheap, but on second thought, decided that it would be wrong.

我想買那張盜版的 DVD，因為它真是便宜，但進一步考慮後，還是認為那是不對的。

0947

on second thought 進一步考慮後

• pirated 盜版的

It may not look serious on the face of it, but the loss could be fatal to our company.

表面上看起來或許不嚴重，但是這筆虧損可能會害死公司。

0948

on the face 表面上

• fatal 致命的（參照 0176）

Jerry is always boasting of his good political connections, but I'm not sure he's on the level.

傑瑞總是吹噓自己的政治關係很好，但是我不確定他是說真的。

0949

on the level 誠實的；正直的

• boast 吹噓；自誇 • political connections 政治關係

I went into the used book store on the off-chance it might have the out-of-print book I'd been looking for.

我抱著一絲絲希望去二手書店，看會不會有我一直在找的絕版書。

0950

on the off-chance 抱著一絲絲希望

• used book store 二手書店 • out-of-print book 絕版書 • look for 尋找

Old bank notes are regularly taken out of circulation and replaced with newly printed ones.

舊紙鈔都會定期停止流通，並換成新印的紙鈔。

0951
out of circulation 停止流通

• replace 取代　• bank note 紙幣

Even if you don't like the present your uncle gave you, you should send him a thankyou letter out of courtesy.

就算你不喜歡你伯父送的禮物，你也應該基於禮貌寄封感謝函給他。

0952
out of courtesy 基於禮貌

• thankyou letter 感謝函

You should buy a flat screen for your computer. Those thick old screens are so out of date.

你應該買個平面螢幕來搭配你的電腦。這些厚重的舊式螢幕早就過時了。

0953
out of date 退流行的；過時的　類 outdated 舊式的

• flat screen 平面螢幕

Sandy's teacher told her to improve her behavior, and that if she stepped out of line once more, she would be suspended from school.

珊蒂的老師要她改正她的行為，假如她再不守規矩，就得休學。

0954
out of line 脫序

• behavior 行為　• suspend 使停職；使休學；暫停；中止

The elevator will be out of service for maintenance until 10 o'clock.

電梯將停機保養一直到 10 點為止。

0955
out of service 暫停服務

- elevator 升降梯；電梯
- maintenance 保養；維修

Granny used to say, "Good fortune doesn't just drop out of the clear blue sky. You have to earn it by working hard."

阿嬤以前常說：「好運不會憑空從天上掉下來。你必須努力去爭取。」

0956
(drop) **out of the clear blue sky** 從天而降

- granny 祖母；外祖母（口語）

Three members of our skating team were out of the running after the first meet.

我們的溜冰隊有三位隊員在初選後就淘汰出局了。

0957
(be) **out of the running** 淘汰出局（無成功的機會）
反 (be) in the running 在競爭行列中（有成功的機會）

I think Joe is really going out on a limb with his plans to expand his company so rapidly.

喬打算把公司擴展得這麼快，我認為實在很冒險。

0958
out on a limb 處於危險狀態；陷入困境

- expand 擴展 • rapidly 快速地

Now that Frank is married with children, his days of going out on the town every weekend are over.

既然法蘭克已結婚生子，他每個週末狂歡作樂的日子也就宣告結束了。

0959
(go) out on the town 狂歡作樂 類 do the town 狂歡一番

• now that 既然

Let's get our work over and done with, and then we can relax and have coffee.

我們先把工作處理完，然後就可以輕鬆一下，喝杯咖啡。

0960
over and done with 處理完；搞定

Bill found the lecturer's explanation was over his head because he didn't understand many of the technical terms.

比爾覺得講師的解釋超出了他的理解，因為他對很多專業術語都不了解。

0961
over one's head 超出某人的理解

• lecturer 講師
• technical term 專業術語

The contents of this package are fragile, so make sure to carry it right side up.

這個包裹裡的東西很脆弱，所以運送的時候一定要正面朝上。

0962
right side up 正面朝上

• contents 內容物（複數形） • fragile 脆弱的；易碎的

MP3 36

The police kept the house under round-the-clock surveillance in case the suspects returned.

警方全天候監視這間屋子，以防嫌犯回來。

0963
round-the-clock 全天候的；24 小時的

- surveillance 監視（參照 0004 ubiquitous）
- suspect 嫌犯

I was relieved to hear that Rob returned safe and sound from his journalistic assignment in Afghanistan.

聽到羅伯自阿富汗的採訪任務安然無恙地回來，我鬆了一口氣。

0964
safe and sound 安然無恙

- journalistic assignment 採訪任務
- Afghanistan 阿富汗

I am second to none in my admiration for Mr. Nelson Mandela and all that he has done for the people of South Africa.

對於曼德拉先生以及他為南非人民所做的一切，我比誰都要崇拜。

0965
second to none 無人能及；首屈一指

- admiration 崇拜；欽佩
- South Africa 南非

Twenty years ago, it was almost impossible to work in a smoke-free environment, but nowadays, smoking is banned in every workplace.

20 年前要在無菸的環境中工作幾乎不可能，但時至今日，各個工作場所都禁菸了。

0966
smoke-free 無菸的

TOEIC POINT free 接在單字後面時，表示「沒有……的」的意思，例如：salt-free diet（無鹽料理）、barrier-free house（無障礙空間的房屋）。不過當 free 放在單字前面作形容詞時，就變成「免費的」的意思。例如：free gift（贈品）、free of charge（免費）、free ride（可免費搭乘）。

Rebecca used her year-end bonus to buy a state-of-the-art computer system.

蕾貝卡用年終獎金買了一套最先進的電腦系統。

0967
state-of-the-art 最先進的；尖端的

This design software allows you to create a three-dimensional image and view from whichever angle you like.

這套設計軟體能讓你做出立體影像，而且想從哪個角度來看都行。

0968
three-dimensional 三度空間的；立體的

The blaze was so fierce that the firefighters' efforts were to no avail, and the building was completely destroyed.

火勢十分猛烈，使得消防人員的努力完全無用，大樓也因此全毀。

0969
to no avail 毫無作用；徒勞

• blaze 烈火 • fierce 猛烈的；激烈的 • firefighter 消防人員

To Carla's disappointment, she failed to win first prize in the photography competition.

令卡拉失望的是，她沒有贏得攝影比賽的首獎。

0970

to someone's disappointment 令某人失望

• fail to 未能…… • photography competition 攝影比賽

During the depression, it was touch and go whether our company survived, but now it is becoming more stable.

在蕭條時期，我們公司岌岌可危，不知能否維持下去，但現已變得比較穩定了。

0971

touch and go 岌岌可危的 類 precarious 朝不保夕的

• depression 蕭條；憂鬱 • survive 存活 • stable 穩定的

The CEO concealed the losses from the shareholders, and under the circumstances, he has no choice but to offer his resignation.

執行長對股東隱瞞了虧損，在這種情況下，他別無選擇只好提出辭呈。

0972

under the circumstances 在這種情況下

• conceal 隱瞞；隱匿 • losses 虧損 • resignation 辭職；辭呈（衍 resign 辭職）

The official lost his position when it was discovered he had been taking under-the-table payments from construction companies.

該官員丟掉了他的職位，因為他被發現私底下收了建設公司的錢。

0973

under-the-table 台面下的；暗中的

• official 官員 • lose one's position 丟掉職位 • construction company 建設公司

Meg is always up and about long before her husband every morning.

梅格每天早上總是比她先生要早得多就起床活動。

0974
up and about 起床活動

※ 本例中的 long 為副詞，表「久；長」。

After all the mistakes made by FGF Corporation, the price of the stock of the company was up for grabs.

在 FGF 公司屢屢犯錯後，該公司的股價便讓人予取予求了。

0975
up for grabs 讓人予取予求的

Despite hours of discussing a possible merger, no decision has been reached. The fate of the company is still up in the air.

可能的合併案儘管討論了數小時，但是並沒有做成決議。公司的命運還是懸而未決。

0976
up in the air 懸而未決；在未定之天

• merger 合併　• fate 命運

TOEIC POINT despite 與 in spite of（參照 0932）意思相同但是不需要介系詞 of。

Rather than spending a lot of money on works by established artists, I decided to take a risk and buy some works by some up-and-coming new painters.

與其花大錢買老牌畫家的作品，我決定冒險買一些後起新畫家的作品。

0977
up-and-coming 後起的；嶄露頭角的

• rather than ... 與其……　• works 作品（複數形）　• established 老牌的；已確立的

Al asked his boss if he could take the afternoon off as he was not feeling up to par that day.

艾爾問他老闆他下午能不能請假，因為他那天覺得不太對勁。

0978

up to par 達到平常的水準

• take off 請假

※ 如本例所示，up to par 通常用於否定。

I often see Tony and Pedro whispering in a corner. I'm sure they're up to something.

我經常看到湯尼和佩卓在角落竊竊私語。我確信他們正在打什麼鬼主意。

0979

up to something 打鬼主意

When the cars reach the top of the roller coaster, they are actually traveling upside down.

當車廂爬到雲霄飛車的最高點時，實際上是頭朝下在前進。

0980

upside down 頭朝下；顛倒

• car（火車等的）車廂；汽車 • roller coaster 雲霄飛車

If you want to cycle all year round, you will need a good set of waterproof clothing.

假如你想一年到頭都騎單車，那就需要一套好的防水衣。

0981

waterproof 防水的

• cycle 騎單車 • all-year-round 一年到頭

※ proof 常置於名詞字後形成另一單字，表「防……的、隔……的」，例如：heatproof（隔熱的）、shockproof（防震的）、bulletproof（防彈的）等。

This beautiful silk dress will stay beautiful forever because it is water-repellent. All you have to do is just wipe off the dust.

這件美麗的絲質禮服可永保美麗，因為它具驅水性。妳只要把灰塵拍掉就行了。

0982
water-repellent 有驅水性的

• all you have to ... 你只要……
• wipe off 擦掉；去除（參照 0878）

※ repellent 由動詞 repel（斥退）而來，可作形容詞（指「令人反感的」）亦可作名詞（指「驅蟲劑」）用。

She's not with it today. At her age, she has her good days and bad days.

她今天不在狀況內。到了這個年紀，她的狀況時好時壞。

0983
with it 在狀況內；跟上潮流

• at someone's age 到了某人的年紀

Martin took my car without so much as telling me.

馬汀連說都沒說一聲，就把我的車開走了。

0984
without so much as ... 連……都沒有；甚至沒有……

That apartment is very expensive but I think it's worth it. If I buy it now, it will definitely go up in value.

那間公寓非常貴，但是我認為值得。假如我現在把它買下來，肯定會增值。

0985
worth it 值得的 類 worth someone's while 值得某人去做

• definitely 絕對地；確定地
• go up in value 增值

CHAPTER 3 UNIT 25

CheckTest

0943 ⇨ 0985

請依照文意將適當的片語填入空格中。可參考第 374 頁的提示來作答。(作答時間：7 分 30 秒)

① Old bank notes are regularly taken ____________ and replaced with newly printed ones.

② ____________ all the members of the department, I'd like to congratulate Harriet on being awarded a Ph. D.

③ I wanted to buy the pirated DVD because it was so cheap, but ____________, decided that it would be wrong.

④ The elevator will be ____________ for maintenance until 10 o'clock.

⑤ Let's get our work ____________, and then we can relax and have coffee.

⑥ I'm ____________ everyone in the office except for Robert. For some reason, he doesn't seem to like me.

⑦ You should buy a flat screen for your computer. Those thick old screens are so ____________.

⑧ I was relieved to hear that Rob returned ________________ from his journalistic assignment in Afghanistan.

⑨ Three members of our skating team were ________________ after the first meet.

⑩ Rebecca used her year-end bonus to buy a ________________ computer system.

⑪ The CEO concealed the losses from the shareholders, and ________________, he has no choice but to offer his resignation.

⑫ I often see Tony and Pedro whispering in a corner. I'm sure they're ________________ something.

⑬ The contents of this package are fragile, so make sure to carry it ________________.

⑭ This beautiful silk dress will stay beautiful forever because it is ________________. All you have to do is just wipe off the dust.

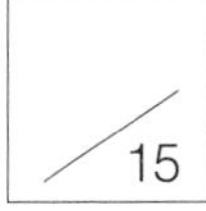

⑮ Despite hours of discussing a possible merger, no decision has been reached. The fate of the company is still ____________________.

參考用字

on good terms with	on second thought	out of circulation
out of the running	out of date	on behalf of
out of service	over and done with	right side up
state-of-the-art	under the circumstances	
water-repellent	up in the air	
safe and sound	up to	

（解答請參閱第 433 頁）

Chapter 4

Customary Espressions

0986 ➲ 1047

慣用表現

Unit 26

MP3 37

Oh, no! I just accidentally deleted this entire document! Back to square one.

噢，糟了！我剛才不小心刪除了整份文件。得從頭來過了。

0986
back to square one 回到原點；從頭來過

- accidentally 意外地
- entire 整個的
- document 文件

Poor Toby has been at wit's end since the editor moved up the deadline. Now he has to stay up all night to get his story in on time.

可憐的托比不知如何是好，因為編輯把截稿時間提前了。現在為了準時交稿，他必須整晚熬夜。

0987
be at (one's) wit's end 不知如何是好；無計可施

- editor 編輯
- move up the deadline 把最後期限往前移
- stay up all night 整晚熬夜
- get something in 交出某物

Your coffee makers are the best on the market. Be that as it may, they are way out of my price range.

你們的咖啡機是市面上最好的。儘管如此，它卻遠遠超出了我的預算。

0988
be that as it may 儘管如此；即便如此

- way out of ... 遠遠超出……
- someone's price range 某人的預算

Daphne is expecting a baby in January. And I was wondering if you might be interested in chipping in for a baby shower.

黛芬妮一月時會生寶寶。我在想你有沒有興趣一起出錢辦個迎接寶寶派對。

0989
be wondering if ... 在想是否……

- be expecting 懷孕
- baby shower 迎接寶寶派對

※ bridal shower 指「歡送新娘派對」。

A: What time is the train supposed to arrive?
B: Beats me. The announcements just keep saying it's delayed.

A: 列車什麼時候會到站？
B: 考倒我了。廣播只是一直說它誤點了。

0990
Beats me. 考倒我了。 類 I don't know. 我不曉得。

The small grocery stores on Tenth Street can't cut it because they are losing business to that new supermarket.

第十街上的小雜貨店都成不了事，因為它們的生意都被那家新超市給搶走了。

0991
can't cut it 不能成功

- grocery store 雜貨店

I can't help betting on horses even though I've been losing lots of money.

就算已經輸了一大堆錢，我還是忍不住要賭馬。

0992
can't help doing … 忍不住做……
類 can't stop doing 停不住做……

• bet on horses 賭馬

I can't stand this coffee. It tastes like mud!

我受不了這個咖啡。它喝起來像泥巴！

0993
can't stand (someone / something) 受不了（某人 / 某事）

Come October, the mountains burn red with all the leaves turning colors.

十月一到，所有的葉子都變了色，山也跟著一片火紅。

0994
come (month)（某月）一到

• burn red（如燃燒般）一片火紅

You're going to fly to Frankfurt and then fly right back to Tokyo the next day? Come off it! That's crazy!

你要飛去法蘭克福，然後隔天立刻飛回東京？別鬧了！那太瘋狂了！

0995
come off it 別鬧了；少扯了

• Frankfurt 法蘭克福
• fly right back 立刻飛回

Come rain or shine, I expect to see all of you on the soccer field tomorrow at 9:00 a.m. sharp!

不論晴雨，明天早上九點整，我都要在足球場上看到各位！

0996
come rain or shine 不管雨天或晴天

expect 這個字通常帶有命令的口吻，例如：I expect your attendance.（請你務必出席）。

Trade shows are the best places to find out about your competitors. Come to think of it, there's going to be one next month in Seattle. Can you go?

貿易展是打探競爭對手的最佳場合。我想起來了，下個月在西雅圖就有一場。你能去嗎？

0997
come to think of it 這樣一想；我想起來了

Come what may, we have to reduce our workforce by 15%. We have no choice.

無論如何，我們都必須削減 15% 的人力。我們別無選擇。

0998
come what may 不管發生什麼事；無論如何

• workforce 勞動力；勞動人口

We opened three new stores in Chicago this year, and they're all doing great. Everything's coming up roses.

我們今年在芝加哥開了三家新店，生意全都很好。一切順利。

0999
come up roses 順利；成功

It costs an arm and a leg to play golf in Japan. Let's go to Hawaii instead.

在日本打高爾夫球所費不貲。我們改去夏威夷吧！

1000
cost an arm and a leg 所費不貲；代價高昂

Jill, I don't care if you hate carrots. You have to eat them or you'll have no supper.

吉兒，我不管妳討不討厭吃紅蘿蔔。妳非吃不可，否則妳就沒晚餐可吃。

1001
don't care if ... 不管是否……

We are giving away 20%-off coupons today on a first-come first-served basis.

我們今天會送八折券，先到先拿。

1002
first-come first-served 先來先招待

Look at how that guy cut in line up ahead! I'm going to give him a piece of my mind.

你看前面那個人竟然插隊！我要去把他臭罵一頓。

1003
give a piece of one's mind 怒斥某人 類 tell someone off 叱責某人

Lenny left his dog out in the cold with no food or water for three days. Yesterday, the dog bit him. I think he had it coming.

藍尼把狗留在外面受凍，三天不給食物或水。昨天狗咬了他，我想他是罪有應得。

1004
have it coming 罪有應得；自作自受

This ad says I'll get my money back if I'm not satisfied, so I'm going to send in my check. I have nothing to lose, right?

這則廣告上說不滿意包退錢，所以我要寄支票過去。我不會有任何損失，對吧？

1005
have nothing to lose 不會有任何損失

- get one's money back 退錢

Josh's father hit the ceiling when he found out that it was his own son that stole the money.

喬許的爸爸在發現是他自己的兒子偷了錢之後大發雷霆。

1006
hit the ceiling 大發雷霆；勃然大怒

A: Do you think we can get on an earlier flight?
B: I doubt it, but it can't hurt to try.

A: 你認為我們搭得到比較早的班機嗎？
B: 我懷疑，但是試試看也無妨。

1007
it can't hurt to try 試試看也無妨

It goes without saying, but if you want to keep your job, you'll have to start coming to work on time.

不用說，假如你想保住工作，就必須開始準時來上班。

1008
it goes without saying 不用說

- keep one's job 保住工作

It looks as if the two sides are going to war. We should evacuate before it's too late.

看起來兩邊似乎要開戰了。我們應該要撤離，以免來不及。

1009
it looks as if ... 看起來似乎……

I'll show you how to program your new phone. It's a cinch.

我來教你新電話要怎麼設定。小事一樁。

1010
It's a cinch. 小事一樁。

• program 為……設計、編寫程式；設定

A: Here comes Carolyn running up the stairs.
B: It's about time she showed up. We've been waiting about half an hour.

A: 凱洛琳跑上樓來了。
B: 她也差不多該出現了。我們已經等了快半個小時了。

1011
it's about time ... 差不多該……

TOEIC POINT 接在 It's (about) time 後面子句中的動詞要使用假設語氣，如本句中的 showed。

A: I hate to ask, but could you pick up the printer at the repair shop for me?
B: Sure. It's no big deal.

A: 我很不願意拜託人，但是你能不能幫我去維修店拿一下印表機？
B: 好啊。這沒什麼大不了的。

1012
It's no big deal. 這沒什麼大不了的。

If a customer cancels an order, it's not the end of the world. There will be hundreds more orders.

假如某個顧客取消訂單，這並不是世界末日。還會有好幾百張訂單的。

1013
it's not the end of the world 這不是世界末日

• cancel an order 取消訂單

No, no. Put away your wallet. Today's your birthday, so it's on me.

不行，不行。把你的錢包收起來。今天是你生日，所以我請客。

1014
It's on me. 我請客。 類 It's my treat. 我做東。

TOEIC POINT 「均攤、各付各的」有下列幾種說法：Let's split the bill. / Let's go fifty-fifty. / Let's get separate checks. 注意，Let's go Dutch. 也可指「各付各的」，但是有歧視的意味，最好不要使用。由於英國與荷蘭之間曾經發生戰爭，而荷蘭人被認為很小氣，因此才出現了 Let's go Dutch 的說法。

They haven't decided on a site for the trade show yet. It's still up in the air.

他們還沒有決定貿易展的地點。還是個未知數。

1015
It's still up in the air. 還是個未知數。

• site 地點
• trade show 貿易展

MP3 38

It might not hurt to bring flowers or something when you go to the Condon's Thanksgiving dinner.

去康登家吃感恩節晚餐時，不妨帶束花什麼的。

1016
might not hurt 不妨

A: Oh, look! You got another love-mail from George!
B: Hey, mind your own business!

A: 噢，你看！喬治又寄了一封情書給你！
B: 嘿，少管閒事！

1017
mind your own business 少管閒事
類 none of your business 不關你的事

Our grandma has a bad leg, but she doesn't let it stop her from going places.

奶奶有隻腳不方便，但是她並沒有因此就不出門走動。

1018
not let it stop (someone) **from doing ...**
（某人）沒有因此就不……

I'm not the cleanest person in the world, but I just can't stand the sight of your room. It looks like a pigsty.

我並不是世界上最愛乾淨的人，但是看到你的房間實在讓我不能忍受。它看起來像個豬舍。

1019
not the (-est) **person in the world** 不是世界上（最……）的人

- stand 忍受
- pigsty 豬欄；豬舍

Did you hear that the company headquarters is moving to Mexico? Nobody expected this. It came out of the blue.

你有沒有聽說公司總部要搬到墨西哥去？沒人料想得到。真是出乎意料。

1020
out of the blue 出乎意料地

• company headquarters 公司總部 • Mexico 墨西哥

What a pain in the neck this new building code is. We can't even put in a new water faucet without a permit.

新的建築法規真是討厭。沒有得到允許，我們連水龍頭都不能裝。

1021
pain in the neck 惹人厭、麻煩的人事物

• building code 建築法規 • water faucet 水龍頭

The CEO doesn't see eye to eye with some of the board members on expanding our overseas markets.

在擴展海外市場上，執行長跟部分的董事看法不一致。

1022
see eye to eye 看法一致
反 not on the same wavelength 意見不合；觀點不一

A: I wonder what time Sanders is going to get here.
B: I don't know .... Well, speak of the devil. Here he comes.

A: 我很好奇不知道桑德斯什麼時候會到。
B: 我不曉得……嗯，說曹操，曹操就到。他來了。

1023
speak of the devil 說曹操，曹操就到

A: You all go on to dinner without me. I'm staying behind to finish up some work.
B: OK. Suit yourself.

A: 你們都去吃飯吧，別等我了。我要留下來把一些工作給做完。
B: 好。隨你便。

1024
suit yourself 隨你便 類 Have it your own way. 隨你高興。

• finish up 完成

A: Look at that man. He looks just like Elvis Presley.
B: You took the words right out of my mouth. I was thinking the exact same thing.

A: 你看那個男的。他長得就像貓王。
B: 你替我說了。我想的跟你一模一樣。

1025
take the words right out of someone's mouth
說了某人想說的話
類 That's exactly what I was going to say. 那就是我想說的。

A bribery scandal involving three city council members has been the talk of the town for the past three weeks.

過去三週以來，三個市議員所涉及的賄賂醜聞是人們議論紛紛的話題。

1026
talk of the town 熱門的話題

• bribery 賄賂（參照 0007 spokesperson 的例句）
• scandal 醜聞
• involving 涉及；牽連
• city council 市議會

A: I just don't like the layout for this ad.
B: That makes two of us.

A: 我就是不喜歡這則廣告的編排。
B: 我有同感。

1027
That makes two of us. 我有同感。

- layout 版面的設計、編排

A: Hey, you! Get your blasted truck out of my parking space!
B: Watch your mouth! Don't be so rude.

A: 喂！把你那台該死的貨車移出我的停車位！
B: 嘴巴放乾淨點！不要那麼粗俗。

1028
watch your mouth 嘴巴放乾淨點

- blasted 該死的
- rude 粗魯的；粗俗的

We go way back. We've been friends since elementary school.

我們是老交情了。我們念小學的時候就是朋友了。

1029
We go way back. 我們是老交情了。

way back 的 way 為副詞，是「非常」的意思，用來強調 back。其他如 way down 指「非常下面」、way up 指「非常上面」、way off 則指「非常離譜」。

A: I had to throw away a whole ream of paper because I spilled coffee on it.
B: What a drag.

A: 我必須把整堆的紙都丟掉，因為我把咖啡潑在上面了。
B: 真是沒趣。

1030
What a drag. 真是沒趣。

• ream 令（= 480 張）；大量的紙
※ drag 指「令人厭煩的人事物」。

A: Are you sure you want to put your house on the market so soon?
B: Yes, of course. What are you getting at?
A: Well, if you wait about a month, I think you'll get a better price.

A: 你確定要這麼快就把房子賣掉嗎？
B: 當然囉。你想說的是什麼？
A: 嗯，假如你等上一個月左右，我想你會賣到比較好的價錢。

1031
What are you getting at? 你想說的是什麼？
類 What is your point? 你的重點是什麼？

• put something on the market 將某物（放到市場上）公開出售

You want me to deposit 2,000 dollars into your bank account for nothing? What do you take me for — some kind of fool?

你要我平白無故地存 2,000 美元到你的銀行帳戶裡？你把我當什麼了——像笨蛋一類的嗎？

1032
What do you take me for? 你把我當什麼了？
類 Who do you think I am? 你以為我是誰呀？（參照 1040）

• deposit 存入
• bank account 銀行帳戶

He laughed at me for failing my driver's test. Then he failed it the next day, too! What goes around comes around.

他笑我駕照沒考過。後來他隔天也沒考過！報應啊。

1033
What goes around comes around. 因果循環，報應不爽。

What in the world is happening in our sales department? We got 12 complaints from our clients in the past 3 days.

業務部究竟是怎麼回事？過去三天內，我們接到了 12 則客戶的投訴。

1034
What in the world ...? 究竟……？ 類 What on earth ... 到底……

※ in the world / on earth 都用來強調說話的語氣。

What's done is done! But don't you dare make the same mistake again leaving frozen food outside the storage overnight!

過去就算了！但是你可別老毛病又犯了，把冷凍食品擺在貯藏室外面一整夜！

1035
What's done is done. 做了就做了，過去就算了。

• don't you dare ... 你敢…… • frozen food 冷凍食品
• storage 貯藏（室） • overnight 過夜

※ don't you dare ... 用於「告誡某人勿做某事以免惹你生氣」時。

Jessica said you wanted to talk to me about something important. What's on your mind?

潔西卡說你有重要的事要跟我談。你想說什麼？

1036
What's on your mind? 你心裡在想什麼？

※ 本例的 what's on your mind? 就是「你想要說什麼？」之意。

What's the point of taking a taxi? Union Plaza is just around the corner.

幹嘛要搭計程車？聯合廣場轉個彎就到了。

1037
What's the point of doing ...? 做……的意義何在？

• around the corner 街道轉角處；在近處

What's with Joey? I said "Good morning" to him, and he just looked away.

喬依怎麼了？我跟他說「早」，他卻轉頭看別處。

1038
What's with (someone)**?**（某人）怎麼了？

When it comes right down to it, I can't afford to buy a new house in my present financial condition.

平心而論，以我目前的財務狀況，我買不起新房子。

1039
when it comes right down to it 平心而論

• afford 買得起；負擔得起
• someone's present financial condition 某人目前的財務狀況

Who do you think I am! I'm a partner in this firm. Get your secretary to make the coffee.

你以為我是誰呀！我是這家公司的合夥人。叫你的祕書去泡咖啡。

1040
Who do you think I am! 你以為我是誰呀！

• partner 合夥人
• firm 公司；行號

Hey! You can't just walk into my office telling me to do this and that! Who do you think you are — the Queen of England?

嘿，你不能就這麼走進我的辦公室，要我做這做那的！你以為你是誰呀——英國女王嗎？

1041
Who do you think you are? 你以為你是誰呀？

• the Queen of England 英國女王

Maybe five hundred people will show up at the news release of our new product. Maybe nobody will. Who knows?

也許會有 500 人出席我們新產品的新聞發表會。也許一個都沒有。誰曉得？

1042
Who knows? 誰曉得？ 類 Nobody knows. 沒人曉得。

• news release 新聞發表會

A: Ben was arrested for taking pictures of the legs of women with his cell phone.
B: That's terrible! Why in the world did he do such a thing?

A: 班因為用手機偷拍女性的腿部而遭到了逮捕。
B: 真是糟糕！他究竟為什麼要做這種事？

1043
Why in the world ...? 究竟為什麼……？
類 Why on earth ... ? 到底為什麼……？

• arrest 逮捕
• take picture 拍照

(Police officer to driver) Excuse me, Ma'am. You didn't yield the right-of-way at the intersection back there. You nearly caused a three-car accident.

（警官對駕駛人）對不起，女士。妳在前面那邊的路口沒有讓路。差一點造成三輛車的連環車禍。

1044
yield the right-of-way 讓路

• intersection 十字路口　• three-car accident 三輛車的連環車禍
※ right-of-way 指「行路權」。

A: This must be one of the worst movies ever made!
B: You can say that again!

A: 這一定是歷來所拍過最爛的電影之一。
B: 說得好！

1045
You can say that again. 說得好。

※ 因為說得很對，所以可以 say that again（再說一次）。

A: Do you promise not to tell anyone what I've just told you?
B: You have my word.

A: 對於我剛才跟你說的事，你保證不告訴任何人？
B: 我可以跟你保證。

1046
You have my word. 我可以跟你保證。
類 I give you my word. 我向你保證。

A: You did an excellent job on the Tillman contract.
B: Thank you, boss. You've made my day.

A: 你在提爾曼的合約上表現得很傑出。
B: 謝謝老闆。你讓我很開心。

1047
You've made my day. 你讓我很開心。

CHAPTER 4 UNIT 26

CheckTest

0986 ⇨ 1047

請依照文意將適當的慣用語句填入空格中。可參考第 396 頁的提示來作答。(作答時間：10 分鐘)

① Daphne is expecting a baby in January. And I ______________ you might be interested in chipping in for a baby shower.

② I ______________ this coffee. It tastes like mud!

③ Trade shows are the best places to find out about your competitors. ______________, there's going to be one next month in Seattle. Can you go?

④ Jill, I ______________ you hate carrots. You have to eat them or you'll have no supper.

⑤ Poor Toby has ______________ since the editor moved up the deadline. Now he has to stay up all night to get his story in on time.

⑥ A: What time is this train supposed to arrive?

B: ______________. The announcements just keep saying it's delayed.

⑦ You're going to fly to Frankfurt and then fly right back to Tokyo the next day? ____________________ That's crazy!

⑧ We are giving away 20% off coupons today on a __________ __________ basis.

⑨ I ____________________ on horses even though I've been losing lots of money.

⑩ It ____________________ to play golf in Japan. Let's go to Hawaii instead.

⑪ A: Here comes Carolyn running up the stairs.
B: ____________________ she showed up. We've been waiting about half an hour.

⑫ ____________________ this country is going to war. We should evacuate before it's too late.

⑬ What a ______________ this new building code is. We can't even put in a new water faucet without a permit.

⑭ Lenny left his dog out in the cold with no food or water for three days. Yesterday, the dog bit him. I think he ______________.

⑮ Did you hear that the company headquarters is moving to Mexico? Nobody expected this. It came ______________.

⑯ No, no. Put away that wallet. Today's your birthday, so ______________.

⑰ You want me to deposit 2,000 dollars into your bank account for nothing? ______________ — some kind of fool?

⑱ It ______________ to bring flowers or something when you go to the Condon's Thanksgiving dinner.

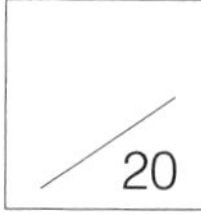

⑲ ________________ Joey? I said "Good morning" to him, and he just looked away.

⑳ The CEO doesn't ________________ with some of the board members on expanding our overseas markets.

参考用字

can't help doing	be wondering if	be at wit's end
first-come first-served	Beats me.	can't stand
come to think of it	don't care if	come off it
cost an arm and a leg	had it coming	It's on me.
it's about time	it looks as if	might not hurt
pain in the neck	out of the blue	see eye to eye
What's with	What do you take me for?	

（解答請參閱第 433 頁）

Chapter 5

Business and Current Topics

1048 ➲ 1507

商務與時事英語

Unit 27

Business

Companies 公司的類型

1048 conglomerate 企業集團
類 Gulliverian company

1049 small and medium-sized enterprises 中小企業
類 small and midsize companies

1050 listed company 上市掛牌公司

1051 delist 下市停牌

1052 multinational company 跨國公司

1053 affiliated company 附屬公司；子公司

1054 dummy company 空殼公司；紙上公司
類 shell company / paper company

1055 joint venture 合資企業

1056 buyout 買斷

1057 M&A (merger and acquisition) 購併

Positions and Ranks 職位與頭銜

1058 CEO (chief executive officer) 執行長
※ 在英國說成 managing director

1059 CFO (chief financial officer) 財務長

1060 CIO (chief information officer) 資訊長

1061 COO (chief operating officer) 營運長

1062 CTO (chief technical officer) 技術長

1063 president 總裁

1064 executive vice president 執行副總裁

1065 treasurer 出納

1066 secretary 祕書

1067 director 董事；主任

1068 outside director 外部董事
※ non-executive director（英國）非常務董事

1069 division manager 部門經理

1070 foreman 領班；工頭

1071 manager 課長 (section~)、店長 (store~)、總經理 (general~)

1072 assistant manager 副理

1073 supervisor 上司；主管

Company Management 公司管理

1074 burden sharing 責任分擔

1075 carrot-and-stick politics 恩威並施

1076 carte blanche 全權委任

1077 Corporate Rehabilitation Law 企業更生法

1078 countdown 倒數計時

1079 crisis management 危機管理

1080 disclosure obligation 揭露義務

1081 foul play 違法行為

1082 lame duck 跛鴨

1083 prime mover 原動力；首謀

1084 win-win 雙贏

1085 working lunch / power lunch 工作午餐 / 巨頭午餐

International Trade 國際貿易

1086 Foreign Investment Law
外商投資法

1087 export letter of credit 出口信用狀

1088 import curb 進口限制

1089 import quota 進口配額

1090 soft currency 軟性貨幣

1091 soft currency country 軟性貨幣國

1092 hard currency 強勢貨幣

1093 tariff barrier 關稅壁壘

1094 trade imbalance 貿易失衡
※ unbalance 的意思不是「不平衡」，在使用上要特別注意。

1095 trade friction 貿易摩擦

1096 trade surplus 貿易順差
※「逆差」可用 deficit 表示

Production and Marketing 生產與行銷

1097 backup stock 備用存貨

1098 brochure 文宣冊
類 pamphlet

1099 bootleg edition 非法製造、販售版
類 pirate edition 盜版；knockoff 山寨版

1100 brain trust 智囊團

1101 capital outlay 資本支出

1102 come-on gift to subscribers
訂閱即贈禮

1103 excessive inventories 過剩庫存

1104 exhibition booth 展示攤位

1105 feasibility study 可行性研究
類 preliminary study 初步研究

1106 market potential 市場潛力

1107 peak output 最大產量

1108 pilot shop 試驗店

1109 pilot factory 試驗工廠

1110 pilot farm 試驗農場

1111 technical innovation 技術創新
類 technological breakthrough

1112 wild goose chase 徒勞之舉

1113 work capacity 運作產能

1114 work count 運作次數

Economy and Finance 經濟與財務

1115 business recovery 產業復甦

1116 economic muscle 經濟實力

1117 economic recovery package
經濟復甦配套措施

1118 economic waters 經濟水域

1119 economic growth 經濟成長

1120 recession 衰退

1121 stagnation 停滯

1122 CPA (Certified Public Accountant) 合格會計師

1123 casualty insurance 意外險
類 nonlife insurance

1124 proxy 委託書

1125 cost accounting 成本會計

1126 costing 成本計算

1127 expense account spending
報帳費用

1128 fiscal year 會計年度

1129 fiscal budget 財政預算

1130 payoff 收益；發餉

1131 petty cash 零用金

1132 prime rate 優惠利率

1133 subprime loan 次級貸款

※ 呆帳的英文說成 bad loan

Employment and Working Conditions 雇用與勞動條件

1134 callback 召回

1135 child-care leave 育嬰假

1136 customized master's program 碩士專班

1137 job interview 工作面試

1138 full-time employment 全職雇用

1139 part-time employment 兼職雇用

1140 maternity leave 產假

1141 permanent employment 終身雇用

1142 temporary employment 臨時雇用

1143 leave of absence 請假

1144 minimum wage 最低工資

1145 net pay (take-home pay) 實付薪資

1146 sabbatical leave 休假研究；支薪長假

1147 severance pay 遣散費

1148 sick leave 病假

1149 SSN (social security number) 社會保險碼

1150 pension 退休金

1151 work hygiene 勞動衛生

Stock Market 股市

1152 all-time high 歷史高點

1153 bear market 熊市（空頭市場）

1154 bull market 牛市（多頭市場）

1155 Black Monday 黑色星期一

※ 指 1987 年 10 月 19 日紐約股市大崩盤

1156 black money 黑錢；非法收益

1157 blue chip 藍籌股；績優股

1158 callable bond 可贖回債券

1159 clearing house 票據交換所

1160 commodity market 商品市場

1161 futures 期貨（複數形）

1162 convertible bond (CB) 可轉換債券

1163 Dow Jones Industrial Average 道瓊工業平均指數

※ Standard and Poor's Corporation Composite Index 指「標準普爾 500 綜合指數」

1164 insider trading 內線交易

1165 LBO (leveraged buyout) 融資購併

1166 money laundering 洗錢

1167 NASDAQ (National Association of Securities Dealers Automated Quotation) 那斯達克

1168 NYSE (New York Stock Exchange) 紐約證交所

類 Wall Street 華爾街

1169 securities exchange (market) 證交所

類 bourse

1170 speculative buying 投機買入

1171 turnover 成交量

1172 warrant bond 附認股權債券

Taxes 稅務

1173 withholding income tax
扣繳所得稅

1174 tax evasion 逃稅；漏稅

1175 tax haven 避稅天堂

1176 tax write-off 稅額沖銷

Kinds of Taxes 稅賦種類

1177 consumption tax 消費稅

1178 federal tax 聯邦稅

1179 state tax （美國的）州稅

1180 gift tax 贈予稅

1181 individual income tax 個人所得稅

1182 inheritance tax 遺產稅
※ 俗稱 death tax

1183 corporate income tax
企業（法人）所得稅

1184 local tax 地方稅

1185 occupancy tax （旅館）營業稅

1186 real estate tax 不動產稅

Daily life

Food and Nutrition 食物與營養

1187 balanced meal 均衡飲食

1188 burnable / unburnable trash
可燃 / 不可燃垃圾
類 combustible / noncombustible trash

1189 recyclable trash 可回收垃圾

1190 chemical additive 化學添加物

1191 eat out / dine out 外食

1192 eater's coma 吃飽後昏昏欲睡

1193 organic food 有機食品

1194 perishable food 易腐敗食品

1195 protein 蛋白質
※ carbohydrate 碳水化合物、fat 脂肪

1196 supplement 補品

Shopping and Merchandise 購物與商品

1197 comparison-shopping 比較式購物

1198 cost performance
成本績效（CP 值）

1199 customer service 客服

1200 cut and sew 裁切縫製

1201 DIY (do-it-yourself) store
自行組裝品商店

1202 mail order 郵購

1203 mall 賣場
類 shopping complex

1204 online shopping 線上購物；網購

1205 online auction 線上拍賣；網拍

1206 mom-and-pop store 小店

1207 polyester 聚酯
類 synthetic fiber 合成纖維

Housing and Real Estate 住宅與不動產

1208 condominium
各戶有獨立產權的公寓大廈

1209 cooperative apartment 合作公寓

1210 lease 租約

1211 mansion 大廈；大樓

1212 sub-let 轉分租

※ 在租約仍有效時，將房子轉租給他人的行為。

1213 prefabricated house 組合屋

1214 real estate agency / agent 不動產業者

1215 right-to-sunlight ordinance 日照權條例

Banking 銀行業務

1216 ATM (Automated Teller Machine) 自動櫃員機

1217 balance 餘額

1218 balance sheet 資產負債表

1219 cash dispenser 自動提款機

1220 commercial paper (CP) 商業票據

1221 certificate of deposit (CD) 定存單

※ fixed deposit 為「定期存款」

1222 personal checking account 個人支票帳戶

1223 savings account 儲蓄存款帳戶

1224 remittance 匯款

1225 interest 利息

1226 withdraw 提款

Transportation 運輸

1227 casualty toll 傷亡人數

1228 clover leaf interchange 立體交流道

1229 lost and found 失物招領處

1230 not-in-service 不營運

1231 tryout run 試營運

1232 detour 繞道

1233 odometer 里程表

1234 tachometer 轉速計

Trains 電車

1235 local 慢車

1236 express train 快車

1237 limited express 特快車

1238 bullet train / super express 子彈列車／超級快車

Health and Medicine 健康與醫療

● Illness and Symptoms 病症

1239 hay fever 花粉症

※ allergy 指「過敏症」

1240 contagious disease 傳染病

1241 infection 感染

1242 angina 心絞痛

1243 fatal disease 絕症

※ terminal cancer 指「癌症末期」

1244 malignant tumor 惡性腫瘤

1245 non-malignant tumor 良性腫瘤

1246 metabolic syndrome 代謝症候群

1247 narcotic addict 吸毒成癮（者）

1248 stroke 中風

1249 flu / influenza 流感

1250 diabetes 糖尿病

1251 anemia 貧血

1252 pneumonia 肺炎

1253 cardiac arrest 心臟病發作

類 heart attack

● Diagnosis and Treatment 診斷與治療

1254 audiometer 測聽器

1255 bone marrow transplant 骨髓移植

1256 bone marrow bank 骨髓銀行

1257 electrocardiograph 心電圖儀

※「心電圖」為 electrocardiogram

1258 chemotherapy 化學療法

1259 daily dose / dosage 每日劑量

1260 over-the-counter drug 成藥

1261 rehabilitation 復健

1262 ultraviolet radiation therapy 紫外線放射治療

1263 vaccination 疫苗接種

1264 vaccine 疫苗

● Medical Ethics 醫療倫理

1265 DNA testing DNA 鑑定

※ DNA 為 deoxyribonucleic acid「去氧核糖核酸」的縮寫，內含操縱遺傳基因的染色體（chromosome）。

1266 external fertilization 體外受精

1267 genetic recombination 基因重組

1268 pro-life 反墮胎的

1269 sex chromosome test 性染色體檢驗

Specialized Fields of Medicine 醫療分科

1270 cosmetic / plastic surgery 美容整形手術

1271 general practitioner 全科醫生

1272 gynecologist 婦科醫生

1273 obstetrician 產科醫生

1274 ophthalmologist 眼科醫生

1275 oncologist 腫瘤科醫生

1276 pediatrician 小兒科醫生

1277 psychiatrist 精神科醫生

1278 surgery 外科醫生

1279 urologist 泌尿科醫生

Occupations 職業

1280 accountant 會計師

1281 bookkeeper 簿記員

1282 financial advisor 理財專員

1283 teller 出納員

1284 paramedic 醫護人員

1285 pharmacist 藥劑師

1286 counselor 顧問

1287 hospital worker 醫院從業人員

1288 computer engineer / programmer 電腦工程師 / 程式設計師

1289 systems designer 系統設計師

1290 graphic designer 平面設計師

1291 contractor 包商

1292 architect 建築師

1293 construction engineer 建築技師

1294 heavy machinery operator 重機械操作員

1295 nonprofit organization (NPO) 非營利組織

1296 sales staff 銷售人員

Nature and science

animals and pets 動物與寵物

1297 canine 犬科動物

1298 CITES (Convention on International Trade in Endangered Species of Wild Fauna and Flora) 瀕臨絕種野生動植物國際貿易公約

1299 endangered species 瀕危物種

1300 extinction 滅絕

1301 feline 貓科動物

1302 pedigree 純種

※ hybrid 雜交種

1303 poultry 家禽

1304 rabies 狂犬病

1305 spaying 切除卵巢

1306 neutering 去勢；閹割

1307 vanished species 消失物種

1308 veterinarian 獸醫（可略為 vet）

Ecology and Environment 生態與環境

1309 animal and bird sanctuary 鳥獸保護區

1310 Clean Air Act （美國）空氣清淨法

1311 compound pollution 複合污染

1312 contamination 污染；毒害

1313 ecologist 生態學者

1314 environmentalist 環保人士

1315 environmental assessment 環評

1316 secondhand smoke 二手菸

1317 fallout 輻射塵

1318 fossil fuel 化石燃料

1319 ozone layer 臭氧層

1320 endocrine disruptor 內分泌干擾物

類 environmental hormone 環境荷爾蒙

1321 hydropower station 水力發電站

1322 wave-power generation 潮汐發電

1323 LOHAS (Lifestyles of Health And Sustainability) 樂活（以健康及自給自足的型態過生活

1324 pollutant 污染物

1325 pollution 污染

Energy 能源

1326 global warming 地球暖化

1327 greenhouse effect 溫室效應

1328 solar energy 太陽能

1329 hard energy 硬能源

1330 hydrogen energy 氫能

1331 nuclear fuel 核燃料

1332 nuclear waste 核廢料

1333 oil well 油井

1334 oil sand 油砂

1335 oil slick 水面浮油

1336 power plant 發電廠

1337 windmill farm 風力發電場

Weather and Natural Phenomena 天候與自然現象

1338 atmospheric pressure 大氣壓力

1339 aurora borealis (northern light) 北極光

1340 aurora australis (southernlight) 南極光

1341 climatic fluctuation 氣候變動

1342 cold front 冷鋒

反 warm front 暖鋒

1343 discomfort index （天氣的）不舒適指數

1344 drizzle 毛毛雨

1345 shower 陣雨

1346 El Ninõ effect 聖嬰現象

1347 foehn phenomenon 焚風現象

1348 high / low pressure 高／低氣壓

1349 precipitation 降水（雨、雪等）

1350 rain front 雨鋒

1351 UV index (Ultra Violet index) 紫外線指數

1352 warm air mass 暖氣團

1353 cold air mass 冷氣團

● **Winds 風的種類**

1354 breeze 微風

1355 gusty wind 陣風

1356 head wind 逆風

1357 tail wind 順風

● **Storms 暴風雨**

1358 hurricane 颶風

1359 tornado 龍捲風

1360 typhoon 颱風

1361 cyclone 旋風

1362 blizzard 暴風雪

Natural Disasters 天然災害

1363 avalanche 雪崩

1364 evacuation order 疏散令

1365 landslide 山崩

1366 lava flow 熔岩流

1367 mudslide 土石流

Telephone and Communication System 電話與通訊系統

1368 area code 區域碼

1369 call waiting 電話插撥

1370 collect call 對方付費電話

1371 person-to-person call 指名通話

1372 radar 雷達

1373 tele-conference 電話會議

1374 videophone 視訊電話

1375 prank call 惡作劇電話

1376 reconnaissance satellite 偵察衛星

1377 virtual reality 虛擬實境

1378 voice mail 語音郵件

1379 ZIP code 郵遞區號

（Zone Improvement Program 的縮寫）

Computer and Cell Phone 電腦與行動電話

1380 attached file 附加檔案

1381 default 預設值

1382 fiber optics 光纖通訊

1383 narrowband 窄頻

1384 broadband 寬頻

1385 shut down 關機

1386 reboot 重新開機

1387 reinstall 重新安裝

1388 customize 自訂

Education / Sports / Culture

Education 教育

1389 literacy rate 識字率

1390 illiteracy rate 文盲率

1391 compulsory education 義務教育

1392 vocational school 職業學校

1393 adult education 成人教育

1394 nursery school 托兒所
※ nursing school 為「護理學校」

1395 kindergarten 幼稚園

● Degrees 學位

1396 B.A. (Bachelor of Arts) 文學士

1397 B.S. (Bachelor of Science) 理學士

1398 M.A. (Master of Arts) 文學碩士

1399 M.S. (Master of Science) 理學碩士

1400 M.D. (Doctor of Medicine) 醫學博士

1401 PH.D. (Doctor of Philosophy) 博士學位

Sports 運動

● Track and Field 田徑

1402 100-meter run 百公尺賽跑

1403 1,000-meter relay 1000 公尺接力賽

1404 10-kilometer walk 10 公里競走

1405 marathon 馬拉松

1406 high jump 跳高

1407 discus throw 擲鐵餅

1408 hammer throw 擲鏈球

1409 javelin throw 投擲標槍

1410 shot put 擲鉛球

1411 pole vault 撐竿跳

1412 horizontal bar 單槓

1413 parallel bars 雙槓

1414 balance beam 平衡木

1415 triathlon 鐵人三項

● Winter Sports 冬季運動

1416 giant slalom（滑雪）大曲道賽

1417 ski jump 跳台滑雪

1418 biathlon 冬季兩項（滑雪射擊）

1419 bobsledding 雪車

1420 luge 滑行雪橇

Society

Crime / Law 犯罪 / 法律

1421 attorney 律師
類 lawyer

1422 ex-con (ex-convict) 前科犯

1423 first offense 初犯

1424 jury 陪審團

1425 imprisonment 監禁

1426 probation 緩刑

1427 prosecutor / prosecuting attorney 檢察官

1428 death penalty 死刑
類 capital punishment

● Kinds of Crime 犯罪種類

1429 bag snatching 搶皮包

1430 bank robbery 搶銀行

1431 blackmail 勒索

1432 bribery 賄賂

1433 burglary 竊盜

1434 counterfeit 偽造

1435 fraud 詐欺

1436 hit-and-run 肇事逃逸

1437 mugging 行凶搶劫

1438 rape 性侵

※ sexual harassment 指「性騷擾」

Process of Indictment 起訴程序

1439 suspect 嫌犯

1440 arrest 拘留

1441 defendant 被告

1442 convict 受刑人

1443 criminal 罪犯

News and Daily Things 新聞與日常事務

1444 baby buster 嬰兒荒時期出生的人

反 baby boomer 嬰兒潮時期出生的人

1445 birds and bees 性知識；性教育

1446 catch-22 兩難困境

※ 這個單字來自 Joseph Heller 的暢銷小說 *Catch22*

1447 famine 饑荒

1448 refugee 難民

1449 nest egg 留窩蛋；儲備金

1450 sibling rivalry 兄弟鬩牆

1451 social background 社會背景

1452 social status 社會地位

1453 the in-thing 流行；潮

1454 tryout 試用；試演

1455 wash-and-wear 快乾的；免燙的

1456 wear and tear 磨損

1457 white paper （政策）白皮書

1458 who's who 名人錄

Public offices and Politics 公家機關與政治

1459 by-election 補選

1460 campaign pledge 競選承諾

1461 casting vote 決定票（兩方票數相同時，主持會議者所投的決定性一票）

1462 caretaker cabinet 看守內閣

1463 stopgap cabinet 臨時內閣

1464 centrist party 中間黨派

1465 civilian control 文人統治

1466 confidence vote 信任投票

1467 hands-off policy 不干預政策

1468 emergency legislation 緊急立法

1469 martial law 戒嚴令

1470 multilateral trade 多邊貿易

1471 national consensus 全國共識

1472 open-ended involvement 全面介入

1473 opinion poll 民意調查

1474 opposition party 反對黨

1475 Peace Corps 和平部隊

※ 由甘迺迪總統設立的部隊，主要在教育、農業等領域上協助開發中國家。

1476 plenary session 全體大會

1477 random sampling method 隨機抽樣法

1478 resident registration 居民登記

1479 swing voter 游離選民

1480 voice vote 出聲表決

U.S. Public Offices

1481 Immigration Office 移民局

1482 U.S. Department of Agriculture 美國農業部

1483 U.S. Post Office 美國郵政局

1484 Post Master 郵政局長

1485 U.S. State Department 美國國務院

1486 Secretary of State 國務卿

與數字相關

Geography and Time Difference 地理與時差

1487 altitude 海拔

1488 altimeter 測高儀

1489 continental shelf 大陸棚

1490 daylight saving time 日光節約時間

1491 Greenwich Mean Time 格林威治標準時間

1492 hemisphere 半球

※ 地區分 northern、southern、western、eastern 等四個 hemispheres。

1493 highlands 高地（複數形）

1494 high seas 公海

1495 International Date Line 國際換日線

※ 即太平洋上東西 180 度子午線

1496 latitude 緯度

1497 longitude 經度

1498 quasi-national park 準國家公園（等級次於國家公園）

1499 plain 平原

1500 plateau 高原

1501 prairie 大草原

1502 terrain 地形

1503 volcano 火山

Time Zones 時區

※ 美國本土橫跨以下四個時區，每個時區時差 1 小時：

1504 EST (Eastern Standard Time) 東部標準時間

1505 CST (Central Standard Time) 中央標準時間

1506 MST (Mountain Standard Time) 山區標準時間

1507 PST (Pacific Standard Time) 太平洋標準時間

附錄

Index【單字索引】

Chapter 1、3、5 所收錄的單字。

C

D

P

T

U

V

Index 【片語索引】

Chapter 2、3、4 所收錄的片語、慣用語。

D

E

F

G

H

I

K

L

附錄 Index 片語索引

R

S

T

U

CheckTest【解答】

解答附有該單字或片語的序號，方便查閱、複習。

Chapter 1

Unit 01 p. 26-27

① co-workers (0010) ② macrobiotic (0013) ③ obese (0020) ④ ubiquitous (0004)
⑤ blogosphere (0003) ⑥ resume (0016) ⑦ outfit (0025) ⑧ emergency (0023)
⑨ commemoration (0030) ⑩ outspoken (0009)

Unit 02 p. 38-39

① average (0052) ② habitat (0048) ③ flyers/ fliers (0037) ④ innovative (0043)
⑤ specifications (0042) ⑥ conserve (0036) ⑦ piracy (0049) ⑧ decades (0031)
⑨ strategy (0056) ⑩ infrastructure (0058)

Unit 03 p. 50-51

① token (0070) ② entrepreneurs (0064) ③ breakdown (0068) ④ conventions (0061)
⑤ asset (0074) ⑥ gain (0085) ⑦ measure (0080) ⑧ fake (0082)
⑨ aphorisms (0078) ⑩ compromise (0088)

Unit 04 p. 62-63

① notice (0101) ② indulgent (0118) ③ reputation (0100) ④ confiscated (0091)
⑤ premium (0105) ⑥ expiration (0109) ⑦ identify (0110) ⑧ impose (0114)
⑨ Alumni (0094) ⑩ beneficial (0120)

Unit 05 p. 74-75

① significant (0128) ② versatile (0125) ③ potential (0122) ④ valid (0131)
⑤ contemporary (0135) ⑥ tactful (0146) ⑦ acquire (0142) ⑧ peculiar (0144)
⑨ runner-up (0139) ⑩ expand (0151)

Unit 06 p. 86-87

① remuneration (0153) ② fatal (0176) ③ refuge (0158) ④ reimbursement (0171)
⑤ circumstances (0164) ⑥ commitments (0167) ⑦ incapacitated (0163)
⑧ privilege (0173) ⑨ endorse (0156) ⑩ consent (0180)

Unit 07 p. 98-99

① terminate (0183) ② persuaded (0195) ③ gourmet (0188) ④ humane (0191)
⑤ hand-me-down (0187) ⑥ candid (0198) ⑦ hefty (0202) ⑧ migrate (0211)
⑨ advantage (0206) ⑩ thaw (0205)

Unit 08 p. 110-111

① unassuming (0225) ② observant (0237) ③ administration (0212)
④ delinquent (0221) ⑤ myth (0228) ⑥ issue (0215) ⑦ Neglecting (0231)
⑧ obstructs (0239) ⑨ procedure (0219) ⑩ racket (0235)

Unit 09 p. 122-123

① ballot (0261) ② hostile (0249) ③ distinguish (0245) ④ retain (0264)
⑤ alternate (0242) ⑥ saturated (0252) ⑦ Consequently (0270) ⑧ evaluate (0255)
⑨ retrieve (0266) ⑩ credible (0258)

Unit 10 p. 134-135

① oath (0283) ② bilateral (0272) ③ conformist (0286) ④ revenues (0276)
⑤ implemented (0279) ⑥ sued (0292) ⑦ deposit (0289) ⑧ adjourned (0297)
⑨ eligibility (0294) ⑩ legislature (0301)

Unit 11 p. 146-147

① vandalism (0306) ② subsidized (0302) ③ expertise (0311) ④ prototype (0323)
⑤ quarantined (0315) ⑥ degrade (0308) ⑦ dehydrated (0329) ⑧ quotation (0326)
⑨ extraordinary (0318) ⑩ provisional (0321)

Unit 12 p. 158-159

① rationalization (0342) ② aggravated (0337) ③ affable (0347) ④ impulsively (0333)
⑤ frantic (0339) ⑥ comprehensive (0344) ⑦ distracts (0356)
⑧ miscellaneous (0351) ⑨ elaborate (0359) ⑩ omnivores (0355)

Unit 13 p. 168-169

① zealous (0371) ② mannerism (0365) ③ mandatory (0377) ④ inadequate (0363)
⑤ commensurate (0382) ⑥ diploma (0368) ⑦ annulled (0375)
⑧ reinforcement (0384)

Unit 14 p. 178-179

① agile (0391) ② manipulating (0398) ③ accountable (0387) ④ criticizing (0392)
⑤ incoherent (0395) ⑥ preoccupied (0405) ⑦ susceptible (0407)
⑧ extravagant (0401)

Unit 15 p. 188-189

① mediocre (0417) ② superintendent (0410) ③ adversity (0421)
④ intermittently (0423) ⑤ reference (0413) ⑥ anonymous (0428)
⑦ confidential (0431) ⑧ attribute (0426)

Chapter 2

Unit 16 p. 208-210

① acting up (0437) ② bears out (0443) ③ Act your age (0436) ④ broken away (0450)
⑤ break in (0458) ⑥ back us up (0440) ⑦ break the news (0471)
⑧ Bringing up (0489) ⑨ blew up at (0447) ⑩ break out in a rash (0466)
⑪ brought down the house (0481) ⑫ broke the ice (0469)
⑬ break the / habit (0468) ⑭ broke through (0475) ⑮ broke up with (0477)

Unit 17 p. 227-229

① burned out (0493) ② called for (0497) ③ burned down (0491) ④ called off (0499)
⑤ carried over (0508) ⑥ came to terms with (0543) ⑦ burn off calories (0492)
⑧ call it a day (0498) ⑨ get / carried away (0503) ⑩ come across (0525)
⑪ caught on to (0515) ⑫ comply with (0547) ⑬ counting on (0548)
⑭ carries a fine (0504) ⑮ come off (0532)

Unit 18 p. 248-250

① do some brainstorming (0560) ② cut down on (0550) ③ cut out for (0554)
④ do the town (0562) ⑤ deprive you of (0556) ⑥ draw the line at (0568)
⑦ cutting in (0551) ⑧ went down the drain (0605) ⑨ fell through (0591)
⑩ driving at (0571) ⑪ ended up lending (0581) ⑫ went into effect (0607)
⑬ get a break (0598) ⑭ fall into a vicious cycle (0587) ⑮ fell apart (0582)

Unit 19 p. 268-270

① grows on you (0618) ② went too far (0617) ③ hang in (0624)
④ go places (0613) ⑤ has a good command of (0633) ⑥ went public (0614)
⑦ have had it up to here (0638) ⑧ gets hung up on (0626)
⑨ hit a new high (0646) ⑩ holding up (0661) ⑪ had no business (0639)
⑫ imposing on (0665) ⑬ having second thoughts about (0643)
⑭ held fast to (0652) ⑮ hold him off (0659)

Unit 20 p. 286-288

① laid off (0684) ② Keep out (0673) ③ keeping track of (0675)
④ keeps company with (0669) ⑤ laid claim to (0681) ⑥ lay over (0686)
⑦ knows the ropes (0679) ⑧ lay hands on (0683) ⑨ looking into (0703)
⑩ make a / issue of (0716) ⑪ make / from scratch (0720) ⑫ make up for (0723)
⑬ live up to (0701) ⑭ make it (0717) ⑮ loses his temper (0708)

Unit 21 p. 305-307

① passed the hat (0727) ② paid / off (0730) ③ picked up the tab (0737)
④ managed to (0724) ⑤ Play it safe (0744) ⑥ passed out (0726) ⑦ pitch in (0738)
⑧ pick on (0733) ⑨ pulling off (0760) ⑩ play it by ear (0743) ⑪ pull a stunt (0752)
⑫ put down (0766) ⑬ put / out (0783) ⑭ pull himself together (0757)
⑮ put away (0764)

Unit 22 p. 324-326

① put / down (0784) ② rub it in (0797) ③ put the blame on (0786)
④ set / back (0814) ⑤ put up with (0792) ⑥ run the risk of (0805)
⑦ raise a racket (0794) ⑧ run in the family (0801) ⑨ took the liberty of (0844)
⑩ spits out (0833) ⑪ sitting in for (0821) ⑫ set me up (0816)
⑬ take / for granted (0843) ⑭ Take advantage of (0839) ⑮ is / spoken for (0830)

Unit 23 p. 341-343

① think twice (0851) ② Try to talk (0860) ③ talked my ear off (0846)
④ turn / over to (0863) ⑤ talk / into making (0848) ⑥ turned out (0864)
⑦ Try out (0859) ⑧ throw out (0855) ⑨ wiped out (0879) ⑩ wore off (0872)
⑪ walking off with (0867) ⑫ wrote it off (0896) ⑬ wore himself out (0873)
⑭ Work off (0885) ⑮ won by default (0877)

Chapter 3

Unit 24 p. 358-360

① As a token of (0902) ② for real (0915) ③ In consequence of (0923)
④ in crisis (0925) ⑤ across-the-board (0899) ⑥ for good (0913)
⑦ brand-new (0906) ⑧ in a jam (0919) ⑨ In other words (0929)
⑩ per capita (0942) ⑪ in for (0926) ⑫ In consideration of (0924)
⑬ In terms of (0933) ⑭ in short supply (0931) ⑮ off and on (0939)

Unit 25 p. 372-374

① out of circulation (0951) ② On behalf of (0944) ③ on second thought (0947)
④ out of service (0955) ⑤ over and done with (0960) ⑥ on good terms with (0946)
⑦ out of date (0953) ⑧ safe and sound (0964) ⑨ out of the running (0957)
⑩ state-of-the-art (0967) ⑪ under the circumstances (0972) ⑫ up to (0979)
⑬ right side up (0962) ⑭ water-repellent (0982) ⑮ up in the air (0976)

Chapter 4

Unit 26 p. 393-396

① was wondering if (0989) ② can't stand (0993) ③ Come to think of it (0997)
④ don't care if (1001) ⑤ been at wit's end (0987) ⑥ Beats me (0990)
⑦ Come off it (0995) ⑧ first-come first-served (1002) ⑨ can't help betting (0992)
⑩ costs an arm and a leg (1000) ⑪ It's about time (1011) ⑫ It looks as if (1009)
⑬ pain in the neck (1021) ⑭ had it coming (1004) ⑮ out of the blue (1020)
⑯ it's on me (1014) ⑰ What do you take me for (1032) ⑱ might not hurt (1016)
⑲ What's with (1038) ⑳ see eye to eye (1022)

Power Builder chart 1

Unit 01-14

學習完每個 Unit 之後，請確實進行 Check Test 測驗，並將正確率記錄於下表。（可參考 p.12 的填寫範例）
正確率＝答對題數 ÷ 題目數 ×100

100%							
90%							
80%							
70%							
60%							
50%							
40%							
30%							
20%							
10%							
	U01	U02	U03	U04	U05	U06	U07

100%							
90%							
80%							
70%							
60%							
50%							
40%							
30%							
20%							
10%							
	U08	U09	U10	U11	U12	U13	U14

Power Builder chart 2

UNIT 15-26

學習完每個 Unit 之後，請確實進行 Check Test 測驗，並將正確率記錄於下表。(可參考 p.12 的填寫範例)
正確率＝答對題數 ÷ 題目數 ×100

100%						
90%						
80%						
70%						
60%						
50%						
40%						
30%						
20%						
10%						
	U15	U16	U17	U18	U19	U20

100%						
90%						
80%						
70%						
60%						
50%						
40%						
30%						
20%						
10%						
	U21	U22	U23	U24	U25	U26

國家圖書館出版品預行編目資料

倒著學New TOEIC新多益字彙 / 大賀理惠, Bill Benfield, Ann Gleason作. -- 初版. -- 臺北市：貝塔出版, 2012. 10
面；　公分

ISBN: 978-957-729-902-4（平裝附光碟片）

1.多益測驗　2.詞彙

805.1895　　101018440

倒著學 New TOEIC 新多益字彙

作　　者 / 大賀理惠、Bill Benfield、Ann Gleason
總 編 審 / 王復國
譯　　者 / 戴至中、許郁文
執行編輯 / 朱曉瑩

出　　版 / 貝塔出版有限公司
地　　址 / 100 台北市館前路 12 號 11 樓
電　　話 / (02)2314-2525
傳　　真 / (02)2312-3535
郵　　撥 / 19493777 貝塔出版有限公司
客服專線 / (02)2314-3535
客服信箱 / btservice@betamedia.com.tw

總 經 銷 / 時報文化出版企業股份有限公司
地　　址 / 桃園縣龜山鄉萬壽路二段 351 號
電　　話 / (02) 2306-6842

出版日期 / 2012 年 10 月初版一刷
定　　價 / 480 元
I S B N / 978-957-729-902-4

SHADOWING DE MANABU TOEIC®TEST 860- TOPPA VOCABULARY-

貝塔網址：www.betamedia.com.tw

喚醒你的英文語感！

斤後釘好，直接寄回即可！

廣 告 回 信
北區郵政管理局登記證
北台字第14256號
免 貼 郵 票

100 台北市中正區館前路12號11樓

貝塔語言出版 收
Beta Multimedia Publishing

寄件者住址 □□□

謝謝您購買本書！！

貝塔語言擁有最優良之英文學習書籍，為提供您最佳的英語學習資訊，您可填妥此表後寄回（免貼郵票）將可不定期收到本公司最新發行書訊及活動訊息！

姓名：____________________ 性別：□男 □女 生日：_____年_____月_____日

電話：(公)__________________(宅)__________________(手機)__________________

電子信箱：____

學歷：□高中職含以下 □專科 □大學 □研究所含以上

職業：□金融 □服務 □傳播 □製造 □資訊 □軍公教 □出版

□自由 □教育 □學生 □其他

職級：□企業負責人 □高階主管 □中階主管 □職員 □專業人士

1. 您購買的書籍是？______________________________

2. 您從何處得知本產品？(可複選)

□書店 □網路 □書展 □校園活動 □廣告信函 □他人推薦 □新聞報導 □其他

3. 您覺得本產品價格：

□偏高 □合理 □偏低

4. 請問目前您每週花了多少時間學英語？

□ 不到十分鐘 □ 十分鐘以上，但不到半小時 □ 半小時以上，但不到一小時

□ 一小時以上，但不到兩小時 □ 兩個小時以上 □ 不一定

5. 通常在選擇語言學習書時，哪些因素是您會考慮的？

□ 封面 □ 內容、實用性 □ 品牌 □ 媒體、朋友推薦 □ 價格□ 其他________

6. 市面上您最需要的語言書種類為？

□ 聽力 □ 閱讀 □ 文法 □ 口說 □ 寫作 □ 其他__________

7. 通常您會透過何種方式選購語言學習書籍？

□ 書店門市 □ 網路書店 □ 郵購 □ 直接找出版社 □ 學校或公司團購

□ 其他____________

8. 給我們的建議：____

____

喚醒你的英文語感！

Get a Feel for English !